922076

Scenes
from
Bedlam

SCENES
from
BEDLAM

A History of Caring
for the Mentally Disordered
at Bethlem Royal Hospital
and The Maudsley

David Russell

formerly Director of Nursing Services at The Maudsley Hospital

Baillière Tindall

PUBLISHED IN ASSOCIATION WITH THE RCN

*London Philadelphia Toronto
Sydney Tokyo*

Baillière Tindall   24–28 Oval Road
London NW1 7DX

The Curtis Center
Independence Square West
Philadelphia, PA 19106-3399, USA

Harcourt Brace & Company
55 Horner Avenue
Toronto, Ontario, M8Z 4X6, Canada

Harcourt Brace & Company, Australia
30–52 Smidmore Street
Marrickville
NSW 2204, Australia

Harcourt Brace & Company, Japan
Ichibancho Central Building
22-1 Ichibancho
Chiyoda-ku, Tokyo 102, Japan

© 1997 David Russell

This book is printed on acid-free paper

A catalogue record for this book is available from the British Library

ISBN 1-873853-39-4

Typeset by Florencetype Ltd, Stoodleigh, Devon
Printed and bound in Great Britain by
Butler & Tanner Ltd, Frome and London

CONTENTS

	Acknowledgements	vii
	Foreword	xi
1	Setting the scenes	1
2	The patient's voice	18
3	Basketmen, keepers, attendants and nurses	35
4	From madmen to service users – social class and treatments	53
5	Matrons – famous and infamous	71
6	Rules for the workplace	85
7	Patients – mostly notorious	99
8	Keeping order	117
9	The public eye	132
10	The 'Golden Bank' – Victorian Bethlem	150
11	Nurses finding knowledge, a role and a voice – the twentieth century	162
12	Women and men – some gender issues	181
13	A search for excellence – the last three decades	196
	Bibliography	216
	Index	219

ACKNOWLEDGEMENTS

The author and publishers are grateful for kind permission to quote the following copyright material:

The table 'Nursing staff: patient ratios 1635–80' from the thesis *Bedlam Revisited: A History of Bethlem Hospital c1634–c1770*, by Dr Jonathan Andrews (unpublished).

Extracts from *Murphy* by Samuel Beckett, published by Calder Publications Limited, London, copyright © Samuel Beckett 1938, 1963 and 1977, and copyright © The Samuel Beckett Estate 1993. Reprinted by permission of the Samuel Beckett Estate and The Calder Educational Trust, London, for the UK and Commonwealth. Permission for America, Canada and the open market territories has kindly been granted by Grove Atlantic, publishers of New York.

Extracts from *Virtuoso – The Story of John Ogdon*, by Brenda Lucas Ogdon and Michael Kerr, by kind permission of the publishers Hamish Hamilton, © Brenda Lucas Ogdon and Michael Kerr 1981.

Extracts from B Thomas, S Liness, S Vearnals and H Griffin (1992) 'Involuntary cohabitees', December 2; A Altschul (1984) 'Psychiatric Nursing: does good practice need good principles?', July 11 and 18; E Skellern (1980) 'Psychiatric nursing for the eighties', September 8; S Ritter (1984) 'Does the team work?', February 8. Reproduced by kind permission of the *Nursing Times* where these articles first appeared.

Extracts from *Beyond the Glass* by Antonia White are reprinted by kind permission of the publishers, Virago Press.

Extracts from *Breakdown* by Stuart Sutherland are reprinted by kind permission of the publishers, Weidenfeld and Nicholson.

The author would also like to thank the following who gave permission to use words or writings: Annie Altschul, Fiona Firmin, Frank Hardiman, Vicki Hayward, George King, Keith Lloyd, Ken Sampson, Margaret Skellern (for F. E. Skellern), Ben Thomas and Pamela Tibbles.

Illustrations appear by courtesy/kind permission of:

Anonymous Collection, London
    Isaac Oliver. Portrait of Lady Eleanor Davies

Bethlem Royal Hospital Archives and Museum
    William Hogarth. A Rake's Progress, VIII The Madhouse, etching 1763
    Bethlem Hospital at Moorfields, print after 1733
    Bethlem Hospital at St George's Fields, as it was in 1815
    Salaries Book, extract, 1815
    Basketmen's Duties from the General Orders 1778
    Minute of the Court of Governors 16 August 1637
    James Hadfield. Poem and Watercolour, 1826
    Richard Dadd, photo of patient, c1856
    Louis Wain. Sweetness Coyed Love into its Smile, painting 1930s
    A women's ward, photo 1912
    A men's ward, photo 1912
    Charles Fréchou. Portrait of Charles Hood, 1851

Bethlem and Maudsley NHS Trust
    John Ogdon, *Bethlem and Maudsley Gazette*, 1982
    Staff demonstrating, *Bethlem and Maudsley Gazette*, 1986

The British Museum
    Margaret Nicholson, portrait, ink and watercolour, after 1786
    The King's Life Attempted, print
    James Hadfield, portrait drawing

The Trustees of Dulwich Picture Gallery
    British School. Nathaniel Lee, portrait painting

Sir Andrew Lloyd Webber Collection
    Richard Dadd. Contradiction: Oberon and Titania: 1854–58, painting

The Museum of London Picture Library
    Bedlam at Bishopsgate, Copperplate Map, 1559

Dr Richard Neville
    Richard Dadd. Portrait of Charles Neville, after 1853

Nursing Times
    Annie Altschul, photo 1950s
    A multi-disciplinary team, 1984

David Russell
    Bethlem Royal Hospital, photo 1995
    Maudsley Hospital, photo 1995

Miss Margaret Skellern
    Eileen Skellern, photo 1960s

The Trustees of Sir John Soane's Museum
    William Hogarth. A Rake's Progress, VIII The Madhouse, painting
    1733–4

Weidenfeld and Nicolson Ltd
    Antonia White, photo c1924

Wellcome Institute Library, London
    The gallery for women
    The gallery for men

Every effort has been made to trace all the copyright owners and obtain permission, but as this has not proved possible in all cases, the publisher will be pleased to hear from the owners.

I should like to thank the staff of the British Library, the Institute of Psychiatry, the Royal College of Nursing, the Royal College of Psychiatrists, the Professional Development Centre at the Maudsley, the Wellcome Institute for the History of Medicine, London, and the Wiltshire Library and Museum Service, Salisbury.

To those who read the manuscript and gave me support and encouragement – Jim McCarthy, Tom Sandford and Pamela Tibbles – I am especially grateful. Much is owed to those who agreed to be interviewed, including Annie Altschul, Les Ayling, Des Doherty, Reg Everest, Peter Eweje, Fiona Firmin, Salleh Gani, Olive Griffiths, Fiby Hare, Vicki Hayward, Chris Heffernan, Russell Horwood, George King, Sue Ritter, John Sims, Anthony Smith, Pamela Tibbles, Eileen Waller, Juliette Wiltshire, Ann Winnicki and Brian Woollatt. It was very helpful to be allowed to use the interview schedule developed by Peter Nolan. I should also like to thank staff of the Bethlem and Maudsley who responded kindly to my frequent requests for information – Nancy Chessum, Richard Cross, Marjorie Harrison, Kay Harwood, Annette Pateman and Cynthia Read.

Many thanks are due to Ben Thomas, who set the work in motion and gave a wealth of assistance in a variety of ways.

Patricia Allderidge, the Archivist at Bethlem Royal Hospital, gave generously of her time and expertise, for which I am grateful.

Finally, I should like to thank my wife Gemma and son Nicholas for most kindly offering helpful comments and giving technical support.

DR

FOREWORD

I am pleased to have been asked to write a preface to this important book on the social history of mental health care at the Bethlem Royal Hospital and the Maudsley Hospital. In 1997, the Bethlem Royal Hospital will be 750 years old. It is all too easy with hindsight to regard the practices of another time as inhumane and ineffective. However, through the following pages, the author presents imaginative and empathetic glimpses of life in the country's longest established mental hospital. With such a rich history and so much archival material to draw upon, the author must be commended for his well-chosen topics. His analysis develops through addressing contemporary issues using historical data. He brings to life many of the characters who cared for the mentally ill themselves. These include many of Bethlem's more famous patients, artists and writers, and, although their stories make for an interesting read, the author has also searched out accounts of people who up until now have remained invisible and unknown.

Not only is this publication highly readable and entertaining, but it also gives the reader insight into the many changes made in the treatment of the mentally disordered over the years and the change in attitude brought about among professional staff, patients, relatives and the public in general. In fact, it is a most appropriate introduction to the anniversary year and will appeal to a much wider audience than just mental health care professionals. Of course, of particular interest to me was Chapter 5, 'Matrons — famous and infamous'. Although the post is now titled Chief Nurse Advisor, the position has existed since at least the reign of King Charles I.

An additional bonus is the illustrations, which have been carefully reproduced. Thanks are due to the Bethlem Royal Hospital Trustees for their generosity in making this possible.

This book is a most significant study. It has much to tell us about the different ways of being a carer and what it was like to look after the mentally ill at different times, and, most importantly, it includes the writings of the mentally ill themselves.

The Bethlem Royal Hospital continues to play an important role in today's modern National Health Service. It provides specialist services, including those dealing with perinatal psychiatry, challenging behaviour, addictions, psychosis, child and adolescent psychiatry, and forensic psychiatry. Here many of the advances, such as neuro-imaging, genetics, biochemistry and neurophysiology, are put into practice, targeting major mental health problems – problems that continue to be a leading cause of illness, distress, disability and mortality. Policy changes in the NHS and Social Services call for the care of the mentally ill to take place in the community; nevertheless, the need for inpatient care continues. There are arguments against the further closure of hospital beds, especially within inner-city areas, and opposite arguments from those who believe the community care programme has not developed enough. I am sure *Scenes from Bedlam* will contribute to these current debates. It should be read by anyone interested in mental health.

Ben Thomas
Director of Clinical Services/Chief Nurse Advisor
The Bethlem and Maudsley NHS Trust

Setting the scenes

The curtain rises on an autumn day in London: Wednesday, October 23, 1247. The principal actor is Simon Fitz-Mary, a landowner, sometime Sheriff and Alderman of the City of London, who is seen gathered with nineteen named men and many others to witness to his grand gesture and noble vision. Some of the land that Simon Fitz-Mary owned in the City, next to the church of St Botolph's, Bishopsgate, was being given to the Bishop-Elect of Bethlehem in the Holy Land, because Simon Fitz-Mary had an especial devotion to the place of Christ's nativity. It was a munificent gesture to donate such a portion of his estate in the capital of England, including houses, gardens, orchards, fishponds, ditches and marshes within its boundaries. The people had come to bear public witness to the Deed of Gift whereby the land was transferred, and prominent among them were the Mayor of London Peter Fitz-Alan, the Sheriff Nicholas Bat, and Aldermen, including master craftsmen – a currier, a loriner and a baker. Simon Fitz-Mary and his household had already removed themselves from the property, and possession had been handed over to Goffredo de Prefetti, the Bishop-Elect.

The vision of Simon Fitz-Mary was that at some time a priory would be founded on this land, with a prior, canons, brothers and sisters, who would wear copes and mantles emblazoned with a star. It would be the Priory of St Mary of Bethlehem, containing a church or oratory wherein the divine office was to be said, with prayers for the souls of the dead. Hospitality would be offered to the Bishop of Bethlehem and his staff when they visited, and donations sent to the mother church in Bethlehem. There was, at this stage, no mention of caring for the sick. All these aspects of the vision were to be accomplished when the Lord Jesus Christ should have poured out his grace more abundantly, namely with material prosperity; and there lay the seeds of a problem, for a foundation without endowments may well run into trouble. But this was the day for the ceremonial confirmation of the Deed of

Gift, so Simon Fitz-Mary sealed the document in the presence of the elder citizens. The story of Bethlem had begun.

In this chapter, the opening scene of the foundation of Bethlem is followed by a discussion of the use and scope of this book, its sources and terminology. We pass then to a consideration of some common images of Bedlam, focusing on the well-known Hogarth picture. The chapter ends with an overview of Bethlem on different sites and a brief chronology of significant events in the history of the hospitals.

The use and scope of this book

The value of historical writing is not always obvious to contemporary health care providers, caught up as they sometimes are in the need to find short-term solutions for those with mental problems. Yet practitioners need a context for their practice. In addition, the relevance of history for mental health care is not confined to seeing problems against a broader backcloth, but is given added urgency by understanding that the problems of today are so often the recycled problems of the past. The history of caring for the mentally disturbed is like the history of psychiatry, which Hunter and Macalpine (1963) aptly described as the 'record of perennial problems, recurrent ideas, disputes and treatments'. If one accepts this approach, the possibility opens of fulfilling the true purpose of historical writing, which is to create interaction between the past and the present.

The people who have been busy with the practical aspects of caring for those with mental health problems have gone largely unnoticed in the history of public provision for illness. Those who looked after the physically sick have attracted attention sometimes as angels of mercy, but, as Carpenter (1981) has pointed out, those who nursed the mentally disturbed seldom achieved public attention except as a result of scandal or alleged ill treatment. Nevertheless, in this book, an attempt is made to write what Thompson (1966) called 'history from below'. Beginnings have been made in writing the general history of mental nursing in the UK (e.g. Nolan 1993), but there is still much local material that needs to be sought out and analysed. This book sets out a record of activities in one organisation, so far as they relate to the delivery of care to people with mental health problems. It is hoped that, because of the long eventful history of the Bethlem and Maudsley, some of the themes and content of this book will prove to be of general relevance, as well as thought-provoking and stimulating in their own right. References to material particular to individual chapters are given at the end of each chapter, but references that concern

2

the Bethlem and Maudsley more generally are given in the Bibliography at the end of the book.

This work does not pretend to be comprehensive, even on the themes selected for consideration, but may provide the ground for further exploration. Few records have been preserved from the earliest days of the hospital before the dissolution of the monasteries, and there are gaps too in later periods, so perforce the accounts of life in Bedlam are somewhat episodic. Some scenes are illuminated, some remain in darkness. This presents unfortunate opportunities for the creation of ill-founded myths. An illustration of this is the alleged treatment of patients by exorcism in Bethlem's early years. Although there is no evidence for this, the imaginative reconstruction of O'Donoghue (1914) has become the 'taken-for granted' fact of Plumb (1972).

An attempt to compensate for the occasionally empty stage has been made by quoting generously from original sources that are available to give the authentic flavour to the narrative and to provide new material for reflection on the evolution of mental health care. This sometimes involves giving details of matters that might not appear significant in themselves but go towards building a picture of the enterprise as a whole. As Maréchal de Saxe (1756; cited in Foucault 1975) wrote, 'It is not enough to have a liking for architecture. One must also know stone-cutting.'

Care should be taken in the interpretation of the episodes described, for what is observed in one situation cannot necessarily be thought of as representative of others or taken as a justification for generalising to different circumstances. Topics such as caring and legislation, patients' food, ethnicity and categories of patients admitted and discharged have not been covered in detail in this book, but would repay study. The development of medical practice and the detailed description of the contributions of individual doctors demands a work of its own.

Sources and terminology

The history of Britain's oldest institution for the treatment of the mentally ill, Bethlem Royal Hospital, remains largely underwritten. Apart from the useful resumé by R.O. Martin for the Charity Commissioners in 1837, there were papers by Bowen (1784), Hack Tuke (1876, 1882), White (1899) and Copeland (1910), but there was nothing of much length until the Reverend E.G. O'Donoghue published his book on the general history of the hospital (1914). This has remained an unquestioned source-book for many subsequent writers. After O'Donoghue, there were further, mostly short, papers by Porter Phillips (1943), Whittaker (1947), Johnson (1953),

Talbot (circa 1969), Lewis (1969) and Cawley (1976), and a book *Bedlam*, by Anthony Masters (1977) (see Bibliography), but there has been no detailed published research covering the whole field, so one is especially grateful for the papers of Patricia Allderidge, the hospital Archivist, although her work does not focus specifically on the carers. She wrote in 1979 that the secondary sources, whether ancient or modern, for the whole history of Bethlem were generally very unreliable, and that would still seem mostly to be the case, apart from her own work and the meticulously researched work on the years circa 1634–1770 by Jonathan Andrews (1991), which is unpublished at the time of writing, but to which I am much indebted. Nevertheless, the archives of Bethlem offer a rich seam of primary source material, some of which has been quarried for this book, as listed in the Bibliography.

Apart from written sources, a start has been made for this book on the oral history of Bethlem and Maudsley, using a series of taped structured interviews of numerous informants who worked at the Bethlem and Maudsley, covering the years from 1928 to the present day. Use was made of the interview questionnaire developed by Dr Peter Nolan (1993) of the University of Birmingham for his book on the history of mental health nursing.

Some key words appearing in this book, such as 'madness', 'insanity', 'mental illness' and 'nurse' and its variants, are sometimes used in particular ways by other modern authors (contrast for example Scull (1982) and Crammer (1994)). For the purposes of this work, an attempt has been made only to use words that were current in the period under discussion. For example, references to mental health nursing are not appropriate before the latter part of the twentieth century; mention of 'mad people' may be made for the seventeenth century, but other words for the mentally disordered may be preferred today.

Images of Bedlam

A problem for writers about Bethlem is that it already possesses an ingrained image in the public mind. The Priory of St Mary of Bethlehem is the institution whose name became corrupted to 'Bedlam', a word that has been, for five or six centuries, synonymous in common speech with a madhouse, scene of uproar, or mental and organisational chaos.

The original name 'Bethlehem' has appeared in a number of other variants including 'Bethleem', 'Bedelem', 'Bethalem' and 'Bedlehem'. The reputation for what appears today as ill-treatment of patients extending to the mid-nineteenth century is difficult to gainsay, but does not represent the whole picture. At least some past visitors found the hospital an admirable place: for instance, an anonymous French author (1788) wrote: 'The poor creatures there are not chained up in dark cellars . . . no bolts, no bars. The doors are open, their rooms wainscotted, and the long airy corridors give them a chance of exercise. A cleanliness, hardly conceivable unless seen, reigns in their hospital.' One wonders whether he saw the entire hospital, but it is still good to know that parts of it appeared agreeable. Some people connected with Bethlem in the eighteenth and early nineteenth centuries, such as Thomas Bowen, governor and chaplain (1783) and the anonymous 'A Constant Observer' (1823), felt able to write about Bethlem in a highly complimentary vein. (Throughout this book it has been assumed, with Alldridge (1993, Sketches in Bedlam), that 'A Constant Observer', the anonymous author of *Sketches in Bedlam*, was James Smyth, as the Governors thought at the time.)

What seems to us as scandalous about the eighteenth and early nineteenth centuries was the way in which people compared the mad to animals – that they were violent, insensitive to heat and cold, and lacking in reason, that quality that distinguishes man from the beasts. Dr William Black (1811) described some of the Bedlam patients as 'ravenous and insatiable as wolves' or 'drenched by compulsion as horses', and the Incurables 'kept as wild beasts, constantly in fetters'. The Parliamentary Commissioners (1815) commented on a room in Bethlem that was like a dog kennel. The Quarterly Review (1857) referred to Bethlem patients being enclosed with iron bars, like the 'fiercer carnivora at the Zoological Gardens'.

These descriptions remind one of the comments on Bedlam by the influential twentieth-century French psychologist and philosopher, Michel Foucault (1961). He follows his description of the chaining of a dangerous madman at Bethlem by reflections on the image of animality prevalent in the hospitals of the late eighteenth and early nineteenth centuries. He writes: 'Madness borrowed its face from the mask of the beast.' The corollary to this was that animality could only be tamed by discipline and brutalising. This may have been true of the French hospital described by Pinel and cited by Foucault, but it can be argued that these methods were not the whole story of Bethlem (Andrews 1991), where the inmates were managed and treated with the aim of achieving cures. It is not that Foucault is singling Bethlem out for individual censure, for he reminds us that La Salpêtrière in Paris had madwomen chained like dogs.

France also paralleled England in the practice of allowing visitors to see the madmen. At Bicêtre in Paris, people paid to see the madmen 'like curious animals', just as people paid at Bethlem to visit the galleries of mad people, although perhaps not in such quantity as Foucault imagined. At the French asylum of Charenton, matters were taken further, when performances were given with madmen taking the parts of actors.

The image of Bedlam as theatre, of patients playing parts as in a play, seems to have been equally if not more pervasive than does the image of the hospital as a zoo. Around 1600, Shakespeare promoted a view of life in theatrical terms – 'all the world's a stage . . . and one man in his time plays many parts'. One of these parts might be that of madman, as played for instance by Hamlet, or Edgar in *King Lear*. Sometimes the Shakespearean characters, for example Malvolio in *Twelfth Night*, were comical, encouraging the audience to laugh at derangement and to be proud of the fact that they were better than the mad people. In early seventeenth-century drama the mad people on the stage were there as a spectacle to amuse by dancing and singing or otherwise offering bizarre distractions. Besides the comedy, there was an element of the macabre and of horror.

People visited Bethlem to be similarly entertained, and they were sometimes stimulated by uninhibited interactions. Sometimes their reactions were more complex than being just simple amusement. For example, Dr Johnson, the great lexicographer, had once been entertained by a furious patient beating straw, supposing it to be the Duke of Cumberland. When he went to Bethlem in 1775, he found nothing peculiarly remarkable, while James Boswell, his companion, found the general contemplation of insanity very affecting. Apart from entertainment or lack of it, Dr Johnson thought that one could also receive a moral warning that madness could be avoided by not indulging the imagination. His friend Mrs Burney, on the contrary, believed that madness was caused by disease or misfortune, rather than by faults, and that thinking of mad people was therefore a melancholy consideration. As in a real theatre, Bedlam could provoke laughter, or sadness and compassion. An attraction for writers was the wealth of incident and the opportunity to reflect on the tragicomic human dramas played out in Bethlem, which added to an understanding of human relationships. This was encapsulated for the eighteenth century in one masterful painting.

The 'Rake's Progress' – a theatrical image

A dominant image of Bedlam, radiating out from the painting's 1733 origin, was that of the final scene of William Hogarth's 'Rake's Progress'. Hogarth said that his pictures were his stage, and here is the climax of a series of dramatic moments in the life of an anti-hero. The engraving made from the painting went through several states and achieved wide circulation, presumably because the morality of the tale was felt to be of universal application. The image of a coin depicting a dishevelled Britannia, fixed to the central back wall in the picture, in later versions of the engraving emphasised the pervasiveness of madness, particularly among the English.

The main figure of Hogarth's masterpiece is the semi-naked Tom Rakewell, reaping the rewards of his dissolute life and now close to death in Bedlam. He is supported by Sarah Young, his discarded mistress and the mother of his child, and behind is a man, possibly Thomas Weston the Steward of Bethlem, while at his feet is a keeper – unnamed – who is either applying or releasing Tom's fetters. The tragedy of this tableau is relieved by the antics of the madmen around, who pursue their fantasies, oblivious of each other and of Tom's end. These men in the male wing are exhibiting what were considered to be types of madness. There is the religious maniac with his Cross and holy pictures, an astronomer/astrologer peering through a paper telescope, a geographer plotting longitude, a tailor with a tape measure and patterns in his hat, a musician with his fiddle, a Papist fanatic and a sad man, crossed in love. In a cell at the back, a naked man with a crown and sceptre urinates, while a lady visitor and her maid giggle pruriently.

Hogarth satirises the Church and the monarchy, while also poking fun at the conventional causes of madness – the influence of the moon, music and love. O'Donoghue (1914) suggested that Bethlem might even have asked Hogarth to paint this picture, although as far as one can tell there is no evidence for this. Hogarth also painted other hospitals, and the patients here displayed were not being ill-treated by the standards of the time, so perhaps this would have been considered to be a favourable representation. At least the Bethlem authorities cannot have been too dissatisfied, for they made Hogarth a hospital Governor in 1752. The chaining seen in the picture was thought necessary for cases of raving madness, and shaving the head for the treatment by blistering was still practised. Public visiting for a fee provided the hospital with a desirable source of revenue. Poor Tom lies positioned in the same manner as Cibber's famous statue showing 'Raving Madness', which surmounted the gatepost outside the hospital. The moral of the drama was clear – a dissolute life brought one to such a place. This was Hell.

Later generations were to see the unclothed, chained state of Tom Rakewell and the frolicking of patients for visitors as unacceptable. The decline in visiting and the advent of moral treatment caused a waning in the theatrical image, as Bethlem moved towards the humane ideals of the Victorian era. Nonetheless, the image of Bedlam at the climax of the 'Rake's Progress' is kept alive by frequent reproductions of Hogarth's engraving and by stagings of the Stravinsky/Auden Kallman opera of the same name. More on other images and public views of Bethlem can be found in Chapter 9.

To provide a framework for visualising the activities of Bethlem, it will be useful in setting the scene to consider briefly the places where the hospital has existed at different times. To start this overview, we shall return to the beginnings of Bethlem's history.

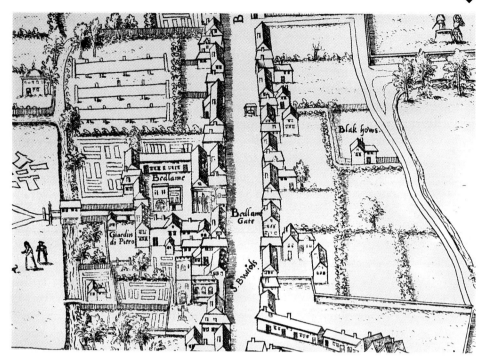

Bedlam at Bishopsgate. Detail from map c1559

Bishopsgate, 1247–1676

While the initial purposes of the Priory were solely to celebrate divine services and to receive the Bishop of Bethlehem and his nuncios whenever they visited, the broader objectives of the monastic order were set out a century later. It was to be an order for contemplation, a military order and an order of hospitallers.

From the beginning, the Priory occupied a relatively rural site in London, being close to Moor Field and Finnes Burie Field. The earliest available drawing of the site (1599) shows an entry through Bedlam Gate from the highway of Bishopsgate, into a courtyard with a cluster of small buildings surrounding a church and, outside, gardens beyond. Round about were houses, shops, gardens and ponds. By 1266, an oratory had been built, but apart from that information is scant. The community does not seem to have thrived, owing perhaps to the obligation to send the monies donated to support the Bishop and the Mother House of the monastery in Bethlehem in the Holy Land. After 1329, Bethlem was no longer being looked after by a Prior but by a Master and brethren, who were looking to the King of England, rather than the Bishop of Bethlehem,

8

for protection. Financial affairs still did not flourish, so in 1346 it was necessary for the Master to ask the Mayor and Aldermen of the City of London for protection and patronage. By the 1360s, a new church and other buildings were being erected, so it would appear that conditions had improved.

The first reference to the 'Hospital of St Mary of Bethlem' comes in the 1329 document, but it is not possible to tell whether the institution was functioning as a hospital for the sick and infirm or as a hospice for travellers, or both, at this date. Sometime during the later years of the fourteenth century, the practice of accommodating the mentally sick became established. This is confirmed by the inquiry report of 1403, which tells us that the poor were being supported in about 1379, and that instruments of restraint had been in the hospital in about 1398. Certainly in 1403, there were six mentally disturbed men, three infirm poor and various other persons who may have been merely lodging there. At this period, there was hardly any institutional provision for the mentally disordered in Europe – only at Gheel in Belgium from the thirteenth century, at Florence in Italy from 1389, and at Valencia in Spain from 1409.

It seems that Bethlem changed from a religious to a secular confraternity some considerable time before King Henry VIII abolished the religious orders and formally transferred the possession of the hospital to the City in 1547. For a short while, Bethlem was managed with Christ's Hospital, but, from 1557 onwards, it was administered jointly with the new foundation of Bridewell, a House of Correction. Bethlem continued as a small hospital that interested the Bridewell managers very little, until in 1598 there was an inspection that found Bethlem in a ruinous condition. At another formal visit in 1624, Bethlem was found to be overcrowded, with thirty-one patients, but only space for twenty-five. The early years of the seventeenth century were notable for mismanagement by Dr Helkiah Crooke, who made money out of Bethlem while keeping the patients short of food. In 1673, the building was judged to be too old, weak, ruinous and small, so a decision to rebuild was taken, in this more confident time following the restoration of the Monarchy in England.

Moorfields, 1676–1815

The palatial new building at Moorfields emphasised Bethlem as standing centre stage in the mental illness scene in England, where it had been the only public institution serving the mentally disordered for about three hundred years. Here began a period when Bethlem was much written about by journalists and men of letters. Visitors were attracted by the new

The HOSPITAL of BETHLEHEM.   L'HOSPITAL de Fou.
Printed for John Bowles   in Cornhil.

Bethlem Hospital at Moorfields, after 1733

pavilion style building and the entertaining madmen within. Designed on the model of the Tuilleries Palace in Paris, the facade was nearly five hundred and fifty feet long, and the interior accommodated one hundred and twenty patients. The front of the building was decorated with Corinthian columns, surmounted with a pediment with the Royal Arms, carved in stone along with massive wreaths of flowers, and the stone balustrade above enclosed an octagonal turret crowned with a cupola. The building gave onto a tree-lined garden, neatly ornamented with freestone promenades, and allowing space for the patients as well as the public to walk and gain refreshment. On the stone piers of the entrance gates reclined the celebrated stone sculptures, representing 'Raving Madness' and 'Melancholy Madness'. This grandiose establishment almost seemed a desirable abode, as the poet and dramatist John Gay (quoted in Hack Tuke 1882) wittily wrote:

> *Through fam'd Moorfields, extends a spacious seat,*
> *Where mortals of exalted wit retreat;*

Where, wrapp'd in contemplation and in straw,
The wiser few from the mad world withdraw.

While the building resembled a palace outside, the inside was plainly a madhouse, consisting of two galleries, one above the other. The galleries were like long corridors with individual cells down one side. In the middle iron gates divided the men from the women. There was some pride initially in having proper facilities in the shape of stove-rooms where the patients could warm themselves, and later hot and cold bathing places below stairs. Yet the place quickly became malodorous and overcrowded, so that extensions were needed and then built. The incurable patients were accommodated in two new wings in 1723–33, and in 1793 further accommodation was added.

In the eighteenth century, visiting reached its peak, and because of the possibilities of various abuses, which will be noted in Chapter 6, restrictions were imposed from 1770. A building whose foundations rested on piles of rubble was scarcely suitable for daily streams of visitors, especially as serious subsidence and settlement began to occur, which necessitated underpinning. A rat-catcher and a man for destroying bugs were periodically needed. In 1799, a committee reported that the building was dreary, low and melancholy, the interior ill-contrived and the accommodation insufficient. Matters came to such a pass that, in 1804, admissions were restricted to those already on the waiting list. Numbers gradually declined, and, in 1807, a move to Southwark was agreed by the Governors.

St George's Fields, Southwark, 1815–1930

By the time of this, the third Bethlem, there were many other institutions for the mentally disordered that had developed in the seventeenth and eighteenth centuries. Hospitals had opened, not only in England and Europe, but also in the USA – in New York, Philadelphia and Virginia. Bethlem set out to maintain its place in the world by erecting another grand building. A flight of steps led up to a fine lofty portico with massive Ionic columns and the Royal Arms in the tympanum above. Originally, there was a low cupola above the central portico, but this was converted in 1844–5 by the addition of a massive dome, under which was enough space for a chapel taking up to two hundred and twenty worshippers. Outside were lawns, a pond, kitchen gardens, airing grounds with privies and yards, stables, a carpenter's shop and a pigsty. The layout inside resembled that of the previous hospital, catering for two hundred patients, with the possibility of enlarging that number. An agreement was made with the government to include accommodation for sixty criminal lunatics.

11

Bethlem Hospital at St George's Fields, Southwark, as it was in 1815

In the basement were the kitchens, laundry, drying room, pantry and cellars, while above were the residences and offices for the Steward, Apothecary and Matron, a parlour for the Physicians and Committee, a Porter's room and a visiting room for patients. A spacious staircase provided the ascent to the principal Committee Room.

Two special blocks were allocated in 1816 for people who had faced criminal charges and been either acquitted or found unfit to plead on grounds of insanity. This provision continued until 1863–4 when such patients were transferred to the newly built State Criminal Asylum at Broadmoor.

The early years were clouded by a parliamentary inquiry into abuses in 1815–6, and an inquiry by the Lunacy Commissioners in 1851, coming before the advent of major improvements under the aegis of Dr Charles Hood in the 1850s. During the later years of the century, occupations and amusements for patients improved, the teaching of doctors became established and the status of attendants steadily rose. It was not until the 1920s that the need became overwhelming for new buildings in a more salubrious area, away from the slums of central London.

Monks Orchard, Beckenham, Kent, 1930 to the present

The fourth Bethlem came into being as one of just under a hundred mental hospitals in Great Britain. It retained some prestige because of its age and Victorian traditions of care. Bethlem took over a country estate that had once belonged to the banker Lewis Loyd. On this land, there had been a mansion house, gardens with ornamental trees, three lakes with cascades, the Monks Orchard Wood and the Park Farm. The hospital built four separate houses with gardens, well spaced out, to accommodate the patients, while the staff residences and administration were grouped round the main entrance. The rural atmosphere was retained by keeping cows and pigs. Within living memory, the adolescent patients used to help with mucking out the pigs. Subsequently some market gardening was undertaken, but all of these activities eventually died out.

The new Bethlem was opened in 1930 by Queen Mary, as the President of the Hospital Board. The wards were carpeted and tastefully furnished with antique furniture and many new additions. On the ground floor the bedrooms opened on to verandahs so that the patients who were being nursed in bed could be wheeled outside to benefit from the healthy country air. The appeal of the place was mainly to middle-class patients who could pay their way, although the Free List was available to those without means.

Queen Mary sometimes returned to visit the hospital she was proud of – for tree planting and for the seven hundreth anniversary celebrations in 1947. By this time, Bethlem was on the eve of great changes. At the inception of the NHS, the historic management ties with Bridewell were severed in 1948 and an amalgamation made with the Maudsley Hospital of Camberwell, London, to form a postgraduate teaching hospital.

Maudsley Hospital, 1923 to the present

While Bethlem was pursuing, at least outwardly, an attempt at gracious living, a hospital of a different type was developing in Camberwell. Dr Henry Maudsley, an eminent doctor in the field of mental illness, had donated to the London County Council a large sum of money for the establishment of a small hospital with research facilities, for the treatment of early and acute cases, in a central position. The Maudsley Hospital opened for its intended purpose in 1923, treating patients who were willing to come, at any rate in the first instance, on a voluntary basis. Dr Edward Mapother, the first Medical Superintendent, wrote that the Maudsley's most distinctive feature was that it combined the characters of the neurological and psychiatric clinics of the continent, and the characters of

Maudsley Hospital, 1995

hospitals in this and other countries. The scene was set for the development of a hospital of international interest.

The Maudsley occupied a site in Camberwell next to the railway and across the road from King's College Hospital. Several Georgian residences continued to co-exist on the campus with the main administration building, which was decorated with white stone and columns, sometimes described as 'Wrenaissance' and reminiscent of Hampton Court. The wards behind were plain and functional in red brick, and later, alas, some prefabricated Ministry of Health and Social Security buildings, fronted by asphalt, were allowed to mushroom on the Denmark Hill side. The hospital was extended several times before World War II, during which activities were dispersed to other sites. The medical school was taken over by the University of London just prior to the amalgamation with Bethlem and renamed the Institute of Psychiatry.

The Bethlem Royal Hospital and the Maudsley Hospital, 1948 onwards

The two hospitals continued to function on their respective sites in Beckenham and Camberwell, growing slowly into one institution, being at first run by a Board of Governors and later by a Special Health Authority, until becoming an NHS Trust in 1994. A unique constellation of specialist units developed, increasingly sited at Bethlem, with the generalist services and the community mental health services focused on the Camberwell district. Parts of the development of the joint hospitals and some of their clinical work will be discussed in Chapters 11 and 13, but, before coming to that, we will focus in the next chapter on what the patients said about their experiences of the services.

A brief chronology

1247   The Priory of St Mary of Bethleem [sic] at Bishopsgate, London is founded by Deed of Gift of Simon Fitz-Mary.

1329   The Priory of St Mary of Bethlem is first described as a 'hospice' or 'hospital'.

1346   Matthew de Norton, Master of the Order, petitions the Mayor of the City of London for help in managing the hospital, and the City takes the hospital under its patronage.

1403   First public inquiry – a visitation by Commissioners of King Henry IV – includes a mention of 'men deprived of reason'.

1547   After the dissolution of the religious order, King Henry VIII grants the government of the hospital of Bethlem to the City of London.

1557   Bethlem and Bridewell, the House of Correction, are united under one management.

1633   Royal Commissioners investigate the problems of the hospital, concerning the Keeper, Dr Helkiah Crooke.

1676   First change of site. Bethlem moves to a palatial new building at Moorfields, London.

1723–33   Wings for incurable patients are constructed.

1733   Hogarth paints 'Bedlam' – the last scene in his 'Rake's Progress'.

1770   Visiting is restricted to those with tickets of admission.

1815   Bethlem moves again, to another site at Southwark, London.

1815–16   Parliamentary inquiry into the treatment of patients. Blocks for criminal patients are built.

1851–2	Inquiry by the Lunacy Commissioners, and major reforms begin.
1863–4	Criminal patients are transferred to the new Broadmoor Hospital.
1870	Convalescent establishment opens at Witley in Surrey.
1882	The Charity Commissioners agree for paying patients to be admitted.
1923	The Maudsley Hospital for early and acute cases of mental illness opens in Camberwell, London.
1930	Bethlem transfers to a country estate at Beckenham, Kent.
1939	The Maudsley Hospital disperses largely to Mill Hill, Middlesex and the Belmont, Sutton, Surrey, because of World War II.
1948	Bethlem Royal and Maudsley Hospitals amalgamate as a single post-graduate teaching hospital in the new NHS.
1967	The Institute of Psychiatry moves to a new building adjacent to the Maudsley.
1991	The Maudsley takes over the management of the District catchment area service for the mentally ill.
1994	Bethlem Royal and Maudsley Hospitals become an NHS Trust.

References and further reading

Andrews, J. (1991) *Bedlam Revisited: A History of Bethlem Hospital c1634–c1770.* Unpublished PhD thesis, University of London

Anon. (1788) *De Londres et ses environs.* Amsterdam (no publisher given).

Black W (1811) *A Dissertation on Insanity.* London: Ridgway, Murray and Richardson.

Boswell J (1799), ed. Chapman RW 1953, corrected 1970. *Life of Johnson.* London: Oxford University Press.

Bowen T (1784) *An Historical Account of the Origin, Progress and Present State of Bethlem Royal Hospital.* London: (no publisher given).

Carpenter M (1981) Asylum nursing before 1914: a chapter in the history of labour. In Davies C (ed.) *Rewriting Nursing History.* London: Croom Helm.

Copeland AJ (1910) Short history of Bethlem Royal Hospital. *Under the Dome,* **19** (74) 47–68.

Crammer JL (1994) English asylums and English doctors: where Scull is wrong. *History of Psychiatry* v: 103–115.

Davies C (1981) *Rewriting Nursing History.* London: Croom Helm.

Foucault M (1961) (translated by R Howard 1965) *Madness and Civilisation: A History of Insanity in the Age of Reason.* London: Tavistock.

Foucault M (1975) *Discipline and Punish: The Birth of the Prison.* Translated by A Sheridan 1977. New York: Pantheon.

Gregory W (1450, reprinted 1876) *Chronicle of London.* London: Camargo Society.

Hunter R and Macalpine I (1963) *Three Hundred Years of Psychiatry, 1535–1860.* London: Oxford University Press.

Nolan P (1993) *A History of Mental Health Nursing.* London: Chapman & Hall.

O'Donoghue EG (1914) *The Story of Bethlem Hospital from its Foundation in 1247.* London: T. Fisher Unwin.

Plumb JH (1972) Bedlam. *In the Light of History.* London: Allen Lane.

Scull A (1982) *Museums of Madness.* Harmondsworth: Penguin Books.

Thompson EP (1966) History from below. *The Times Literary Supplement* 7 April: 279–280.

Tuke DH (1876) The history of Bethlem Hospital. *Proceedings of the medico-Psychological Association at Bethlem Royal Hospital*, May 10.

Tuke DH (1882) *Chapters in the History of the Insane in the British Isles.* London: Kegan Paul, Trench and Co.

White JG (1899) *A Short History of the Royal Hospitals of Bridewell and Bethlem.* London (printed privately).

*T*he patient's voice

'**A** client-centred approach' is what many mental health professionals aim for nowadays in their clinical practice. There has been a growing desire to listen more attentively to what the clients or patients have to say about their conditions, treatments and perceptions of how the care is delivered. At Bethlem over the centuries, patients have voiced their opinions on a range of circumstances that have affected them. In this chapter, we consider what patients have written themselves and also what patients are reported to have said. For practical purposes, generalised descriptions of the hospital and literary texts with an intended fictional element have been avoided in this chapter.

The material considered has been divided into four types, although this is not to suggest that other classifications might not be equally valid. Roy Porter, for instance, in *Mind-Forg'd Manacles* (1987) divides the Voice of the Mad according to the types of complaint – melancholy in its various manifestations, those adrift from public reality, those with delusions – and other themes.

The categories considered here are:

1. material obtained by direct inquiries;
2. congratulatory literature;
3. protest/complaint literature;
4. autobiographical texts.

It will be seen that the material does not always fit neatly into one category, but may have elements of several. Much of the material was composed after patients had been discharged, so certain allowances need to be made by the reader for distortion either in a favourable, unfavourable or inaccurate way, because of the effect on memory of the passage of time. There are also the effects on perception and rationality that may arise from being mentally disturbed. The extracts have been chosen, not only for their descriptive qualities of the hospital and patients' attitudes, but to illustrate comments on the carers, be they keepers, attendants or mental health nurses.

Inquiries

Until recently, it was not common for patients' ideas to be solicited and then recorded in written form, except when there were glaring problems. At the Bethlem and Maudsley Hospitals it has now become the practice to consult patients about current issues that affect them. An example of this is the study carried out in 1992 by Thomas et al, entitled 'Involuntary cohabitees', which addressed the issue of having mixed-sex wards, and the needs of patients, particularly the need for privacy. Here is an extract from the findings from 150 participants in the study:

> When asked whether they preferred being cared for by a male or female nurse, eighty-two (55%) said they preferred a mixed ratio because men and women offered different approaches. Thirty-six (24%) had no particular preference. To them, gender was less important than the individual nurse's personality or experience. Sixteen (11%) of the women respondents said they would have preferred to have been cared for solely by female nurses. Some said female nurses had a better understanding of women's problems or they found other women easier to talk to. Five said they could not bear men and felt quite unsafe being supervised by them, while two said they liked having male nurses around because their presence helped to protect the women in the ward and made it safer. One patient said he liked female nurses because he could talk to them about his feelings, but liked male nurses because they talked to him about football.

Already in this short extract several ideas emerge, helping to identify what patients want from nurses. While experience and understanding of problems are important, so also is the nurse's personality, and this is a recurring theme. Different nurses will have various skills in interaction, some helping the patient to relate to his everyday world, some helping him to explore specific reactions to his current situation, each offering complementary types of support. Safety is seen as a prerequisite; the question is, who will provide it?

Mixed-sex wards are largely a phenomenon of the second half of the twentieth century at Bethlem, although the social mixing of male and female patients was recognised as problematic at least as early as 1663.

Bethlem has been the subject of numerous Public Inquiries across the centuries, the earliest being in 1403. In the report of the external Commissioners who visited Bethlem, we find the evidence from one of the earliest named patients:

> *Agnes Coteneys, a woman lately residing within the aforesaid Hospital, in the year*
> *and a half past, gives evidence that she herself, the self-same witness, was conveyed*
> *to the aforesaid hospital by her neighbours for the recovery of her health there,*
> *because at that time she was seriously ill, and she says that much alms was*
> *collected for her by her parents and other worthy people: and that on many*
> *occasions it was stolen by Peter Taverner, the Porter, to such an extent that she*
> *was unable to get that which had been collected for her, and that the aforesaid*
> *Peter, or at any rate his wife, carried away and kept for their own private uses*
> *each thing and everything that was meant for her benefit.*

Agnes goes on to press for the return of her property. If, as a discharged patient, she had at least partially recovered, it may have been easier for her to criticise the staff and seek reparation. She was assisted by the evidence of staff who were able to support her testimony of the abuses of Peter Taverner. So begins a long story of patients who, with a minimum of encouragement, were able to provide useful accounts of their experiences.

Patients have not always been so forthcoming when questioned by external inquirers, especially while still inpatients. The responses to questions sometimes show a passivity that suggests that the patients were either unable, unwilling or fearful of giving comments that would have assisted their questioners.

Edward Wakefield visited the hospital on April 25 and May 2 1814, and on the women's galleries the patients complained of being deprived of tea and sugar. They did not complain about being chained to the wall, or only having a blanket gown to cover their nakedness. In the men's wing, even James Norris, an American marine who had been chained to the wall for 14 years, at first merely said that it was in consequence of attempting to defend himself from what he conceived to be improper treatment by his keeper. James Norris (sometimes known as William Norris) described how he was fastened by a long chain, which, passing through a partition wall, enabled a keeper, by going into the next cell, to draw him close to the wall at will. He also told Edward Wakefield that 'he read a great deal of books of all kinds, history, lives or anything the keepers could get him; the newspaper everyday, and conversed perfectly coherently on the passing topics and the events of the war, in which he felt particular interest'.

The fact that the patient had been chained up for several years was regarded by the visitors as scandalous, but the hospital staff pointed out that in 1803 he had stabbed William Hawkins, one of the keepers, had also stabbed a patient and had bitten off the finger of a man named Thompson.

On closer questioning, one of the members of the committee, Charles Western, found that James Norris had some insight into his condition:

He talked freely, and not altogether irrationally; he told us he was aware of his own situation, and of his occasional violence, and confessed that he was not fit to be trusted without some restraint, as he could not answer for himself, and that he might otherwise do mischief to somebody, as he had tried to do before; his mind therefore was not in such a state as to render him insensible to his situation, nor to deprive him of all social enjoyments; and in proportion as his mind was rational, his suffering must have been increased during his long and dreadful confinement.

Elinor Webb, an ex-patient, had, in 1851, the ordeal of appearing before a panel of Commissioners in order to describe her stay in Bethlem. The transcript of the proceedings shows that she was asked 145 questions, which covered topics such as forced feeding, the amounts of bedding used, bedtimes, observation at night, washing, physical abuse and bad language. Although the Commissioners were not asking her directly about how she herself was treated, Elinor Webb volunteered information when she got the chance:

Question 1638. Did you ever see any of them struck with a broom? – No; I was struck with a broom once.
1639. Who struck you? – Mrs Turner.
1640. Did you ever see her strike anyone else? – No.
1641. What kind of a blow was it? – She hit my knuckles as hard as she could hit them.
1642. What for? – Because I climbed up to the window.
1643. Did you ever see Ellen strike any of them? – No, only push them about.

and later:

1653. Did Ellen use any bad language to other patients as well? – Yes, she used it to me.
1654. What language did she make use of? – That I was 'a rotten Westminster whore;' that was her frequent language.'

The Matron poured doubt on Mrs Webb's testimony, dismissing it as conjectural evidence, unsupported by a single witness. 'During the time this patient remained in the basement-ward, her habits, disposition, and violent conduct were such that great caution would have been necessary in receiving any statement from her.'

Whatever the behaviour of this patient was, there were substantial accounts of dubious practices by attendants. One might wonder how the Commissioners set about distinguishing the truthfulness or otherwise of their interviewees. The transcripts leave the reader feeling at some distance from the meetings on which they report. There was undoubtedly some condensation of material, otherwise there could not be such a coherence of style throughout. Yet the oft-repeated allegations, for instance of the unsatisfactory nature of the bedding and clothing, eventually added up in the Commissioners minds to a view on which they felt able to act.

In this Inquiry one begins to encounter the same sort of material as that found in protest/complaint literature, but, before looking at that, here is a digression into writings that praise.

Congratulatory literature

This is the sort of writing that might have been commissioned, or at least suggested, by the management of the hospital. Although it is often for the consumption of the general public, it sometimes seems to be for boosting the morale of the staff. The tone can occasionally be thought sycophantic, but the writing may include a softly worded critique of hospital life.

In 1744, Bethlem published a broadsheet to be handed to visitors to the hospital, purporting to be written by a patient, J. Clark. It followed a known format, for example that of Thomas Fitzgerald (1733) and Hildebrand Jacob (1723), which started by praising the institution – buildings or staff – described the mad people and sometimes ended with a moral.

Mr J. Clark expressed his gratitude to the Governors and said that what he wrote would be strictly truthful. He then began the poem proper:

> First, to our Governors due praise be given;
> Who, by just care, have changed our Hell for Heav'n:
> A Hell on Earth no truer can we find,
> Than a disturbed and distracted Mind;
> And, of all the Charities that, sure, is best,
> That soothes the troubled Soul to quiet Rest.
> For this, our learned Doctor gives his Aid,
> And for his Care, with Blessings ever paid;
> This all those happy Objects will not spare,
> Who are discharged by his Skill and Care.
> Our trusty Steward, next demands our Praise,
> And, without Doubt he'll have it all our Days.
> We must not now forget old honest Wood,
> Who to us all is civil, kind and good.
> The Keepers, mild to those who well behave;
> But some there are, who always curse and rave;
> Are justly chain'd, confined within each Room,
> Altho' they know, full well, their certain Doom:
> If Keepers should neglect at this just Call,
> It would, no doubt, go badly with us all.'

The poet continued, describing the food, the treatments and the causes of madness. He ended by saying that trusting too much to some led to the doom of madness, but there were really too many causes of madness for him to describe them all.

In the above extract, Mr Clark praised the Governors again, and, by way of the Doctor, Steward and Porter came to the keepers, who were given the most space. There the poem took a slightly unexpected turn. The keepers, although mostly mild in manner, have to restrain and seclude patients. The poet/patient seemed to feel the need to justify this, putting the blame on the disturbed patients and stressing that it was for the good of all. We hear that the keepers' role was to maintain a safe environment.

For another example of congratulatory literature, one can look at the house magazine, *Under the Dome*, for 1905. In an article entitled 'Tempus fugit', a patient who only identifies himself as 'An Impatient Patient' describes his stay in Bethlem. The first half of the article was written at the request of the hospital chaplain, the Reverend E.G. O'Donoghue, while the author was still an inpatient: the second half was written after convalescence when he had returned home. He wrote of the great kindness that he received within Bethlem's hospitable walls and claimed that in no place can time be made to fly more quickly and pleasantly. This patient expressed himself in pompous, moralising, slightly comic metaphors, which were perhaps what he thought the chaplain would like. The hospital was compared to a railway train – 'some of us are destined for a shorter, some for a longer trip, but all of us, one may hope, will be the better for the journey, and will alight at our respective stations with none but pleasant feelings – feelings of gratitude towards those who have so well ministered to our creature comforts'.

It was only when the author had arrived home that he was able to tell the reader of the 'sad experiences which are inseparable from any sort of restraint'. He had been indignant at being deprived of his freedom and tried to persuade the doctors that they were wrong with 'not-always-too-carefully-worded remonstrances'. What seemed to have been most therapeutic was his curiously worded interactions with other patients. One of his fellows addressed him as follows:

> 'My dear young friend, you are very eloquent, very plausible, and very amiable, but you are extremely cocky!'
> 'Cocky!' I exclaimed, in high dudgeon, 'I consider that is a most offensive term, and I must request you to withdraw it. I know I have my faults, but I am convinced "cockiness" is not one of them; in fact, to be "cocky" is that which I have striven all my life – and I am persuaded successfully – to avoid becoming.'
> 'Well,' said my friend, 'If you object to the word "cocky," I have no objection to substituting the word "strutty." You will surely not deny that you are very "strutty."'
> 'Heavens!' cried I, '"strutty!" If anything could be worse than "cockiness," it would be "struttiness," and I cannot for a moment admit your soft impeachment.'
> 'I would not for worlds hurt your feelings,' returned my accuser, 'and I will

23

cheerfully retract both the expressions to which you take exception, provided that
you, on the other hand, will only admit that you are very arrogant.'
I admitted nothing and the conversation ceased.

The author seemed to have taken his friend's comments to heart and was able after a pause to continue the relationship. He concluded his article by saying that in trying to give hope to other patients, he was 'insensibly cheered and refreshed' himself, and finally suggested that a society should be formed to continue and complete the admirable work carried out at Bethlem. The management at this period needed some impetus to organise follow-up care in the community.

Protest/complaint literature

In this section, we will consider some examples of literature that is primarily directed towards an exposure of a corrupt or cruel system, where ex-patient authors have sought publication to alert a wide public.

The magazine *Pearson's Weekly*, on May 30, 1912, published an article that superficially might almost pass for a congratulatory text. The anonymous ex-Bethlem patient writes that force-feeding was not 'torture' as some had supposed, that the patients were not ill-treated as in the county asylum, and that the Bethlem staff were quite pleasant to her – some of them, some of the time:

> *Three Years in Two Madhouses, by One Who Endured It.*
>
> *The particular place to which I was taken, and in which I was confined during the first year of my madness, was the Bethlem Royal Asylum (or 'Hospital', as it is officially designated), in the Lambeth Road, London. This really splendid institution is intended for the care of lunatics likely to be cured within one year, and preference is given to patients of the educated classes. It has an income from investments of £80,000 a year, and everything possible is done for the poor demented creatures it harbours, both as regards skilled medical attendance, and diet, and in other ways.*

She wrote that she was suffering from 'acute melancholia' and wished to die as soon as possible, so she refused to eat. A doctor and five nurses force-fed her using a gag, stomach tube or nasal tube:

> *Presently, realising even in my poor mad brain that my attempt at suicide by starvation was doomed to failure, I gave it up for a bad job and consented to take my food in the ordinary way.*
>
> *As soon as I started doing this, the harsh looks and words that had been used to me by doctors and nurses – and which were really, as I found out afterwards, purposely assumed for my own good – entirely ceased, and I was treated with every kindness.*

24

In Bethlem Hospital each ward is a little world of its own, with its separate staff, consisting of a sister, nurse, and about four probationers.

I was posted to Mary Ward, and remained there during the entire twelve months I was an inmate of the institution.

Sister Wheeler was in charge, and I took a great fancy to her from the very beginning. She was one of the sweetest and kindest and most patient women it has ever been my lot to meet, and one of whom it might be truthfully said that she was a born nurse.

This patient perceived the staff carrying out the difficult treatment procedures as harsh. This is hard to avoid, even with the best explanations, if the procedure has happened without the patient's cooperation. Patients in their writings express ambiguous feelings about nurses who need to be firm and discourage some sorts of patient behaviour. The writer later described the probationers as being either nice, or hasty and ill-tempered. She had to see somebody as a positive understanding person, and in this case it was the Sister in charge. One wonders if the Sister participated in the feeding procedure. It is likely that she attracted at least some of this flattery by virtue of the power inherent in her role, which must suggest caution in self-appraisal by those in positions of authority.

Not all protests are as subtly worded as this *Pearson's Weekly* article, and for a full-bodied attack on the behaviour of the staff of the hospital one can hardly do better than read the diatribe of Urbane Metcalf (1818) entitled *The Interior of Bethlehem Hospital*. Metcalf, previously a hawker of laces, garters and braces, was a patient at Bethlem in Moorgate, 1804–6, and at Bethlem in Southwark in 1817. He itemised the misdemeanours of the staff one by one and presented a lurid picture. The person who attracted the most of his venom was Rodbird (actual name Rodbard) keeper of the Fourth Gallery:

Another patient of the name of Leonard, is in a general way a very quiet man. I have known Rodbird the keeper, abuse him repeatedly and set other patients on to do it: I remember well I was once at the pump and Rodbird came out to rinse a drinking horn. Rodbird said he had been giving Leonard physic, and there were two doses of it, and damn the B–gg–r he wished it was poison. And though it was Dr Tothill, his physician's order that he should go to chapel when he chose, he [Rodbird] used to hinder him whenever he pleased.

Another patient of the name of Brown, some months back it was thought necessary to keep in a strait jacket, but afterwards he was allowed in the daytime to have it off. On Tuesdays, Thursdays and Saturdays, the evenings that Rodbird went out, he would put the jacket on before Brown had had his supper, and I have seen him put to the greatest difficulty to contrive to eat his supper as he had not the use of his hands. And this was done merely to save Blackburn, who on those evenings supplied Rodbird's place, the trouble of putting the jacket on at bedtime.

Metcalf had scarcely less severe words for the Matron, Elizabeth Forbes, whom he appeared to find irresponsible and self-seeking:

> *I do think that a greater abuse cannot exist than the permission extended to the servants of the institution, to take in private patients, setting aside the injustice of making a public establishment subservient to private interest; they cannot if they are occupied with the care of private persons devote their time to the exercise of those duties they are hired to discharge. During the last summer, Miss Clarke [a patient] and the matron went to Worthing, and were absent for a fortnight; Miss Clarke's liberty is indisputable, but surely the matron ought not to absent herself, at any time. It is a gross violation of her duty, and calls for the severest reproof if not a dismissal.*

One can feel some sympathy with Metcalf's point regarding the activities of Mrs Forbes. There has been conflict at several points in the history of Bethlem for staff between their responsibilties to the institution and the compulsion to follow other occupations for some part of their time, for financial advantage. This must, on many occasions have been because of the meagre salaries paid to staff, but it could also have been a response to the demands of a more or less total institution, where staff had to live and be frequently available, with very little official time off. Was this, for instance, Mrs Forbes' only way of getting some respite? The regime confined both patients and staff.

In the activities of Rodbard, however, one reads, even in this short episode, of something that appears inhumane and malicious. It is not known how far Metcalf caricatured Rodbard's behaviour, and there is another side to the story. The medical notes are revealing. Thomas Rodbard, the keeper, reported to the doctor (1818) his observations of the patient Metcalf's condition.

> *July 1: I am informed by Thomas Rodbird the Keeper of No 4 in which gallery this patient has constantly resided, that he has now ceased to consider himself as heir to the Throne of Denmark – and I observe that he does not seem so depressed.*
> *September 1: This patient appears rather irritable at this period and has complained to me about the badness of the provisions and of the ill treatment which some of the patients have endured from their respective keepers. He has also made the complaints to Dr Munro – but I cannot ascertain any fact upon which his accusations are grounded – his health is improved and he continues to take the Pills.*

We have here encapsulated one of the problems of patients' complaints. This patient had a long standing delusional belief, and this may have militated against the managers taking seriously his complaints of ill-treatment, especially if they were not very coherent. Dale Peterson (1982) says that Metcalf's writing resembles a blurred photograph. This seems apt when one reads his allegations of the murder of a patient, juxtaposed with the failure of the keepers to provide clean socks. It is, nevertheless, as Peterson says, a noteworthy contribution to the history of protest.

Lastly, we turn to the protests of a naval office ticket clerk, James Carkesse, which appeared in verse in his book of 1679 entitled *Lucida Intervalla*. Although fiercely critical of the conduct of the institution, he did not write as if expecting redress for the way he was treated, so his work could just as easily be discussed in the next section of this chapter under autobiographical writings. Carkesse is concerned to hold a glass up to society. As Porter (1987) wrote, 'Carkesse's barbs against the asylum are not those of a Benthamite reformer avant la lettre, but those of a railer against the human tragi-comedy'. Carkesse believed that he was a poet of genius, but critics have not been impressed with his verses.

Transferring to Bethlem from the Finsbury madhouse, Carkesse arrived in a frenzy, breaking the windows of the coach and tearing his clothes. He had high expectations of Bethlem, but warned that unless the staff were civil, he would behave like a madman. This mad behaviour seems to have occurred, for he wrote that he had been confined in darkness and in chains, given Physick, beaten, bled and made to vomit. Carkesse railed against 'Sir Madquack', his doctor, Dr Allen, protesting that he was only acting mad.

Joseph Matthews, the Porter, and the keepers (basketmen) come in for particular criticism, being compared to the dogs of Hell. Of the three keepers, Jones and Langdale were 'fierce' to the patients and fawned on their superiors, while Whetstone was weak, a 'tail with no sting'. The records show that Whetstone had had a long period of illness.

Carkesse acknowledged the importance of the keepers, who at that time wore azure-blue uniform coats, saying that his madness was not controlled by the moon, but by the demeanour of the keepers:

> *His*
> *Rule of Behaviour:*
> *If you are Civil,*
> *I am Sober.*

> *Porter and Keepers, when they're Civil,*
> *They charm in me the Madmens Devil;*
> *The Roaring Lyon turns to Lamb,*
> *Lies down and couches wondrous Tame:*
> *For though at Bedlam Wits ebb and flow,*
> *As wandring Stars move swift or slow;*
> *My Brains not ruled by the Pale Moon,*
> *Nor keep the Sphears my Soul in Tune;*
> *But she observes, and changes notes*
> *With th' Azure of Sky coulour'd Coats.*

Autobiographical writings

This category of patients' writings is composed of material from authors who wish to share their experiences of mental illness in Bethlem, for reasons that may include instruction of others, financial gain or maybe a desire to externalise their illnesses. These texts were unsolicited and do not appear to be written in expectation of changing the institution. The authors describe, rather than praise or blame.

In 1976, Stuart Sutherland, a psychologist, wrote his book *Breakdown*, which he subtitled 'A personal crisis and a medical dilemma'. The first part of his book described his experiences of mental breakdown and the treatments he received. Chapter 4, 'The hospital', covered his time as an inpatient in a place that was not positively identified as Bethlem. He wrote of a renowned hospital that was an NHS show-piece, and one of the best equipped in England.

This is one of the most detailed accounts by a patient of life in a ward for the mentally ill in the 1970s, and it deals with aspects of ward life not much commented on before. One of these is the potential problems of understanding between people with different cultural backgrounds. Sutherland wrote:

> *On the evening of my first day there, my anxiety began to build up. Over half of the nurses were coloured. I remember wondering how nurses with home backgrounds in Jamaica, India, Pakistan, Ceylon and many different African countries could have such sympathy with the absurd neuroses of the British middle and working classes. On my first night on the ward, an attractive and vivacious little African nurse was exceptionally kind to me. She chatted over my problems and inveigled me into playing table tennis and snooker with her, and this distraction from my anxieties was extremely helpful.*

He did not, however, see some of this nurse's subsequent interventions as helpful, and was upset when the nurse accused him of always blaming his troubles on something else. Although there were so many nurses from ethnic minorities, it was not matters concerning cultural differences that caused him most difficulty. He wrote about his frustrations with the ward routines, which included much time devoted to group meetings, the point of which was not clear to him. He described two groups, one for the whole ward and one for a small group of patients:

> *The following day my anxiety gradually built up throughout the morning. After lunch there was a group meeting of the whole ward: these meetings occurred weekly and were attended by nurses, occupational therapists, psychologists and doctors, as well as patients. I was unable to sit through the meeting – I began to wring my hands and moan and eventually I rolled on the floor. The male nurse who admitted me took me outside and we walked round and round the grounds together. He allowed me to pour out the tale of my sufferings in an attempt to talk me*

John Ogdon (1937–1989) pianist, composer and patient, 1982.
Photo: Denise Binks

down. For the rest of the afternoon nurses took it in turns to walk with me
through the beautiful park in which the hospital was situated . . .

In addition to individual therapy, there were twice weekly group therapy sessions
attended by my group as a whole. They were conducted by the registrar and were
also attended by a senior nurse – a brisk but pleasant man from India, who was
always neatly turned out. He had a ready smile, which was perhaps sometimes
lacking in warmth, but he had considerable patience and rarely became ruffled,
though he could be peremptory with recalcitrant patients. Each group session lasted
for an hour; about half the time passed in complete silence, and we spent the
remainder in sporadic discussion of what we ought to be talking about. Neither the
registrar or any of the nurses present offered guidance on this point.

A somewhat more positive view was expressed by John Ogdon, the
concert pianist, about his experiences of groups in 1973. He was admitted
to the Maudsley several times in the 1970s, the account of which was
written down by his wife, Brenda Lucas. She wrote:

There was one hour's group therapy every day in the Villa – and as a result,
John began to experience a sense of camaraderie with the other patients. Sick as
many of them were, they shared a common awareness that they were all in the

29

same boat together; also, whereas the sane visitors to the ward tried to carry on sensible conversations with them, and did their best to make sense of the answers, they themselves had a more relaxed attitude. As a rule, if one of them interrupted another, or a second replied in non-sequiturs, no one felt threatened or hurt: if a third walked away in mid-sentence, no one took any offence.

In the early 1970s, group meetings were a highly thought-of activity among many nurses and junior doctors. Such methods provided an alternative to the sometimes sterile routine of playing games and other diversional activities that Sutherland also describes, but the therapeutic effectiveness of group methods of treatment remained a matter of debate.

Before the twentieth century, female patients did not find the opportunities to comment on their care nearly as much as did male patients. This now seems to have changed, and the next author is a woman who presented her own distinctive viewpoints on hospitalisation.

'Clare Marc Wallace', writing in 1964, was herself a psychiatric nurse who became a consumer of the services. She was admitted to the 'Wilton Clinic', a London teaching centre, said to be 'a centre for ideal nurses and first-rate doctors – home of psychiatry at its best'. As in Sutherland's case, the ward was staffed mainly by 'coloured nurses'. Clare related how she tried to commit suicide by stepping in front of a bus and slashing her wrists. She was treated with electroconvulsive therapy (ECT) while the nurses tried to set limits as to what was acceptable behaviour. What is spelt out very clearly in this narrative is the centrality, in the whole process of care and cure, of the ward Sister, who had a strong and distinctive personality. It was through the relationship Clare built up with the Sister that she progressed to discharge:

I grew very attached to the Sister over the weekend, for she was about my own age, volatile but kind, and very intelligent despite her ultra-feminine gestures with her hands and shoulders, and her eyes raised to heaven if she was in disagreement with anything one said. It was rumoured that she was always quarelling with her husband, who was also a Continental. As I lay back on the pillows, I wondered idly how she ever got round to saying 'yes' and 'I do' instead of her usual 'we do'. It must have been quite a ceremony, her wedding . . .

But even though she was eccentric, she would do anything to help her patients, even if she lost her temper with them sometimes. She never bore malice, and all the time I was on her ward, I never heard her say a spiteful word about anyone. She would always manage to find a good point in everyone's favour. I was often bitchy, but Sister Zukov brushed my catty criticisms aside. She had no repressions. If she was cross with someone, she came out and said so quite forcefully, but no matter how childishly the patient was acting, she would often soften her harsh words by calling her 'dear'. Everyone was 'dear' from the patients, to the porters, to the doctors. Somehow she made herself avoid this term when talking to Dr Marx [the consultant], but it must have cost her a great deal of effort. (She spent the twenty minutes before he came to the ward making up her face.)

Zany, crazy, kind, intelligent, batty, and yet an individual – this was Sister Zukov.

This passage displays a degree of emotional attachment that is more intense than that in the earlier extract from *Pearson's Weekly*. The relationship that Clare valued had elements of dependence that were likely to create problems for the Sister and require careful handling, especially as the time for discharge from hospital drew near. It also created problems for the other ward staff whom Clare cast in a negative role and with whom she disagreed. It was to the credit of this Sister that she had learned to handle such relationships, so that she could negotiate agreements or contracts with the patient, for example that the patient did not harm herself and took the necessary diet. Clare Marc Wallace was writing about skilled psychiatric nursing, in which the Sister made use of her own personality in a nurse–patient relationship, to telling therapeutic effect.

Earlier comments on care come from a Bethlem inpatient Arthur Legent Pearce, who in 1851 arranged to have his poems published. One of the sonnets expressed the terror and anger rising up inside him in the course of a long admission:

> *When on my bed, fond memory brings the days*
> *Of youth and freedom back to this sad heart,*
> *Life lies once more before me like a chart,*
> *And forth I wander in a dreamy maze,*
> *On breathing pictures as it were to gaze.*
> *Sudden my bosom seems to rend apart -*
> *A fiend appears who shakes a dreadful dart:*
> *'Behold thy tomb – these madhouse walls,' he says.*
> *And then I burn in anger and despair,*
> *And tears fall down in torrents from my eyes.*
> *My tears cannot my fever fires impair -*
> *Still less my fires consume the tears and sighs.*
> *O cruel fate! to be confin'd as mad,*
> *For years, in scenes so wretched and so sad.*

The poem was said to have been written as 'a solace and amusement to the writer in his weary and melancholy confinement' and 'to afford pleasure to the public, awaken sympathy in his behalf, and in the behalf of the many wretched persons who have fellowship with him, both in Bethlehem and in other asylums'. Pearce's poem still has power to involve us in his plight. One hopes it was an imaginary apparition rather than a member of staff who was cruelly confronting him with his fate. His situation was comparable to that of the poet John Clare in a Northamptonshire asylum, who maintained some hope and animation until he realised that the staff were never going to release him. The outlook was gloomy for Pearce, a former doctor, who had attempted violence against his wife

31

many years before and was confined as a criminal lunatic during Her Majesty's pleasure.

It was not merely the prospect of long incarceration that upset Pearce but the company of other miserable and disabled patients. He was unable to see himself as helping his fellows, but was sucked into their dejection – a problem staff need to be alert for in any group of patients.

Another poet already mentioned, James Carkesse encouraged staff to consider the patient's situation and the effects of the hospital environment, including the behaviour of the staff themselves. In his reflective, more than his polemical mood, Carkesse tried to draw the staff back to first principles when he reminded them of the Founder of Bethlem's intention. In spite of the fact that he did not know the real founder's name and the thought was a little confused, he made valid points:

> Henry the Eighth this Hospital Erected,
> Madmen to cure, with lunacy infected:
> But Anger, a short Madness call'd, and Passion
> Here to arraign was ne're the intent nor fashion:
> This kind in Porter and Keepers raigns,
> And they should wear, who fasten on our chains.

He seems to be saying that the hospital is in the business of curing the real madness, rather than the types of anger and passion mostly seen in the Porter and keepers. Yet their behaviour is so unreasonable that they should be the ones to be considered mad. There is an element of wanting the argument both ways in Carkesse here. The implication is that when patients become angry, that is not the proper madness needing cure, but that when the staff become angry, they should be chained up like patients. The last point is one that arises fairly often in patient literature. Who are the real madmen? The staff or the patients? When a patient is confronted with some apparently non-rational piece of staff behaviour, he may reasonably question who is the mad person, especially when the patient feels that staff are punishing him for his 'mad' behaviour. This questioning by patients has the useful function of directing attention to dubious procedures and focusing minds on the perpetual need for auditing clinical practice.

Finally, we go back to the early seventeenth century to find the Bethlem patients most well-known appearance in an anonymous popular song, 'Loving Mad Tom', purported to be sung by the beggar who had been a patient in Bedlam, but had been discharged and wished to appear harmless, an object of pity. It is a companion to the other type of Bedlam popular song in which the maiden, confined and made mad by love, sighed and sang of her lover as she rattled her chains.

Tom O'Bedlam was out in the community begging and perhaps stealing for his living. He was not exactly cured, as his disordered thought in the song is meant to show, but he could present himself as a sympathetic figure. Shakespeare might have expected his audience to recognise this character, which he put on stage in his play *King Lear*. The British Library manuscript of this song has eight stanzas and refrain, of which the following is a sample.

From the hag and hungry goblin
That into rags would rend ye
All the spirits that stand by the naked man
In the Book of Moons defend ye!
That of your five senses
You never be forsaken
Nor wander from yourselves with Tom
Abroad to beg your bacon.

While I do sing 'Any food, any feeding,
Feeding, drink, or clothing'
Come dame or maid, be not afraid,
Poor Tom will injure nothing.

O thirty bare years have I
Twice twenty been enraged,
And of forty been three times fifteen
In durance soundly caged
On the lordly lofts of Bedlam
With stubble soft and dainty,
Brave bracelets strong, sweet whip's ding dong,
With wholesome hunger plenty.

And now I sing . . .

Poor Tom has been stripped, starved, confined in chains and whipped. His sins have been expiated; as a patient, he has suffered. The community must now support him. He implies that if you show charity, you may mysteriously ward off the evil spirits of madness from yourself.

Conclusion

The above examples of patients' writings and utterances have been selected to illustrate a variety of moods and feelings, produced as a reaction to their environment and the people in it. There has been misery and cheerfulness, love and hate, bitter denunciation and servile praise. The modes of treatment were commented on, but in this group of authors it was the behaviour and personalities of the staff that attracted the most attention. Much has been said about the use and abuse of power in the mental hospital/asylum. One might have wished for more material to draw on, or more space to develop the themes emerging. There is enough to demonstrate the richness of the patients' contribution to health care over several centuries.

In the next chapter we turn from the patients towards those staff who were themselves delivering care.

References and further reading

Anon. *Loving Mad Tom.* British Museum MS Additional 24665.

Carkesse J (1679) *Lucida Intervalla.* London (no publisher given).

Clark J (1744) *Bethlem, A Poem.* A broadsheet sold to visitors to Bethlem.

Fitzgerald T (1733) Bedlam. In *Poems on Severall Occasions.* London (no publisher given).

Jacob H (1723) *Bedlam, A Poem.* London (no publisher given).

Metcalf U (1818) *The Interior of Bethlehem Hospital.* London (published by the author).

Ogdon BL and Kerr M (1981) *Virtuoso: The Story of John Ogdon.* London: Hamish Hamilton.

Perceval JT (ed.) (1851) *Poems by a Prisoner in Bethlehem* (Arthur Legent Pearce). London: Effingham Wilson.

Peterson DA (1982) *A Mad People's History of Madness.* Pittsburgh: University of Pittsburgh Press.

Porter R (1987) *Mind-Forg'd Manacles.* London: Athlone Press.

Sutherland S (1976) *Breakdown.* London: Weidenfeld and Nicolson.

Thomas B, Liness S, Vearnals S and Griffin H (1992) Involuntary cohabitees. *Nursing Times,* 88(49): 58–60.

Wallace CM (1964) *Portrait of a Schizophrenic Nurse.* London: Hammond, Hammond and Co.

Basketmen, Keepers, Attendants and Nurses

Those who have cared for the inmates of Bethlem across the centuries have had differing roles and titles, ranging from 'brother' to 'mental health nurse', and these matters are discussed in the first part of this chapter. To start to define features of their employment more closely, there are sections on the number of carers, their uniforms, residence, staff stability and absences, and salaries.

Brothers and Sisters

The brothers of the Priory of St Mary of Bethlehem developed a special responsibility for gathering money to support the Mother House of the monastery in the Holy Land and also their own house, the London Priory. They went out with baskets to collect food, which was donated from the tables of the rich in London. This eventually led to the coining of the word 'basketman' for one who cared for the inmates at Bethlem.

By the fourteenth century the house was being run by a Master, who was expected to be in Holy Orders, and by 1400 the day-to-day management was being controlled by a Porter. This Porter, sometimes called a Janitor, also had there his wife and servants, together with a chaplain, at least one other priest and sundry lay people. The Brothers and Sisters had disappeared, except for one Sister, Alicia Lincoln, who was non-functional. She said that she was willing to resume her duties, which were probably to do with the giving and receiving of alms. The residents, besides the poor and sick, also included labouring men and children who lodged there.

Basketmen and Maidservants

In the sixteenth century, the inmates became the responsibility of a Keeper, who replaced the Master. The Keepers came from a background in trade, for example Richard Munnes, draper (1561), Edward Rest, grocer (1565) and Roland Sleford, clothworker (1580). This changed in 1619 with the first medical appointment as Keeper of Dr Helkiah Crooke, also physician to King James I. Dr Crooke left the care of the hospital to a steward, and there were numerous complaints of bad conditions and the ill-treatment of patients (Allderidge 1979, Management and mismanagement at Bedlam). This in turn led to inquiries, which resulted in the office of Keeper being abolished. A resident Steward in 1635 became responsible to the Governors for the day-to-day management.

The staffing gradually becomes more explicit in the hospital records. From the time of Dr Crooke, there start to be Matrons, for example Elizabeth Withers (1633–54). The Matrons were unsalaried and, apart from a few minor exceptions, they were the wives of the Porters or, later on, the Stewards. The office of Nurse for the physically sick patients was first held by Elizabeth Clashby, 'an experienced and able person', wages £6 per year, who started on January 27 1693. This post continued inter-mittently until it was combined with the office of Matron in the person of Mary Spencer in 1765. The following Matron and Nurse, Mary White was also the wife of the Steward.

These officers were assisted by basketmen, maidservants and their assistants who worked directly with the patients. There were also support staff, such as the cook, washerwomen, gardener and nightwatchman.

In the eighteenth century, although the patients were being segregated by sex, the basketmen worked on both the men's and the women's side, where they were assisted by gallery maids (Bethlem Rule Books 1778). The segregation of distracted women and men patients had initially been formalised by the Governors in 1663, when a 'discreet, careful and single woman' had been appointed to take care of the distracted women.

Keepers

Although the term 'keeper', meaning a servant who looked after mad people, was in popular use throughout the seventeenth and eighteenth centuries, Bethlem adhered, for official purposes, to its own terms – basketman and gallery maid. These terms fell out of use in the early nineteenth century, and, in 1815, the Bethlem Salary Books called such staff male keepers and female keepers. Some of these keepers were illiterate, as is illustrated by the fact that two of the female keepers in 1815 were unable to sign their names in the Salary Book and merely made their mark.

John Haslam, Apothecary at Bethlem, had at first a somewhat low opinion of keepers, as instanced in his book of 1809, where he wrote: 'Although an office of some importance and great responsibility, it [being a keeper] is held as a degrading and odious employment, and seldom accepted but by idle and disorderly persons'. He commented that the public hospitals acquired better staff, who wanted to be kept on because of the better pay, than was the case in private institutions, where recruitment was from 'the plough, the loom, or the stable'. However, in a later book of 1817, Haslam made a passionate plea for starting a contributory pension fund and establishing a register of keepers. He reflected on the predicament of the keepers, of whom there were considerable expectations, but who were exposed to personal hazard with scant pay, and who were disqualified from working when their bodily vigour had declined. This seemed unjust.

The word 'keeper' was used in a fairly loose way in the first half of the nineteenth century to denote not only those who were working on the wards, but also other hospital staff who were following the trades of painter, plumber, plasterer, engineer and bricklayer. Details of the roles connected with patients are set out in Chapter 6, 'Rules for the Workplace'. It does not appear that the Bethlem keepers had such extensive calls as elsewhere to function as artisans in addition to their ward duties, for example as at Worcester County Asylum in 1851 (Nolan 1992). Nevertheless, in the early nineteenth century, two of the five keepers in rotation performed the offices of cook and cutter of meat. There was no very obvious use of recovered patients as keepers, for example as at Stafford in 1819 (Smith 1988), although they sometimes assisted with domestic tasks, such as distributing provisions (Sub-Committee 1769).

Attendants

By Lady Day 1843, the staff have been renamed again and are called male attendants and female attendants. Ten years later the first Head Attendant for the male patients was appointed, namely Charles Neville. He is remembered as the man who looked after Richard Dadd, patient and distinguished artist. Dadd painted Neville's portrait, and he appeared as a person of substance. He strikes one as a different class of person from keepers such as Rodbard and Blackburn, so reviled by Metcalf forty years before for their violence and thieving. However, there is little evidence on which to construct a picture of the social origins of the Bethlem attendants of this period. Elsewhere, the asylums employed persons qualified to be 'upper servants' (Hanwell, 1847) or 'the upper domestic servant type' (Northampton, 1900). Conolly of Hanwell sharply criticised the appointment of men as Male Attendants just because they had the frames of prize-fighters. We do hear at Bethlem in 1879 of some anxiety regarding possible changes in the social class of attendant, stemming from the experience of having probationer nurses from St Bartholomew's Hospital on ward placements. An anonymous writer voices this concern in the house journal *Bethlem Star*.

> *I believe that young active women of the lower middle class are best suited for such work as they have here, and I do not believe that lady nurses would succeed so well. The duties of the attendants are very onerous and often very unpleasant; hard manual labour is required as well as cheerful association. In Bethlem we have such a very large area per patient, that the mere keeping it clean is no light business, and we should require a large staff of scrubbers as well as lady nurses, which would make the administration costly as well as cumbrous.*

This view was not shared by the Physician Superintendent in 1887, who wrote in the Annual Report, 'We have tried the experiment of having a limited number of lady probationers in the wards to learn mental nursing, and at the same time to act as lady companions. There can be no doubt that the more refined our attendants are the better'.

It seems that this may have had some influence on recruitment policy, although it was hard to persuade the brighter, more 'refined' attendants to stay. We read, in 1897, that it was difficult to get young attendants of fair education and good manners who did not leave for more rapid promotion elsewhere. Bethlem Matrons from the mid-nineteenth century were recruited from among those who had held posts of responsibility in asylums or schools; for instance, in 1869, Elizabeth Wright came from her post as Matron at Wellington College; in 1893 William Slattery, Head Attendant, came from Cane Hill Hospital, Surrey; and in 1916 Sarah Hearder, Matron, came from the Royal Edinburgh Asylum.

Mental nursing

In 1854, the post of Night Watch was created, first for a woman and then a second post for a man. This was, in effect, the beginning of a night nursing service. At this time there was a growing awareness all over the country of the need to employ separate staff for night duties. In 1856,

Jane Slack, the female post-holder, was being described as the 'Night Nurse'. This job title continued to be used until 1901 when all female attendants, day or night, were retitled as either Sister, Staff Nurse or Nurse. This reorientation, influenced by what was happening in surrounding general hospitals, did not affect the male attendants, who continued to be known as Charge Attendants, Second in Charge attendants, Ordinary Attendants and Temporary Attendants. Although six Attendants qualified for the Medico-Psychological Association Certificate and badge 'For Proficiency in Mental Nursing' when it was first issued in 1894, the attendants were never called 'mental' nurses, not even after 1919 when those holding the certificate were eligible for admission to the supplementary section of the national Nurses Register for mental nurses.

At the end of the nineteenth century, attendants still occupied a lowly position in the hospital hierarchy. In the two previous centuries, the Steward, Porter and Matron were of the level of inferior officers, and all the rest – keepers, gallery maids, attendants and nurses – were servants. In the 1893 Annual Report, the attendants and nurses were still being referred to as 'servants', although some had already trained for and passed the examination for the Certificate of Proficiency in Mental Nursing. Yet, reading the staff magazine, one gains the impression that Bethlem attendants shared in the improved status of asylum attendants generally, which was said to have been 'distinctly raised in recent times' (Tuke 1892).

Male staff drained away in 1899 as they left for military service in the South African War; again, in 1914 onwards, men were called to the Colours to serve in World War I. It was not until after 1919 that the titles were changed to conform to those of the female nurses, and men began to be known as Charge Male Nurses, Second in Charge Male Nurses, Male Nurses and Temporary Nurses.

During this period, the hospital functioned strictly in separate sides – the wards for male patients being staffed by male nurses, the wards for female patients being staffed by female nurses. This did not altogether meet the approval of the Royal College of Nursing, who, in 1928, wrote that 'no woman nurse is employed on the male side which is a pity'. In fact, the Matron of Bethlem was finding it difficult to obtain enough suitable female staff to go round, which is scarcely surprising in view of the opening of the prestigious Maudsley Hospital only eight miles away. This was in spite of Bethlem paying higher salaries than the Maudsley, at least initially. By 1936, the Bethlem Matron was having to relieve her shortage of females by recruiting student nurses from 'continental countries and the colonies'. The problems were compounded in 1939 when male nurses once again went off to fight, this time in World War II.

The Maudsley Hospital opened in 1923 with wards entirely staffed by female nurses, except for three male probationers on the ward containing the more acute male cases. All Sisters and Staff Nurses were required to possess a certificate of general hospital training, with the sole exception of those nurses who were employed as masseuses. Lectures and demonstrations were given to enable all these staff to obtain the Medico-Psychological Certificate or registration by the General Nursing Council. The policy of having female nurses everywhere continued until the early 1930s, without any reasons being given in justification. The employment objectives stated in 1926 were: 'to supply nurses who have had a general training with another [training] in mental work, and so provide doubly trained candidates for the higher posts elsewhere'. These objectives were fulfilled, so that, in 1935, the Maudsley could boast that fourteen of its nursing staff had become Matrons in other hospitals, and eighteen had become Assistant Matrons. Meanwhile, male nurses had been accepted as Staff Nurses, but if wanting further promotion, they had to leave. Parity was only achieved at the time of the amalgamation of the Bethlem and Maudsley hospitals, when it was resolved that promotion be awarded on the basis of merit without gender restriction.

After amalgamation, one of the Matrons was designated Superintendent of Nursing, although the position could theoretically have been taken by a man. The post of Head/Senior Male Nurse disappeared. The Superintendent was supported by a Deputy and Assistant Matrons, while the ward staff continued to be called Sister, Charge Nurse or Staff Nurse. The titles of the senior nurses changed again in the early 1970s, when the Salmon structure was introduced, clearly delineating the managerial responsibilities for nurses and nursing. The titles used were Chief Nursing Officer, Principal Nursing Officer, Senior Nursing Officer and Nursing Officer. This changed again in the 1980s, when the posts were reorganised into Chief Nurse Adviser, Director of Nursing Services and Nurse Manager, only to diversify as the management responsibilities were gradually withdrawn and different structures introduced.

The registered mental nurses, who gradually became known as psychiatric nurses from the 1960s onwards, started to adopt the name 'mental health nurses' in the 1990s.

Numbers of staff

One of the more persistent myths about the Bethlem and Maudsley hospitals has been that they have always been highly staffed with nurses. This has not been the case for long periods of the hospitals' history, as

Table 3.1 Nursing staff : patient ratios, 1635–1780[1]

Date	Officers	Servants	Total	Patients[2]	Ratio
1635–43	3	4	7	25	1:3.6
1644–76	3	4	7	47	1:6.9
1677–80	3	5	8	90	1:11.3
1681–92	3	6	9	117	1:13.0
1693–1701	4	6	10	128	1:12.8
1702–05	4	6	10	136	1:13.6
1706–29	4	6	10	144	1:14.4
1730–50	4	6	10	242	1:24.2
1751–64	4	6	10	263	1:26.3
1765–68	3	8	11	267	1:24.3
1769–76	3	10	13	270	1:20.8
1777–80	3	10	13	280	1:21.5

[1] Table excludes officers' assistants, washerwomen, nightwatchman, gardener and ratcatcher.
[2] Patient numbers are rough (Easter) averages, derived from Spital reports, and Court and Committee Minutes.

This table is reproduced by kind permission of Dr Jonathan Andrews.

can be illustrated from the records.

In the late 1300s, when Bethlem was starting to care for the mentally disturbed there seems to have been only a Master, a Brother and a Sister, and, by 1403, a Master, a Porter and his wife, with an indeterminate number of servants. The number of patients rose from 9 in 1403, to 20 in 1598, and 31 in 1624. By 1635, the patients were looked after by 3 officers, the Steward, Porter and Matron, and by 4 basketmen or servants. This continued with only small increases in the number of servants, although the number of patients grew apace, especially with the opening of the new hospital building in 1676. Jonathan Andrews (1991), to whom I am much indebted for research on this period, has an informative table that shows only 9 staff for an average of 117 patients for the years 1681–92 (Table 3.1).

The situation deteriorated to a nadir between 1751 and 1764, when 4 officers and 6 servants were looking after an average of 263 patients at a time, which is a staff ratio of 1:26.3. An increase in accommodation of 100 cells for incurable patients had not been accompanied by a rise in staff establishment.

The Salary Books for Bethlem, our main source of information on staff numbers, are extant from 1777, and, for Lady Day that year, show a resident staff of a Steward, Porter and Matron, plus 3 Basketmen, 3 Assistant Basketmen, 3 Maid Servants and 1 Assistant Gallery Maid. They were helped by 2 Laundry Maids in their task of maintaining an average number of 280 patients. This Salary Book ends its record in 1815, when there were still only 10 servants – 3 Keepers, 2 Assistant Keepers and 5 Female Keepers.

There is a gap in the Salary Books after this, and the next book starts in 1842. The published Annual Reports for Bethlem do not start until 1843. Nevertheless, it is clear from what figures we do have that the staff ratios at Bethlem compared unfavourably with those at some other places. Dr John Conolly improved the ratio of attendants to patients at Hanwell on his arrival there in 1839 from 1:25 to 1:17, to cope with his non-restraint policies. By 1842, Bethlem still had only 1:20.5 patients. The Retreat in York at this period was doing much better with 1:4.5. Bethlem caught up somewhat (to 1:7.1) when Dr Hood insisted on non-restraint policies in the 1850s. This was not too different from the New York State Lunatic Asylum at Utica in 1869, which used 1:9 patients for males and 1:6 for females (Santos and Stainbrook, 1949). However, it was not until the 1880s that Bethlem reached the staffing levels of the Retreat.

Bethlem had moved to Southwark in 1815 to a new building with a bed complement of 200, but the number of patients and staff proceeded to grow. It has been said that mental nursing was a somewhat arbitrary creation of the Victorian lunacy legislation (Dingwall et al 1988), but, apart from the growing population, the check on restraining practices and locking up patients must have had at least as great an influence on the growth in attendants numbers. During the stay in Southwark, which lasted until 1930, the numbers of Keepers, Attendants or nurses (whatever they happen to be called at the time) increased, as is shown in Table 3.2.

The ratios are not given after 1948 because of the increasing specialisation of the wards, which meant that wards were staffed to differing levels according to the nature of the work. The 1981 numbers were composed of 16 Nursing Officers, 87 Sister/Charge Nurses, 140 Staff Nurses, 130 State Enrolled Nurses, 3 Nursery Nurses and 159 Nursing Assistants. A labour-intensive service had developed, for which nurse:patient ratios varied between a highest of 1:0.4 for the Secure Unit and a lowest of 1:3.58 for night duty general psychiatry wards. This alerts one to the need for caution in the interpretation of the above figures unless one has accompanying information on how the staff were deployed. Skellern (1978) pointed out that for a 24-hour, 7-day week, 52-week service the Bethlem and Maudsley Hospitals needed 5.7 or even 6.0 whole-time equivalent nurses to obtain just one nurse on duty all the time, although that target was not always achieved. She went on to stress the wide variety of clinical skills needed in specific clinical areas, in addition to educational and management skills needed overall.

Table 3.2 Nurse : patient numbers 1815–1991

Year	Attendants			Patients	Ratio
	Male	Female	Total		
1815	5	5	10	122	1:12.2
1836	10	11	21	258	1:12.2
1842	7	10	17	355	1:20.8
1856	21	27	48	340	1:7.1
1863	14	26	40	333	1:8.3
1871	21	27	48	258	1:5.4
1886	32	34	66	270	1:4.1
1896	36	38	74	226	1:3.1
1901	31	35	66	206	1:3.1
1913	33	38	71	187	1:2.6
1923	37	45	82	228	1:2.8

In 1930 Bethlem moved to Beckenham, with a bed complement of 250 (109 males and 141 females).

Year	Male	Female	Total	Patients	Ratio
1934	41	49	90	203	1:2.6
1940	47	44	91	212	1:2.3

The Maudsley opened in 1923 and the years up to 1935 were as follows:

Year	Nurses	Students			Patients	Ratio
		Male	Female	Total		
1923	27	12	23	62	157	1:2.5
1931	29	12	34	75	189	1:2.5
1935	35	17	42	94	195	1:2.1

When the two hospitals amalgamated in 1948, the figures together were:

Year	Nurses	Male	Female	Total	Patients	Ratio
1948	–	–	–	224	318	–
1960	–	–	–	343	481	–
1971	342	58		400	494 (beds)	–
1981	532	104		636	397	–
1991	–	–	–	850	577	–

Uniform

The earliest mention of clothing for the basketmen is in the Bethlem Court of Governors Minutes for 1675, where one reads that the coat and breeches issued every Easter were to be made 'of a sad muske Collo [colour] in regard of their frequent Imployment in workes that will Soyle the same'. As Andrews remarks, the sombre colour would be a mark of the humble station of a servant. It also would show the dirt less, in an environment not noted for its sanitation and hygiene, where patients were wont to throw filth, excrement and other noisome things into the yards or even over the attendants. That was still going on at a much later date (1816), when Simmonds the Head Keeper complained that James Norris, a patient, had thrown his filth all over him.

In 1676, there was an alteration of policy, presumably connected with the move to the new hospital building, for the servants' coats were changed to blue, as worn by the staff of charitable organisations:

> It is ordered by this Court that a blew cloth Gowne be made and provided for the Hospitall of Bethlem And that the same be lined with blew. And also that a good large staff and tipt with silver with the Armes of the said Hospitall engraven thereon be bought for him. And that [?he] doe, in the said blew Gowne, with the said Staffe give his Attendance at the passage next the poores [gate] leading to the said Hospitall.
>
> ALSO that the three men Servants or Baskettmen in the said Hospitall have blew coats provided for them to be made in such a manner as the Beadles Coates in the Hospitall of Bridewell. And that silver badges with the Armes of the House engraven thereon be fastened to the Sleeves of the said coates. And that William Cuthbert, a Goldsmith do make the same Badge.

It was agreed in 1680 that the Porter and servants should be allowed coats of blue cloth every year in the future. Pairs of shoes and stockings were also provided. An eighteenth-century illustration of the blue coat can be seen in Hogarth's 'Rake's Progress – The Madhouse' painting, where it is worn by the basketman kneeling with the manacles at the feet of Tom Rakewell. The coat appears quite substantial, which may have been advantageous in winter. A round, tiered, dark hat is also worn, which may possibly have been part of the official garb. Clothing and hats were still being supplied to patients and servants at the end of the eighteenth century, although we do not know of what pattern. Male nurses were issued with hats well into the twentieth century.

For the nineteenth century, we are lacking in information about keepers' and attendants' dress, as the hospital clothing ledgers have not survived for that period. We know from the Steward's Account Books that patients continued to receive clothing, for example in 1830, including shoes, belts, gloves, stays, muslin caps and the occasional shawl or wig.

One illustration surviving is the painting of the Head Attendant, Charles Neville, in mid-century, where he appears somewhat formally dressed in wing-collar, cravat, waistcoat and three-quarter length coat, looking unlikely to be involved in the 'hands on' care of the patients. Presumably this was his office, or Sunday-best attire.

In 1891, female attendants were at long last granted a type of nurses' uniform. It was to be a uniform approved by the Resident Physician,

Ward F2 c1907 at Bethlem, Southwark

costing £3 each, remaining the property of the hospital and to be returned when one left the service. About the turn of the century a photograph was taken of the workroom of F2 ward, in which a nurse stands in the doorway. She wears a cap, a deep high-necked collar and a white apron over a dress that stretches almost to the floor.

Uniform for nurses in 1928 was described as 'a dark blue dress 9 inches off the ground with a very stiff white collar, cuffs and belt; Sisters wore navy, and all wore chatelaines around the waist with keys, scissors and a whistle to summon assistance'. Male nurses were issued with two suits a year and an outdoor coat.

When the hospitals amalgamated the arrangements for uniform were:

- Superintendent of Nursing: green dress;
- Deputy and Assistant Matrons: grey dress;
- Sisters: navy blue dresses;
- Deputies, Staff Nurses and SENs: cornflower blue dress with belt colour according to rank;
- Nursing Assistants: purple/white striped dress;
- Male nurses: white coats.

It was reported to the Nursing Committee in 1962 that the uniform dresses were shrinking badly. Uniform was discussed again the following year and remained a popular topic of debate for the Committee. The question was raised of whether or not the national nurses' uniform should be adopted.

In 1971, proposals were put forward for nurses to come out of uniform, and, in June of that year, some nurses started to wear their own clothing. These nurses were given dockets that they could exchange at Marks and Spencers stores for clothing they had bought there. By 1973, every nurse was allowed to wear his or her own clothing, and gradually all the nurses in the psychiatric services, even those who had initially opposed this development, abandoned their uniforms. The reasons for this change were that uniform was seen as a barrier between nurse and patient. The nurse was not to hide behind a uniform but was to interact with the patient as if in normal everyday life. In spite of occasional discussions about the economic or clinical usefulness of standard clothing, nurses continued to have the personal choice of clothing. A dress policy was formulated to help nurses to avoid provocative or dangerous attire.

Residence, staff stability and absences

For at least the first four centuries of its life, Bethlem was a hospital where most of the staff were expected to be resident. At the beginning, the Brothers and Sisters were sometimes absent on fund-raising trips around the country. By the 1400s, there is some evidence that other trading interests preoccupied members of staff, which, although pursued on the site, must have taken their attention away from the poor and sick. For instance, Peter Taverner, the Porter, was discovered to be running an ale house and a common lodging house for itinerant labourers and children, as well as renting out part of the cemetery for a bakery.

The most notable absentee of early modern times was Dr Helkiah Crooke, physician to King James I, who was installed as Keeper in 1619, but for years left Bethlem in charge of a Steward. This sort of arrangement was not really available to the lower-paid servants, who had to confine their absences to trips to the ale houses, from whence they returned sometimes the worse for drink. For much of the seventeenth century, such matters remained a difficult problem for the Governors. The Stewards George Foye (1644–7) and Matthew Benson (1648–58) were not always resident, which may have posed problems in carrying out their duties of supervising inferior staff.

Joseph and Millicent Matthews, and John Green – Porter, Matron and basketman respectively – were running a victualling house in the 1680s.

Matron was recorded as constantly attending the Bull Alehouse, which was in fact owned by Bethlem. The Governors made numerous attempts to control this, trying to get the Stewards to fulfil their obligations, restricting the Matthews and setting curfews for the servants, even stipulating bedtimes. It had already been formalised in 1672 as regards the servants – 'their personal Attendance is continuall required both day and night'.

During the eighteenth century, there is little mention of these matters in the Bethlem records, but this should not be taken to imply that the problems were solved. In 1785, it was necessary for the Governors to forbid resident staff to sleep outside the hospital without permission. The basketmen and keepers slept in the galleries, so were actually living on the wards. Patients such as Urbane Metcalf still, however, had tales of absentee keepers. Rodbard, keeper of the Fourth Gallery was said to be frequently absent, spending on average not more than three hours a day in his gallery, which must have been with the connivance of the Steward. Allen, keeper of the Basement Gallery was said to be 'so much out', and Matron would go off to the seaside at Worthing.

The increasingly repressive regime undoubtedly contributed to the institutionalisation of staff, bringing them a closer identification with patients. Both patients and their keepers were confined in movement as well as being behaviourally controlled. It should not be surprising that this culture of restraint was the seedbed for the scandals of 1815 and 1852.

It is evident from the Salary Books that keepers and attendants in the late eighteenth and early nineteenth centuries did not change places of employment. They lived out their lives almost entirely within the confines of the hospital. In 1848, we read 'Many of the servants of these classes have passed many years in the hospital and have become long habituated to their duties'.

Length of stay in employment was regarded as a matter for congratulation. It became an established pattern for a core of staff members to stay up to thirty or forty years in the service of Bethlem, and this continued throughout the nineteenth and first half of the twentieth century, as is seen from the Annual Reports.

For instance, in 1936, Charge Nurses Leary and Baldi retired after thirty-three and thirty years service respectively. In 1947, Charge Nurse Bowditch left after thirty-four years' service. The remarkable Kenneth Cantle, once Chief Male Nurse, retired in 1957 after fifty-four years, bringing to an end the reign of a family dynasty that included his father (thirty years service), and uncle (thirty-five years). That said, generations of families working at Bethlem appear to have been less common than elsewhere.

At the opening of the Maudsley in 1923, it was decided that residence should be offered to only about half of the staff. To those resident, a charge of 9 shillings and 11 pence per week would be made for lodging and washing. Meals could be obtained by all staff on payment. This system was said to have worked well in the first year. Dr Mapother remarked, 'it certainly increases the chance of selecting staff owing to the preference of many nurses for living out. Its chief objections are, perhaps, in connection with staff who fall ill'. There are no records for sickness at this time, but, in view of the high staff turnover, Mapother might reasonably have had cause for concern over staff whose illnesses could not be so easily checked.

In spite of what he says about the attractiveness of living out, the life of the Nurses' Home was not without its diversions, in the form of a Social and Sports Club and weekly dancing classes and Dances. In fact, the demand for extra accommodation grew, as did the number of staff, over the years to 1935. The Bethlem Nurses Home in the 1930s was a place of great restrictions but liked by its occupants. Vicki Hayward wrote:

> *Bedrooms were not heated nor were there any mirrors until Queen Mary suggested that we needed one – then joy of joy – every room was fitted with a full length one, also we had a hospital iron bedstead, a dressing table, plus a Lloyd Loom chair . . . Our morning call at 6 am was night sister walking all floors ringing a bell. Breakfast at 6.30 am and on duty at 7 am and even a day off it was breakfast at the same time.*

In addition to the residences, some staff still slept on the wards, up until the 1960s. Thereafter the residences received progressively less supervision, and the staff living in them were encouraged to take control of their own patterns of living. In the 1990s, the larger residences were converted for use as offices and for clinical purposes.

Salaries

The question of salaries for staff would not have arisen in the early years of Bethlem, for the monks and nuns were vowed to holy poverty and were not expected to accept money for themselves. They begged for the maintenance of the poor and sick for whom they cared, but for themselves would expect no more than food, a habit and lodging. Long after Bethlem ceased to be a monastery, the Lord Mayor, Sheriffs and Chamberlain of the City of London sent victuals to the hospital, in the form of bread, oatmeal pottage, beef and beer.

By the beginning of the seventeenth century, the practices of staff had become distinctly mercenary. In 1631, we find that the Keeper was getting a cut of 10–20 shillings as part of the admission fee for each patient. The staff were also charging the patients for food. The Commissioners wrote:

From the Bethlem Salaries Book. Note Elizabeth Forbes (Chapter 2), Thomas Rodbard (Chapter 2) and the marks of the female keepers (Chapter 3)

> *It is a very usual and daily practice [for the Steward] to sell unto the poor of the house, such bread and meat as is sent in from the Lord Mayor, Sheriffs and out of the markets, and that at excessive rates, as ordinarily a penny loaf for a groat or 6d, and sometimes 2 pennyworth of bacon for 12d.*

There was nothing new in the urge to make money, for, even two centuries earlier after the decline of the monastery, staff were using their entrepreneurial instincts to develop small businesses on the side, such as a bakery, a lodging house and an inn.

The servants did receive wages, but at the level of £2–£5 10s. per annum for the hundred years between 1635 and 1735, which, as Andrews pointed out, encouraged them to devote their energies to embezzling, extortion and petty profiteering. Andrews' studies showed that Bethlem staff received less in wages than did their colleagues at other London hospitals, but that the cases were not entirely similar. The best comparison was with St Luke's Hospital, which opened in 1751, and there the wages surpassed those of Bethlem. The Governors at Bethlem had preferred to allow their staff to receive tips from visitors in the servants box, and, from the 1680s,

49

gratuities were given also from the Governors. The latter were not won without agitation, as the basketmen found it necessary to complain and ask for a rise. On March 7 1684 there is what seems to be the first evidence of a persistent theme – the dialogue between workers and management about levels of remuneration, which were conducted with varying degrees of good-nature or acrimony. The basketmen complained again in 1685, 1686, 1687 and 1690, but they did not achieve real increases in their basic wages until 1765 and thereafter. Their wages eventually rose from £12 per annum in 1765 to £20 in 1769 and to just under £50 in 1775. Like the monks of old, the servants could still expect to get free furnished accommodation, meals, clothing, occasional heating and medical cover.

Detailed Salary Books from 1777 tell precisely what each member of staff was paid each quarter. As the number of staff increase, one can see hierarchies of payments emerging, which, from the names of the employees, seem to relate to length of stay and presumably experience.

On Lady Day 1777, Matron was paid £15, the Porter £14 5s, the three Basketmen £12, three Assistant Basketmen £6 5s, three Maidservants £6 5s, and one Assistant Gallery Maid £4 10s. The 1777 entry shows an increase in the status of the Matron, in that she was being paid more than the Porter.

At Michaelmas 1842, the Matron was paid £45, two Keepers £12 10s, two Keepers £10, one Keeper £6 5s, two Assistant Keepers £5, nine Female Keepers £5, and one Assistant Female Keeper £4. This 1842 entry shows that, apart from the Matron, the female staff were not managing to keep pace with their male colleagues in terms of financial reward. They were, however, doing better at £20 per annum than were the female attendants at Hanwell Asylum, for example, who only received £14. The men were soon, in 1853, to get another rise in their status, with the appointment of the first male Head Attendant, Charles Neville. However, this appointment was a relatively minor achievement when one considers that the quarterly payments were for the Steward £66 5s, for the Matron £32 10s, and for poor Charles Neville only £15 10s. In fact, this was a presage of the future, for although the post of Head Attendant, later Head Male Nurse, continued well into the twentieth century, the men never achieved parity with the Matrons. Even after 1947, when, at least in theory, a man could have become the Superintendent of Nursing/Chief Nursing Officer or Chief Nurse Adviser, no man was appointed until 1991 to the top nursing post.

One positive point was that it was possible to make small amounts of progress from lower-paid to higher-paid positions, although this might have taken many years, as shown in the Salary Books.

During the nineteenth century, attendants still had access to some advantages, in the shape of lodging, laundry and washing allowances and, most notably, beer. The latter was freely available from a tap, maintained by a hydraulic mechanism, in the common passage on the men's side. This beer machine was accessible to attendants at all hours and was thought, by a writer in the Asylum Journal, to have contributed to making the fat and formidable keepers look more satisfied than cheerful. Dr Hood took away the beer machine in the 1850s, but lunchtime drinking continued. In 1886, the Governors, motivated by their concern about this, offered the attendants an annual allowance of £3 for men and £2 10s for women in lieu of the beer. Quite a lot of staff took up the cash offer, and it was noticed that there was a substantial increase in alertness among the attendants in the afternoons!

At the end of the century staff were changed over from quarterly to monthly payments, signalling a new era when staff were no longer all expected to be resident or dependent on being given lodging and allowances in order to survive. Wages and staff numbers were gradually increasing. The quarterly bill for nursing staff on Lady Day 1900 was £973 9s 8d, whereas it had been £71 5s in 1815. By 1919 the Head Male Nurse, Ernest Clark, was getting £14 11s 8d a month, almost as much as Charles Neville was getting for a quarter, sixty years before.

During the first year of the Maudsley Hospital, levels of pay quickly became a major issue. Staff were being paid at rates set by the London County Council for the staff of county asylums, and, because of the relative smallness of the new hospital, the Maudsley Matron and her general trained staff found that they were being paid less than the rates offered at the Bethlem for mental nursing staff. In spite of this, the Maudsley Hospital managed to recruit sufficient female nurses to staff the wards almost exclusively with women. A particular item of dissatisfaction was that probationers (nurses in training) at Bethlem were paid £50 18s all found, while at the Maudsley they would only get £33 11s 8d per annum. The salary problem was seen to be affecting all the Maudsley nurses by 1924, and most of them signed a petition to the London County Council, which was supported by the Medical Superintendent, Dr Mapother. The National Asylum-Workers Union also joined in the fray, particularly because of the hardship to married male nurses. Eventually, an uneasy compromise was reached, whereby the nurses got a little more pay by dint of adjusting their notional starting date in the service.

This theme of disputes over pay continued, especially in the 1940s, 1970s and 1980s, and these episodes will be discussed in Chapter 11.

The attempt in this chapter to start describing the Bethlem care staff and their work is followed in Chapter 4 by a look at aspects of who the patients were and what sort of treatments they could expect to receive.

References and further reading

Andrews J (1991) *Bedlam Revisited: A History of Bethlem Hospital c1634–c1770.* Unpublished PhD thesis, University of London.

Anon. (1855) General reports of the Royal Hospitals of Bridewell and Bethlem. *The Asylum Journal.* July 2.

Dingwall R, Rafferty AM and Webster C (1988) *An Introduction to the Social History of Nursing.* London: Routledge.

Haslam J (1809) *Observations on Madness and Melancholy.* London: J Callow.

Haslam J (1817) *Considerations on the Moral Management of Insane Persons.* London: Hunter and Otridge.

Hayward V (1982) *Bethlem Royal Hospital, its beginning in 1930 at Beckenham, Kent.* Unpublished paper in the Bethlem Archives.

Metcalf U (1818) *The Interior of Bethlehem Hospital.* London (published by the author).

Nolan P (1992) Trained for what? A history of mental nursing and its training. *Royal College of Nursing History of Nursing Journal,* **4**: 131–142.

Santos EH and Stainbrook E (1949) A History of Psychiatric Nursing in the Nineteenth Century. *Journal of the History of Medicine and Allied Sciences.* **IV**: 48–74.

Skellern E (1978) *The Nursing Service at the Bethlem Royal Hospital and the Maudsley Hospital.* Unpublished paper in the Bethlem Archives.

Smith LD (1988) Behind closed doors: lunatic asylum keepers 1800–1860. *Social History of Medicine* **1**(3): 301–327.

Tuke DH (1892) Insane, attendants on. In *A Dictionary of Psychological Medicine,* vol. 2. London: J. and A. Churchill.

From madmen to service users – social class and treatments

After listening to the voices of individual patients in Chapter 2, we now turn to considering patients as a group, taking one aspect that was accessible in the documents: patients' social class as revealed by their occupations. To help build up pictures of different periods, the material has been divided according to the site of the hospital at the time. Occupation is, of course, only one of many ways of looking at a group of patients, and a more complex picture could be built up using records of problems, history of illness, diagnosis, gender, religion and length of stay. In the confines of this chapter, it has been decided to complement the information about social class with a survey of the treatments given to the patients, ranging from the early types of restraint to the eighteenth-century medical treatments, and through the later 'moral' treatment up to twentieth-century physical and psychological methods.

Classes of patient by occupation

At Bishopsgate

The first document to give information about the sick and those deprived of their reason who lived in the hospital is the report of 1403. The descriptions are brief and tantalising, confining themselves to such phrases as 'a certain man from Westminster' or 'a merchant from Exeter'. Apart from the oft-quoted report that the hospital at that time contained six men deprived of their reason and three other sick people, we know some patients were discharged, although whether cured or uncured is not clear.

Agnes Coteneys, from what she said, seemed to have regained her health, although the ex-Bethlem man described by Sir Thomas More still seemed to have been displaying signs of disturbance.

Bethlem was a charitable institution, open to meeting the needs of poor patients who could not afford to pay for their own keep. The hospital contrived to get friends and relatives to contribute to their support, and the City of London also contributed. We have already seen that patients who came from outside the capital were being accommodated, and the hospital, not unnaturally, looked for funds from the people who had sent them.

A hospital inspection in 1598 of 'Bethalem where the lunatick people are kept' gave details of the twenty 'prisoners' who were currently resident. There were eleven men and nine women who had been there for various periods between one month and twenty years. Among them were three widows, a fellow of Pembroke Hall in Cambridge, a Dutchman, an almswoman and a gentleman of the Queen's Chapel. Six of the residents had been sent there paid for by the Governors of Bethlem, but the others were variously maintained by parishes, private persons, churches, other hospitals and City livery companies.

Another list, produced in 1624, is composed of eighteen men and thirteen women, who had been there for periods from fourteen days to upwards of twenty years. Many are not described, but those who are include two simple fellows, a poor idiot, a pensioner, a property owner, an apprentice and a 'mad woman sometime servant to the Matron of Bridewell'.

This was during the time of Dr Helkiah Crooke. It was his boast that he cured seventeen patients when he first came to the hospital in 1619. He was subsequently inactive in this field, which was unfortunate as Bethlem was still the only organisation in England providing specifically for the 'lunaticks'. As the century progressed, demand for admissions increased, which meant, in turn, pressure for discharges and more accommodation. From Dr Crooke's time, there appeared to have been some effort to improve the throughput of mad people, although the managers seem to have accepted that some would stay without restiction of time.

The listed occupations of patients admitted to Bethlem from 1640–80 are dominated by vagrants, apprentices and servants, with a sprinkling of scholars and gentlemen. Of the fifteen vagrants, eleven were women, which was the largest female group. The remainder included clerks, grocers, tailors or weavers (Andrews 1991).

At Moorfields

In the new Bethlem, the idea of curing patients was still paramount. Dr Edward Tyson recorded that, between 1684 and 1703, 890 of the 1294 patients who had been in the hospital had been discharged cured. Jonathan Andrews, from his study of parochial records, throws doubt on the ability of Bethlem to live up to its aspirations to cure patients, his view being that the majority of patients failed to sustain their remissions or had been discharged unrecovered. He thinks also that the parishes who sent them to Bethlem were in fact concerned primarily with custody and safe-keeping.

Where recorded, the occupations from 1694–1718, out of a total of 251, show a shift away from vagrants, apprentices and servants, towards seamen, mariners, labourers and gentlemen. Perhaps the figure for labourers conceals the former vagrants. The rest are partly or semi-skilled tradesmen, as before.

Early in the eighteenth century, a rule was operated that prevented patients remaining more than twelve months in the hospital, whether cured or not. Admissions were selected from those with newly arising illnesses, which might be thought more likely to be curable. Nevertheless, the problem of the incurable patients did not go away, so in 1728 Bethlem opened a wing to accommodate fifty men, and in 1736 another wing for fifty women, whom it had failed to cure after they had been over a year in the main part of the hospital. These were patients considered dangerous to themselves or others.

Bethlem continued to receive as 'objects of charity' dangerous and insane paupers. Not all patients were penniless, and, of the incurable for 1733–1800, between 35 and 39% were private patients (Andrews 1991). Some patients were in business or skilled trades. After 1733, some patients, such as a gentleman, farmer, yeoman, haberdasher, tailor and attorney-at-law, were ordered to be discharged as unfit for Bethlem because of their higher level of income.

At Southwark

O'Donoghue (1914) wrote that 'The patients of the first half of the nine-teenth century were largely of the labouring class', but in the lists of Occupations of the Curable Patients for 1845 one can see a preponderance of patients with partly skilled occupations (Table 4.1).

In 1845, among all the 'tradesman of every description', there were 'others better born', whose families were not able to provide for them but who were thought to be peculiarly suitable objects for Bethlem's charity. The 'better class of patients' were, when they recovered, thought to be appreciative and grateful, which pleased the officers after their 'long months of superintendence and anxious watching'.

During the nineteenth century, Bethlem cared for ever larger numbers of disturbed patients. In the Annual Report for 1868, we read that out

Table 4.1 Occupations of the curable patients admitted during 1845

Males

Attorney's clerk	1	Medical student	1
Bakers	5	Painters	4
Barrister	1	Pattern designer	1
Blacksmith	1	Pianoforte tuner	1
Blind maker	1	Plumber	1
Bookbinder	1	Police clerk	1
Bookseller	1	Policeman	1
Cabinet-makers	2	Pork butcher	1
Carpenters	5	Porter	1
Chair-maker	1	Printers	2
Cigar-maker	1	Provision broker	1
Clerks	6	Publican	1
Cooper	1	Sadler	1
Corn Chandler	1	Sail-cloth worker	1
Curriers	2	Salesmen	2
Divinity student	1	Sawyers	2
Draper's assistant	1	Seaman	1
Engineers	2	Servant	1
Excise officer	1	Shoemakers	5
Farmer	1	Silversmith	1
French teacher	1	Soldier	1
Furrier	1	Son of musician	1
Glover	1	Stationer	1
Gold chain maker	1	Stonemason	1
Green grocers	3	Tailor	1
Grocer	1	Teacher of music	1
Groom	1	Tobacconist	1
Hairdresser	1	Waiter	1
Hatter	1	Waterman	1
Hawkers	2	Whitesmith	1
Hosier	1	None	1
Labourers	11	Not stated	1
Lightermen	2		
Mariners	2	*Total*	110

Females

Artificial-flower maker	1	Hawker	1
Corn dealers	2	House agent	1
Dressmakers	9	Housekeepers	3
Embroiderer	1	Lace-makers	2
Furniture broker	1	Lady's maid	1
Governesses	11	Laundresses	2

Lodging house keeper	1	Widow of a teacher	1
Milliners	4	Wives of a messenger, a	
Needlewomen	7	clerk and a mariner	3
Nurses	2	Wives and daughters of	
Paper-makers	2	farmers	9
Schoolmistress	3	Wives, widows and	
Servants	33	daughters of tradesmen	60
Shopkeepers	5	Wives, widows and	
Shopwoman	1	daughters of mechanics	
Straw bonnet maker	1	and labourers	33
Watergilder	1	No occupation	4
		Total	205

of the 246 patients, 140 were thought to be suicidal. Nor was the likelihood of cure any more certain than before. Of the 270 patients recorded for 1876, there were 112 discharged as 'not recovered'.

Soon after this, in 1882, Bethlem was, for the first time, officially allowed by the Charity Commissioners to take paying patients. Whether for this or for other reasons, some problems of class distinction started to emerge among the patients. Bethlem in its time at Southwark was constructed on the single-room system, which meant that patients could be separate at night, but during the day they would have to associate in the male or female galleries. In 1884, it was noted by the Physician Superintendent that as asylum treatment was eminently social, and class distinction important, it was not suitable for patients of the servant class to mix with governesses and cultured ladies. It had already been noted in 1873 that almost a quarter of the female admissions were governesses – young women who were thought to have found the duties of teaching too onerous. These were presumably the 'class of quiet, ladylike, melancholy patients' referred to in the Annual Report, many of whom were intensely suicidal.

In almost forty years up to this period there had been a noticeable change in social class. Labourers had disappeared from the male list and been replaced by clerks as the dominant group. The ranks of tradesmen had been infiltrated by professionals – architects, barristers, clergymen, army officers, surgeons and solicitors. In the female list, apart from the unemployed wives, the preponderance of servants had been replaced with governesses and housekeepers.

The last of the Annual Report tables of 'Occupation of Direct Admissions' was for the year 1916 and showed a similar picture (Table 4.2).

Table 4.2 Occupations of the direct admissions during the year 1916

Males

Government postal servant	1	Civil servant	1
Navy	1	Army	2
Solicitors	4	Clergymen	2
Dispenser	1	Medical practitioner	1
Shorthand writer	1	Schoolmasters	2
Architect	1	Consulting engineers	2
Accountant	1	Actor	1
Clerks	4	Manufacturers' agents	3
Warehouseman's assistant	1	Tax collectors	2
Cabinet manufacturer	1	Jeweller	1
Leather case maker	1	China salesman	1
Hotel managers	3	Law stationer	1
Apprentice	1	Sponge dealer	1
Schoolboy	1	No occupation	4
		Total	47

Females

Assistant nurses	3	Masseuse	1
Governesses	12	Art pottery painter	1
Singer	1	Stage	1
Blouse designer	1	Hospital nurses	2
Household duties	8	Book-keeper	1
Clerks	8	Drapery assistants	2
Dressmakers	2	Dairy maid	1
No occupation	48	Student	1
Housewives	10		
		Total	103

At Maudsley and Bethlem

The Maudsley Hospital began by admitting patients only on a voluntary basis and not taking patients requiring certification or with definite psychosis. Those who lived in London had to contribute according to their means, while those from elsewhere had to pay the full maintenance rate, which at that time was £5 per week. Private rooms were extra, but these were only open to those who were neither dangerous to themselves, nor seriously objectionable to others. There also had to be a guarantee that, if the patient's condition changed for the worse, alternative arrangements for care would be available. The limitations of this system were illustrated in the remarks of Dr E. Mapother, the Medical Superintendent (1924):

> *Social Class of Patient: Though admission is determined solely on medical grounds and in no degree by social or financial considerations, a considerable proportion of the patients has been of the well-educated classes, including a number of clergymen and doctors, hospital nurses and school teachers. The record of occupation of husbands or other relatives not having been kept this year in the case of female patients, statistics would be of little value. Social differences have never given rise to difficulties.*
>
> *Sex: There has been considerably less pressure on the male wards than on the female. This was anticipated, as it is universal in similar hospitals elsewhere. The cause is probably in large part economic, as male patients, especially now, [during a recession] cannot afford to give up employment on account of neuroses.*

In practice, it became necessary to make exceptions to the admissions policy, so that cases of scientific interest could be admitted for teaching and research purposes. This, in turn, meant that, by 1932, special quarters had to be made available in a garden villa for patients 'liable to be disturbing to each other'. Facilities were also made for the more educated patients to be grouped together.

These arrangements were interrupted by World War II, but afterwards, following the amalgamation with Bethlem in 1948 and the inception of the NHS, the Maudsley and Bethlem Hospitals adhered to the policy of taking only voluntary patients. Patients, arriving at Outpatients with a view to admission who did not look suitable were sent to the assessment ward at St Francis Hospital, Dulwich. Patients becoming long-stay were transferred to Cane Hill Hospital, Coulsdon, Surrey.

Starting from 1949, the Hospitals Triennial Statistical Reports analysed the patients by social class and occupation, as required by the Registrar General at a census. The first Social Class table showed relatively more inpatient males of social classes I and II (professional and intermediate occupations) than there were in the population of Greater London. This higher social class was partly explained by selective admission policies, which favoured patients who were not certified, who were at an early stage of their illnesses, but who were thought to be remediable and possibly suitable for teaching purposes or research projects. If these criteria did not produce the right class of patient, there was always the stated desire to preserve standards and the reputation of the hospital. It was said that the reputation of a hospital depended not just on the qualities of the medical and nursing staff, but on the behaviour and demeanour of the patients. 'A ward which contained for more than short periods an excess of psychopaths of low intelligence and dirty habits, or of thieves who stole the property of other patients, would quickly acquire a bad reputation'. It was to take another twenty years to modify this system of selectivity.

Mr George King, a Charge Nurse at Bethlem working in the period soon after amalgamation in 1948, remembered good-humouredly the men of higher social class, referred to in the table mentioned above. He painted a picture of Bethlem where nurses still appeared to be treated as part of the servant class and had to facilitate the following of rural pursuits. A peer of the Realm was to be admitted. Mr King said (oral history interview 1994):

> *The thing is if he comes in under his [own] name, he'll be pestered by the other 59 patients we have got over here, and for heaven's sake, we must grant him some immunity from that . . .*
>
> *But if you had seen the Rolls Royce that came up, and his wife like a ship of state, you know, all bust and behind, and she inspected all the rooms. I had a beautiful white coat on that day, and she said 'who are you?' And I said 'I happen to be the Charge Nurse, Madam.' I didn't pull my forelock, but I felt I should. Well anyway, he came and I said, 'I can offer you an upstairs or downstairs room'. He was ever so nice. He had his fags on a chair, and every morning I helped myself to one of his cigarettes, took him a cup of tea, you know.*
>
> *I had an awful job about this, – he borrowed a bagging hook, and cut the path either side from round the ward, right the way round the woods to the bowling green up at the far end. I had an awful job to get it [back].*
>
> *Then he got his guns, and I had to go and see this consultant and said, 'well, I'm agreeable, but I want them locked up at night in the store'. So anyway it was decided that the Hospital Secretary would come down, and he said 'I've done a bit of shooting'. So I went to the [patient] next morning, I said to him 'how did you get on?' and he said 'I bagged six pigeons'. 'And how about the Hospital Secretary?' 'Oh he peppered a nurse's hat.' So I said, 'where's the pigeons?' He said 'oh, [another male nurse] had them'. Just my luck, I was telling my wife, with a bit of luck we would have a brace of pigeons, and have something to eat'.*

The female inpatients in 1949–51 had a distribution of social class showing conspicuously more of them in class III for skilled occupations. The Triennial Report suggested that this might be because in the lower middle classes, where appearances had to be kept up on relatively small incomes, more stress was produced in women than in men.

Regarding occupation, while there was variation by locality, the most prominent feature was the higher figures for clerical occupations among male and female patients than in the general population. This was followed by occupations in metal-working, manufacturing, engineering, transport and communications among male patients, and by occupations in personal service among females. This pattern did not vary significantly for the next two decades.

The last chart of male patients' occupations covering the years 1961–3 gave the highest numbers in the professional and technical, clerical and unskilled categories. The female patients' occupations were dominated by the clerical category, followed by professional and technical, and personal service. The drift towards having a spread of patients whose social class reflected that of the surrounding community continued inexorably and, by 1969, although there was still an excess of patients in classes I and II at the expense of class III, the proportion of the two lowest social classes was much the same as in the general population of London.

The Bethlem and Maudsley Hospitals only took in patients of informal status until the late 1960s, when the first patients were admitted on a section of the Mental Health Act 1959. The selectivity of the admission policy was further broken down in the early 1970s, when the Maudsley accepted some responsibility for patients from Camberwell, the catchment area within which it was situated. This broadened the social spectrum of patients considerably, as the predominantly middle-class clientele became gradually mixed with the inhabitants of Camberwell, a deprived, multi-ethnic, inner city area. The responsibilities for Camberwell were shared with King's College Hospital District Health Authority until, in 1991, the process of change was largely completed by the Maudsley taking over the management of all the psychiatric services for the catchment area. Nevertheless, the Maudsley retained the right to treat patients from whatever other sources it wished.

The treatments

Early forms of patient management

Bethlem's intention and expectation was to cure patients, unlike most ecclesiastical, mediaeval hospitals, which concentrated on caring (Clay 1909). An early reference to Bethlem's work of curing is in the 1450 manuscript containing William Gregory's *Chronicle of London*:

> *A church of Our Lady that is named Bedlam. And in that place be found many men that be fallen out of their wit. And full honestly they be kept in that place; and some be restored unto their wit and health again. And some be abiding therein forever, for they be fallen so much out of themselves that is incurable unto man.*

Little is known from the Bethlem records of the earliest methods of treatment. The most likely form of intervention in mediaeval England for mental disturbance was some kind of restraint or confinement. Although Bethlem was initially a monastic establishment, there is no available evidence for specifically religious types of treatment, such as exorcism or locking up in a church overnight. The first indication of Bethlem's methods is the mention in 1403 of the following articles in the inventory: six chains with locks and keys belonging to them, four pairs of iron manacles, five other chains of iron and two pairs of stocks. The mentally disturbed and the physically sick at Bethlem profited from Christian alms-giving, which provided shelter, bedding and food. They were perhaps more fortunate than the rest of the mentally deranged in England, who were dependent on whatever care the community might offer in a generally unplanned and unsystematic way. Some depended on their families for maintenance, some wandered from place to place begging, and those who were not cared for in ecclesiastical hospitals were confined in local jails (Scull 1993).

The extent to which Bethlem during its history had recourse to whipping as a method of treating or controlling the patients is a matter of conjecture. While there is no evidence from the Bethlem archives on the subject, it seems to have become accepted in the public mind that whipping occured.

An example of this is in the mediaeval song relating to Bethlem, 'Loving Mad Tom', which speaks of 'sweet whips ding dong'. More factual is the account of Sir Thomas More (1553) who reports of a man who had 'ben put uppe in bedelem, and afterwarde by betyinge and correccyon gathered hys remembraunce to hym'. This report bears evidence of the use of whipping for therapeutic effect, but in Elizabethan and Jacobean drama, the use of the whip is portrayed as being more for control. For instance, in the play *The Changeling* by Thomas Middleton (1622), the Keeper turns on a patient who tries to seize him; 'Is't come to this? Nay, then my poison comes forth again. (Flourishes whip.) Mad slave, indeed, [to] abuse your keeper!'

During the seventeenth century, the tide of opinion seems to have turned against rough treatment. On July 18 1646, the Court of Governors ordered 'that no officer or servant shall give any blows or ill-language to any of the mad folks on pain of losing his place', and again, in 1677, the Governors propounded a rule that 'No Officer or Servant shall beat or abuse any Lunatik, nor offer any Force to them, but upon absolute Necessity, for the better governing of them.' This seems to imply that harsh methods had been used, although discouraged, but that, because of the escape clause, such methods could still, on occasions, be used. There is nothing further in the records, and there is no reference to beating in patient complaints much after this period.

Medicines and other treatments

An early reference to the use of medicine appears in the Court minutes of 1578:

> It is granted that the olde woman the wife of Davie Thomson which hath given medicine to the poor at Bedlam shall have viiid [8d] a weeke to kepe 2 lunaticke

> *persons in Bedlem in rooms there provided for her. she to finde them diett and medicine this to continue at pleasure of the governors.*
>
> *She reporteth that she hath cured one William Horne at North Cray in Kent a rich man which was frantic and also she hath cured manye others.*

In 1628, a London merchant left £50 to the hospital in his will to provide a weekly administration of physic for the patients, and later in the century a fund was set up to provide medicines for those who had been discharged, on an outpatient basis to prevent their relapse (Allderidge 1993, The First Four Centuries). There is no mention of the medicines administered until 1679, when the Governors discussed the duties of the surgeon (Andrews 1991). Whatever it was, the medicine was not appreciated by all; James Carkesse in 1670 writes of the 'Hellish Physick, Quack down my throat does pour'. Andrews (p. 301) reports that 'many patients rejected contemporary physic as "poison", when its operation was often so uncomfortable, painful and debilitating, producing voiding from both stomach and bowels, scarification, sores and bruises'.

The Governors in 1750 were worried about the bills for medicines, which had risen to £372 17s 10d, and enquired into the goodness of the medicines and whether any alternatives were proper. They were assured that no bad medicines were administered. In the following year, the first dispensary, or 'apothecary's shop' was set up at Bethlem, which was followed in 1772 by the creation of the office of 'Resident Apothecary'.

John Strype in 1720 gave an overall view of the general treatment of patients:

> *Those that are fit for it, at convenient Hours, have liberty to walk in the long galleries which are large and noble. In the Summer time, to air themselves, there is two grass plats, one for the Men, another for the Women. And in the Winter a Stove for each apart, where a good fire is kept to warm them. In the Heat of the Weather, a very convenient Bathing Place to cool and wash them, and is of great Service in airing their Lunacy; and it is easily made a hot Bath for restoring their limbs when numbed, or cleaning and preserving them from Scurvey, or other cutaneous Distempers. Their Diet is extraordinary good and proper for them.*

Strype points out that many of the patients, having found better usage at Bethlem than elsewhere, have desired to continue at Bethlem rather than be turned out: 'There is nothing of Violence suffered to be offered to any of the Patients, but they are treated with all the Care and Tenderness imaginable.'

The treatments themselves do not appear to us to be characteristically tender. Bethlem seems, during the eighteenth century, to have settled into a routine of bleeding, bathing, vomiting and purging the patients. These treatments were in addition to the continued use of manacles and chains for restraint. The general principle was that of the 'antiphlogistic' (Black 1811), literally anti-inflammatory, or 'depleting' system, which was

63

designed to lower the turbulent spirits. Dr Thomas Monro in 1815 described the regime that had been carried out from at least the time of his father, and maybe even before, for generations of the Monros had been physicians at Bethlem between 1728 and 1853:

> *In the months of May, June, July, August and September, we generally administer medicines; we do not in the winter season, because the house is so excessively cold that it is not thought proper . . . We apply generally bleeding, purging and vomit; those are the general remedies we apply . . . all the patients who require bleeding are generally bled on a particular day, and they are purged on a particular day.*

All the patients, except those who were too weak:

> *are ordered to be bled about the latter end of May, or the beginning of May, according to the weather; and after they have been bled they take vomits once a week for a certain number of weeks, after that we purge the patients . . .*

Other treatments included the use of blisters applied to the nape or vertex of the head after the head had been shaved, or to the legs. Blistering was intended to act as a counter-irritant or shock.

Cold baths are also referred to as a treatment in the poem of 1744, allegedly written by a patient, J. Clark. This is confirmed by Thomas Bowen (1783) who wrote: 'There are certain days fixed for the proper medical operations; and the cold, or hot bath is used in those cases where it is judged to be salutary'.

The use of fear in the management of patients was a sinister method that staff did not hesitate to use with uncooperative patients. Some patients who starved themselves or declined medication had their mouths forced open by introducing a metal key, specially designed by John Haslam, the Apothecary, in about 1797. Sometimes a patient resisted having the key in his mouth, and, if a strait waistcoat or restraint by two or three keepers was not enough, Haslam remarked that 'he [the patient] may be blind-folded at the commencement, which never fails to alarm him, and urges him to enquire what the persons around him are about'. To balance any revulsion we might feel for such methods, one should also take into account the fact that the use of fear was not uncommon for that period. This is witnessed by the practice of Benjamin Rush at the Pennsylvania Hospital in Philadelphia, who commented (1812) when listing remedies for mania that 'terror acts powerfully upon the body, through the medium of the mind, and should be employed in the cure of madness'. He also did not balk at modes of coercion, such as the strait waistcoat and shower bath, which he described frankly as 'modes of punishment'.

'Punishment' was a word not much in use at Bethlem (except by Haslam 1809), but the idea was not far from the surface. When the Head Keeper in 1816 was publicly asked whether James Tilley Matthews had been put in irons 'to punish him' for criticising the Apothecary, the Keeper answered 'yes'. The answer had been forced from him. One wonders whether he already knew the rule later propounded by John Conolly (1847) that attendants should never employ the term 'punishment' in relation to anything done to patients.

Moral treatment, electricity and bathing

Well before the end of the eighteenth century, there were the stirrings of change in the approach to patients. John Haslam, in spite of his odious key, and although still supporting bleeding and purging, had started to turn against vomiting, cold baths, blisters on the head, setons and the use of opium. He disdained whimsical modes of treatment such as whirling, or spinning a madman round on a pivot. John Monro (1758), who thought that management was the most important thing in treatment, recommended that patients should be 'talked to kindly' and 'used with the greatest tenderness and affection'.

The introduction of 'moral treatment' by Tuke at The Retreat in York affected attitudes to care widely in the direction of more humane and less punitive approaches, including a stress on the value of occupation to combat the dangers of idleness. Mr and Mrs Jepson, Apothecary and Matron at the Retreat, took meals with the patients; Miss Powell, Matron at Hanwell Hospital in 1841, was using kind and soothing words to the suicidal patients. The previous Matron at Hanwell, Mrs Ellis had, in the 1830s, pioneered the development of suitable occupations for patients, making fancy articles that were sold, the profits being ploughed back into extra comforts on the wards. This welcome trend in treatment was evident also at Bethlem. Mrs Forbes, Matron from 1815, had been busy setting an example to the English asylums by liberating the patients from personal restraint. Some customarily called 'blanket Patients', who had been forced to wear confining blanket gowns, were also chained to the wall by hand or leg, but Mrs Forbes let them loose. James Smyth, a keeper (1823), wrote, 'The grand principle of this establishment is mildness; for it is now generally acknowledged that this mode of treating the maniac is much better calculated to restore reason than harshness or severity.'

The Bethlem Annual Report for 1845, written by Drs E.T. Monro and A. Morison, stressed, under the heading General Treatment, the kindness of the officers and attendants, and the very few patients who required restrictive treatment, by which they meant padded rooms and canvas mufflers. The occupations, which were said to fill a considerable portion of the patients' time, were gardening and the workshops for the men, and laundry and needlework for the women. The men formed into groups for digging, sweeping, rolling and weeding in the gardens, while in the workshops they followed the trades of carpenter, smith, cooper, plumber and mason. Apart from the washing and ironing, the women sewed men's shirts, women's caps, gowns, shifts and aprons, and also made up pairs of sheets, bed-ticks and pillowcases. To counterbalance all this industry, the amusements consisted of the library, billiard and bagatelle rooms, along with cards, draughts and dominoes, chess and piano-playing.

The Annual Reports comment periodically on the introduction of new treatment methods, which were thought of as improvements consequent on the humane and enlightened principles that guided the moral and spiritual treatment of insanity. Dr W. Rhys Williams, in his 1873 account of the treatments used during the year, referred to the moral influence, but concentrated on the physical treatments. The drugs used to quieten patients were conium, digitalis, antimony and chloral. One of the manic patients improving on conium, who had displayed terrible fury and blasphemy, was described as having, previously for many years, spent two-thirds of her time in seclusion.

At that time, galvanism, the application of direct-current electricity, was a chosen method for various types of problems, including melancholia, hypochondriasis, mania, dementia, sexual irritability and constipation. The use of electricity in treatment was not new at Bethlem, for Dr Monro had acquired an electrical machine with medical apparatus as early as 1796. For galvanism, a Weiss' battery was used, the negative pole applied to the nape of the neck and the positive pole to the forehead, using between five and fourteen cells, for five to ten minutes daily. Some patients complained that they could not bear it, and even the medical staff were not entirely convinced of its value. Dr Williams wrote:

> After a careful use of galvanism, almost daily since May, 1873, we have been rather disappointed in the direct results of the galvanism. Undoubtedly much good is done by the influence of a doctor brought directly to bear on a certain number of patients for some time daily, and I must own that I consider as much was due to the moral influence, and the repeated assurance that the galvanizing was done to cure them, as to the galvanism itself.

Some patients improved up to a certain point only to relapse, as was the case with one woman who did not appear to welcome the treatment. Dr Williams wrote, 'Shower baths have produced the same temporary recovery. One case of melancholic stupor became much roused under galvanism, and on several occasions astonished us by sudden fits of violence. She seemed for a time to improve but after six months of daily galvanism, we gave her up.' The showers, given as a shock, were shorter than galvanism, only lasting for a second or two, and being followed by a good drying to improve the general condition and hasten cure. Sadly, Dr Williams did not refer to the role of nurses or attendants in these treatments, although no doubt their assistance was essential.

'Daily teazing' was one treatment that he thought had some effect. He wrote, 'By insisting that the patient shall, against her will, walk up and down the gallery with you, you rouse her to resist, and this daily rousing does good; in fact, galvanism acts in these cases in the same way.' This sort of reasoning now appears alien, opening the door for possible ill treatment simply for the sake of arousal.

Specific treatments for some complaints were given, for instance nitrate of amyl inhalations for epilepsy, belladonna and cold sponging for enuresis. Some attempt was being made to have a scientific approach, for the doctors took sphygmograph readings, measured urine volumes and performed post mortem examinations of the brain.

In spite of doubts about the efficacy of electricity, it continued to be used in various ways, as did bathing. In 1881, a French method was adopted of prolonged baths at 85°F for eight or nine hours at a time, and even for days together. A decade later, prolonged tepid baths were freely used in the treatment of excitement. Hydrotherapy continued throughout the first half of the twentieth century, and is remembered by some nurses as still being used in the early 1950s.

A physiotherapy department was created in October 1931, where treatments such as hydrotherapy, electrotherapy and heliotherapy (sunbathing) were carried out. This department also organised indoor and outdoor physical exercise, such as folk dancing, netball and eurhythmics.

Insulin, more electrical and other treatments

At the same period the use of insulin was being tried out, but it was not until 1946 that insulin shock therapy started. Fiona Firmin, a staff nurse, told of her work on the insulin ward from 1951 (oral history interview 1994):

> The deep insulin treatments were every morning, Monday to Friday. The aim was that the patient had a total of thirty comas in all, and these were induced by insulin. You started in the morning at 7.15 am by giving the insulin injections. They started on a lowish dose and worked up to coma. There was the sopor stage prior to coma, so they didn't have a coma from the word go. But once they had reached the coma state, you expected them to have a coma every day for thirty comas. The first coma would be five minutes, and then ten minutes, maximum half an hour. Then we would interrupt the coma with glucose – insert a nasal tube – a pint of glucose solution and bring them round. If they didn't come round fairly quickly, the doctor immediately gave them intravenous glucose. We had the patients in one room, and it was small, I think seven beds. There wasn't a nurse per patient, but there was always a minimum of 2 nurses in there, probably 3, and the Sister was permanently there. I would be in and out once the trollies were ready.

67

We were fairly well staffed, and I always say I think a lot of the recovery rate was due to the care they had. They had round the clock care. They would get up and be helped to the bath. You were constantly on the alert. You never left the ward without a bottle of glucose solution in your pocket if you had patients with you. We did lose one patient who went into an irreversible coma, and we just could not do anything. When I think of how dangerous the treatment was, I reckon that wasn't bad in five and a half years.

Earlier in the century, the emphasis at Bethlem had been largely on physical treatments, which were also embraced by the Maudsley Hospital at its opening in 1923. One might have had gland therapy, insulin or malarial treatment, massage, remedial exercises, galvanism, faradism, high-frequency current, vibromassage, continuous or prolonged baths and sedatives. In addition, there were psychological treatments, including all the then-current forms of psychotherapy, exploration under hypnosis and complete psychoanalysis.

Dr Eliot Slater, arriving at the Maudsley in 1931, found that the daily task of treatment was control of feverish emotions, agitation and excitement, for which drugs such as paraldehyde, barbiturates, morphia and hyoscine had to be given, sometimes in heroic doses at the risk of serious toxic effects. This was a feature that has sometimes bothered nurses much later in the century.

The physical forms of treatment continued side-by-side with the psychological forms. Continuous narcosis and the use of endocrine preparations were in favour in 1939–40. Group therapy commenced in 1943. The post-war years saw the building and opening in 1952 of a Neurosurgical Unit, with Guy's and King's College Hospitals. Surgical procedures used to relieve agitating mental conditions included leucotomy, which was at its peak in 1952–4 when ninety-one patients (2.5% of inpatient discharges) had the operation. Insulin coma therapy was likewise at its height then, but was abandoned in 1958.

Electroconvulsive therapy (ECT) grew from small beginnings at Bethlem in 1940, when it was called electrical induction therapy. It reached a peak for the Maudsley and Bethlem of 1328 treatments (33.6% of inpatient discharges) between 1958 and 1960, but thereafter its usage declined. For the triennium 1967–9, the proportion of inpatients receiving this treatment had fallen to 21% yet in 1976 there were still enough ECT treatments being carried out to warrant the Maudsley erecting a new wooden hut especially to accommodate the twice-weekly sessions. Dr George Stein (1976) gave a black comedy account of the initial experiences there:

The first patient arrived and climbed up onto the modern collapsible trolley, which duly collapsed, and he fell to the floor with a loud thud. Fortunately neither the patient or trolley were broken and so we were able to resume the proceedings, only to find that when he was fully anaesthetised one of the oxygen cylinders was empty. Although the spare cylinder was rapidly brought in, the patients in the waiting room had the pleasure of sharing both our surprise and relief as the oxygen arrived.

Even the rhythmical pumping of the anaesthetist's bag could be overheard, no doubt evoking enough erotic and disgusting fantasies in our anxious patients to keep the psychotherapy department gainfully employed for several years to come.

In the 1980s and 90s, the administration of ECT continued in both hospitals on a fairly regular basis, primarily for the treatment of patients with manic–depressive illness. In 1994, provision was still being made for twice weekly treatment sessions in both hospitals.

The treatment patterns for patients were substantially altered by the advent of medicines such as the major and minor tranquillisers and anti-depressants in the 1950s, and later on lithium, in the 1970s. These drugs produced more rapid improvements in the patients' conditions than was the case with earlier treatments. They also caused nurses to devote more time to the giving of medication, ensuring that the tablets were swallowed, observing the patients' progress after taking the drugs and watching for side-effects.

Of particular interest to nurses was the development of behavioural psychotherapy in the early 1970s, which research showed was a treatment that nurses could carry out at least as successfully and cost-effectively as could other professionals. This was a sizeable step forward for nurses who subsequently began to establish themselves as specialists using other therapeutic methods.

Subsequently, the Bethlem and Maudsley hospitals have engaged in varying forms of physical and psychological treatments, according to the specific needs of individual patients. This has been done in the context of a wide range of specialist services provided for the mentally disordered with developmental, behavioural or social problems.

More on treatment methods and care in the latter part of the twentieth century appears in Chapter 13, but next we shall look at three distinctive figures at the head of care staff.

References and further reading

Andrews J (1991) *Bedlam Revisited: A History of Bethlem Hospital c1634–c1770.* Unpublished PhD thesis, University of London.

Black W (1811) *A Dissertation on Insanity.* London: Ridgway, Murray and Richardson.

Clay RM (1909) *The Mediaeval Hospitals of England.* London: Methuen.

Gregory W (1450, reprinted 1876) *Chronicle of London.* London: Camargo Society.

Haslam J (1809) *Observations on Madness and Melancoly.* London: J. Callow

Mapother E (1924) *Maudsley Hospital, Report of Medical Superintendent to the London County Council.* London: Maudsley Hospital.

Middleton T (1653) *The Changeling.* London: H. Moseley.

Monro J (1758) *Remarks on Dr. Battie's Treatise on Madness.* London: Clarke.

More T (1533) *The Apologye of Syr T. More, Knyght.* London: Rastell.

O'Donoghue EG (1914) *The Story of Bethlehem Hospital from its Foundation in 1247.* London: T. Fisher Unwin.

Rush B (1812) *Medical Inquiries and Observations upon the Diseases of the Mind.* Philadelphia: Kimber and Richardson.

Scull A (1993) *The Most Solitary of Afflictions.* New Haven, Connecticut: Yale University Press.

Slater E (1975) Psychiatry in the thirties. *The Bethlem and Maudsley Gazette*, Spring: 8–10.

Stein G (1976) E.C.T. *The Bethlem and Maudsley Hospital Gazette*, Summer.

Strype J (1734) *A Survey of the Cities of London and Westminster . . . Written at First in the Year MDXCIII.* By John Stow. London: A. Churchill.

Matrons – famous and infamous

The four major Royal Hospitals of London in 1557 were St Bartholomews', Christ's, Bridewell and St Thomas's. Bethlem was managed with the latter. The larger hospitals had lists of duties for Matrons at least from 1557, but Bethlem, being small, may not have had a Matron of its own. By the seventeenth century, it had become customary to use the Bethlem Porter's wife as an inferior officer responsible for admitting and supervising the female patients and one or two maids. In a 1630 document, the Privy Council of Charles I required the Justices of the Peace of the City of Westminster to send three mentally disordered persons 'to the Master and Matrone of Bedlame, for the receiving of them' (Walker and McCabe 1973).

From the time of Charles I, the list of names of Matrons continues unbroken until the present day. The titles have varied since the amalgamation of the Bethlem and Maudsley Hospitals, and there have been Superintendents of Nursing, Chief Nursing Officers or Chief Nurse Advisers, all of which have been names for the principal post for a nurse in the organisation. (see Table 5.1 on page 83).

There follow three vignettes of women who held the most senior post. In reading these narratives, it must be remembered that each Matron had a different role. This is highlighted, for example, in the number of staff they controlled – Mrs Withers 2, Mrs Hunter 10, Miss Skellern approximately 700. One should beware of comparisons between differing sets of social circumstances, which have changed markedly over the centuries. The vignettes below stand as independent pictures, but collectively they illustrate some of the diversity of Matrons at Bethlem.

Elizabeth Withers, 1633–54

One of the earliest Matrons was Elizabeth Withers, wife of Humphrey Withers, who was appointed to the post of Porter on July 5 1633. Humphrey Withers had been previously employed at Bridewell, as an arts-master in charge of sieve-makers, and before that had worked as a merchant tailor. Mrs Withers' previous employment is not known. At this time the Matron's role was that of a superior domestic servant, working as an adjunct to the Porter, and there was no salary apart from that which was given to her husband. The Matron supervised a single maidservant in the duties of laundering and cooking, as well as looking after the care of the female patients. Both Mr and Mrs Withers also assisted in the bathing and bleeding of both male and female patients (Andrews 1991). There were at this stage no explicit directions to segregate male and female patients.

The career of Elizabeth Withers appears to have started quietly, but, by late 1636, discord was developing between Mr and Mrs Withers, and Mr and Mrs Langley. Richard Langley had been appointed as Steward in February 1636, and, by the end of the year, the disagreements between the families had become so serious that they needed airing in the Court of Governors. Humphrey Withers threatened to resign and let it be known that he had an offer of alternative employment with the almon(g)er of the City of London. Fortunately for him, the Court found that the Langleys had committed 'abuses in words, blowes, assaults and fowle carriages' against him and exonerated Withers as a 'honest, diligent and faithful' officer, not to blame for the dissensions. The Governors also found a scapegoat and dismissed one of the maidservants for vicious gossiping and disturbing the relationships between the Steward, the Porter and Mistresses Withers and Langley.

Matters did not improve. Two years later, the Langleys were found guilty of returning drunk to the hospital late at night. Richard Langley was also found to have stolen hospital provisions and falsified the accounts. The Withers as well as the Langleys seem to have been given to heavy drinking, for, in 1641, both parties were admonished by the Court of Governors about 'being drunk [and] . . . abuseing each other with evil language'. The Withers were in further trouble two years later for extortion and embezzlement. They were accused of extorting money from patients to supply market bread and selling the house suet to a chandler. At the same time, they were accused of shutting the door against visitors, in order to force them 'to give more money to the [Poores] Boxe than they are willing to give'. The Court found them 'too faultie' but, surprisingly, did not dismiss them. Furthermore, in 1651, Humphrey Withers was admonished for alehouse tippling, embezzlement and absenteeism. On this occasion, Withers and other servants were found guilty of 'curring provisions to Alehouses and abiding there to tiple and disorder themselves and neglect their service and staying out late in the evening'.

This particular pattern of events was brought to an end by the death of Humphrey Withers in 1654, and this should also have brought to an end the employment of Elizabeth Withers, as her post as Matron was dependent on being the wife of the Porter. The Court of Governors, in their generosity, retained Mrs Withers on the staff as a maidservant. Alas, a pattern of becoming the worse for drink had been established, and one can read in the Court minutes of 1655, 1657 and 1662 about the Widow Withers not behaving 'herself in orderly manner'. Two basketmen, who seem to have accompanied her on the 1657 drinking bout, were sacked for being rude and disorderly persons, but Mrs Withers was allowed to remain. In the event of future problems, the Porter, then John Hopkins, was instructed to 'locke her upp in one of the roomes appointed for Lunatique persons there'. Unfortunately, after this Elizabeth Withers is mentioned no more, so we do not know how her story ended. After her tenure of the post finished in 1654, no Matron was appointed for another nine years.

The only known documentation about Elizabeth Withers is the Bethlem Court of Governors' Minutes. These do not record what she herself said, so we only have the official viewpoint on her activities. During this period, she would, as an inferior officer, most likely be mentioned in the Minutes only if there were some problem that needed resolution. We are confronted with an unsavoury story of disturbed staff relationships, characterised by heavy consumption of alcohol.

There is no evidence of how this affected the patients, and, at first sight, one might suppose that here was an episode in hospital life that needed no further comment. O'Donoghue (1914) managed to gloss over these events, but Andrews (1991) made many references to the leading persons in this story. He hypothesised that Elizabeth Withers may have been a patient herself in 1655 and 1662, but eventually decided that, as Withers was such a common name, it was unlikely that the maidservant and the patient were one and the same person. Nevertheless, the provision for her to be locked up argued a considerable recurring amount of disturbed behaviour.

Andrews observed that the Governors were less interested in how patients might be affected by staff misconduct and more concerned with the disobedience to the Governors themselves. He also comments on the leniency with which offending staff were treated, and we might feel astonishment that such people were able to remain in employment. Yet staff were periodically admonished and dismissed, so one can view the existence of the documentation on these topics as evidence that the management were concerned and trying to control the situation. The background is of an institution where the consumption of alcohol, both on and off the premises, was part of the culture, and this naturally gave rise to long-term problems. It was not for another two and a half centuries that the beer allowance to staff was withdrawn.

As we do not know anything about Elizabeth Withers that does not relate to troublesome behaviour, it is not possible to arrive at a balanced assessment of her place in the life of the institution. Then, as now, there were profound problems posed to colleagues on the way to treat a staff member with a drinking problem, especially when there had been hostility in interpersonal relationships and ultimately a decline into mental instability.

Henrietta Hunter, 1840–52

Over two centuries later, in 1840, Mrs Hunter was appointed to the post of Matron. Mrs Hunter was the daughter of Dr John Haslam, a former Apothecary to Bethlem. She herself worked with Dr Edward Thomas Munro, whose father had worked with her father. During the early part of her tenure of the post, the physicians Dr Edward Thomas Monro and Dr Alexander Morison reported with approval the conduct of Matron and the attendants in their Annual Report to the Court of Governors. In the Report for 1845, they write that 'the personal care and forbearance of the male and female attendants on each side of the Hospital respectively, cannot be too highly appreciated. The unwearied kindness of the Matron, on the one hand, and the indefatigable assiduity of the Steward, on the other, can be equalled only by the unvarying attention and benevolent demeanour of the resident Medical Officer [the Apothecary]'.

Mrs Hunter was proud of the alterations and improvements that she had introduced during her years at Bethlem and listed them herself for the Commissioners who visited the hospital in 1851:

1st	*Religious service daily in every gallery, but the refractory.*
2nd	*The removal of several restraint chairs.*
3rd	*The removal of eight large iron gates from the galleries.*
4th	*The introduction of ordinary beds in the front basement ward, instead of loose straw, which had been the previous practice: and the substitution of a wooden floor for stone pavement, thereby materially increasing the warmth and comfort of the ward.*
5th	*Building a new workroom and parlour for convalescent patients.*
6th	*Having an airing ground laid out as a flower garden for ditto.*
7th	*Introduction of a pianoforte for ditto.*
8th	*Introduction of bagatelle and pope-joan boards, and materials for drawing and painting for ditto.*

9th	Introduction of a select library for ditto.
10th	Introduction of fancy works and straw plaiting.
11th	A large increase in general employment throughout the galleries.

The above facts will prove that I have, with the kind assistance of the Governors, been an active agent in carrying out their philanthropic views for the amelioration of the condition of the insane; and that I have studied to act, with a faithful and an upright heart, the part assigned to me – even to the sacrifice of my health and domestic comfort.

There was a pleasing account in the 1843 Report of Mrs Hunter providing fruit and cakes for an end of year party, when patients played the new pianoforte and danced quadrilles. Patients were said to show pleasure whenever she visited the wards. The report also noted the importance and responsibility of her role: 'The matron regulates the classification, occupations and amusements, and to a great extent the general treatment of her patients.'

The first signs of tension between Mrs Hunter and Mr Wood the Apothecary came in 1845, when they disagreed about which of them was going to order a strait waistcoat to be worn by a patient named Sarah Love. The necessity for this was dubious since the patient was said to be in a 'decline'. Mr Wood was not amused when, an hour and three quarters after she had died, the nurses included Sarah Love amongst the list of patients wearing strait waistcoats. Mrs Hunter was made to carry the blame for this inaccuracy of recording.

Two years later, the friction between Mr Wood and Mrs Hunter was serious enough to require a Committee of Investigation. It emerged that Matron had taken some of the control over the female wards that had previously been the responsibility of the resident medical officer. Mr Wood felt that his authority had been limited. The Governors found that there had been 'infirmity of temper on both sides' and called on them not to interfere with one other's province. Mrs Hunter had undisguisedly displayed her bad temper to Committees, for which indiscretion she was cautioned in writing not to resist or dispute the wishes of the Governors.

Matters came to a head once again in 1851 when complaints were received from relatives about the treatment of two patients, namely Miss Morley and Miss Hannah Hyson, who had since died. These patients were said to have been subjected to 'harsh and improper usuage' by the attendants. This provoked an Inquiry as to the management and treatment of patients at Bethlem by the Metropolitan Commissioners in Lunacy, chaired by Lord Shaftesbury. Copious evidence was taken from all grades of staff and patients, and the detailed verbatim replies to questions were published. During the course of the lengthy investigation in which many hundreds of questions were asked, Mrs Hunter had personally to face 217 questions about how she had carried out her role, including the following:

> *Question 465. What are your duties, especially in reference to female patients? –*
> *To visit them daily, and more frequently, if I think it necessary; to see whether*
> *every kindness and attention is paid to them by the nurses; to report to the medical*
> *man, and to see the nurses report also any case of necessity that may occur during*
> *his absence; to send up their medicines, and various other things that can contribute*
> *to the comfort and security of the patients.*

The Commissioners went on to ask her questions about the extent of her authority, her visits to the wards, patients' complaints, mechanical restraint and seclusion, the use of padded rooms, the placement of patients on different wards, patients who refused food, staff discipline, accidents, sleeping arrangements, bathing, physical abuse and bad language. Mrs Hunter denied any current ill-treatment of patients, but, rather suspiciously, it emerged that some staff had recently resigned their posts. She denied having seen dirty patients mopped down with cold water. The Commissioner pressed her further:

> *Question 621. You never see them washed of a morning? – I see them when they*
> *are bathing the patients occasionally.*
> *622. It would be a good thing for you to recollect what a responsible situation you*
> *hold; it would have a beneficial effect if you brought the weight of your authority*
> *to bear upon all this. Why do you not go? – It is not my habit, and I cannot*
> *affect it.*
> *623. It is not your habit; I hope it will become your habit; you hold a most*
> *responsible situation. – I am aware of it.*

And later on:

> *674. Have you ever had cause of complaint stated against any, and which of the*
> *nurses during the time of your being matron? – Upon several occasions when I*
> *have found neglect, I have discharged the nurse instantly; and if I have only had*
> *complaints made of what I considered unkind treatment, I have immediately*
> *requested permission of the Treasurer to discharge the woman instantly.*

In addition, a patient, Elinor Webb, stated that Mrs Hunter tried to discourage her from complaining. An attendant, William Marston, complained that he was badly treated and abused by Mrs Hunter.

The Commissioners were agreed that Henrietta Hunter had neglected her duties, and said:

> *Adverting to her duties to see that the linen of the patients is properly changed,*
> *washed and returned, and that it is her duty to look to the personal comforts of the*
> *patients, it might be inferred, that the fact of as many as 15 female patients*
> *sleeping naked in the basement ward must have been known to her; but this she*
> *assures us was not the case – a fact that can only be attributable to her imperfect*
> *and not very frequent visits to this part of the hospital, and to the fact of her never*
> *seeing these patients after their being placed in their beds at night.*

Mrs Hunter was not satisfied with the impartiality of the Inquiry, particularly as regards herself. In her letter of resignation from her post, she wrote, 'I cannot believe that it is consistent with the ordinary practice of common justice for any person to be persecuted as I have been; and my reputation, which was my all, assailed by witnesses behind my back; or that I should be examined and harassed upon evidence taken in my absence, and which I was not even allowed to see and answer.'

As well as Mrs Hunter, the Steward and three of the medical staff resigned or changed post.

In contrast to the previous vignette, in which the concerns of the staff and governors were central, we have now moved to the Victorian age, when the Governors were said to be motivated by philanthropic views on ameliorating the condition of the insane, and the staff were thought to wish to make the patients comfortable. As Mrs Hunter herself said, 'My wish and aim is to do everything that is humane and kind.'

Unlike Mrs Withers, she was not the wife of another officer, and, having an independent appointment, was paid a personal salary of £180 a year. Her duties had been clearly outlined and she was interested in making improvements. Did she deserve the censures of the Commissioners and a banishment into obscurity?

Mrs Hunter comes over as a forceful lady who managed to extend her sphere of authority, particularly over the female patients. Her earlier struggles had not been with other inferior officers but with medical staff. She acquired the right to move female patients from the admission or convalescent wards to the basement wards if they became disturbed. This may not seem unreasonable, but in practice it led to a communication gap. Mrs Hunter and Mr Wood, the Apothecary, operated independently. The ward staff were answerable to Mrs Hunter for general management of the patients, and to Mr Wood for the medical treatment. This might have worked adequately were it not for problem patients and staff misbehaviour. Mrs Hunter did not seem to have felt the need to share difficulties that arose with other officers. She did not herself ill-treat patients and professed to be unaware of the abuses complained of by the patients and their relatives. Is it possible that Mrs Hunter was only blameworthy in a minor way and mainly made a scapegoat in an attempt to conceal the deficiencies in medical supervision?

O'Donoghue, (1914) sided with the staff on this issue. He wrote:

> [My] bewilderment only increased with each reading [of the Commissioners Report]; but if I had to give judgment on appeal I should admit that the report justly condemned some features in the system under which the hospital had been – conscientiously enough – administered up to this period ... On the other hand, I am of the opinion that the Commissioners, and for that matter the governors, did serious injustice to some of the individuals who had endeavoured to carry out the system in force in accordance with the decisions of the courts and committees.

The Commissioners found that Mrs Hunter had been negligent in not fully observing what her staff were doing in controlling the more disturbed patients. It is apparent from her evidence that she was more interested in the work of the convalescent wards, but that could not excuse her from her overall responsibilities. One cannot help thinking that, if she had thoroughly investigated the complaints that had previously come to her attention, it might have been a different story. She could then have made reports to the medical staff and the Governors, which would have assisted them in running the organisation. She paid a heavy price for her misjudgments, but this might not be thought unjust in view of her authority and responsibilities.

Alternatively, one might see Mrs Hunter as a victim of her own success in carving out a sphere of authority of her own. She was one of the new breed of Matron who alarmed Dr John Conolly with their assertion of power in the institution. Her tragedy was that she was unable to handle the additional responsibility that she had undertaken, but she could nevertheless be regarded as having pioneered an expanded role. Henrietta Hunter was not unfamiliar with a situation such as that in which she found herself; over thirty years before, her father, John Haslam, Apothecary at Bethlem, had been dismissed because gross malpractices were discovered at the hospital. She left in bitterness, feeling that she had been misrepresented and that the Commissioners had been prejudiced and had disregarded her conscientious discharge of duty during twenty-two years of service to the mentally afflicted. Nevertheless, she had failed to make the reality of the hospital wards conform to Victorian high idealism.

Eileen Skellern, 1963–80

Just over a century later, Eileen Skellern was appointed as Superintendent of Nursing at the Bethlem and Maudsley Hospitals, taking up her post in 1963. She came from St Bartholomew's Hospital, London, where she had been a Sister Tutor. Before that she had been employed at the Cassel Hospital, London, with Dr Tom Maine, pioneering psychotherapeutic and psychosocial treatments for patients with neurotic illnesses, and then with Dr Maxwell Jones at the Belmont Hospital, Surrey, developing social rehabilitation by group methods. She had been at the centre of some of the most progressive work of that time. On behalf of the Royal College of Nursing she had also produced a pioneering piece of research on the role of the Ward Sister (1953), which is rightly remembered as one of the earliest nursing research studies ever done by a nurse in the UK.

Miss Eileen Skellern, Superintendent of Nursing, photo from the 1960s

Eileen Skellern was a warm, outgoing, articulate person, quick to forge relationships, who in the 1960s was regarded as a national leader in her field. Much of her work in the first years of her appointment was done outside the Bethlem and Maudsley in promotion of the hospital's national and international role, for which she travelled widely, talking to nurses and hospital staff world wide. Eileen Skellern lectured at many conferences, sat on committees, some at the King's Fund College, and pursued interests with such bodies as the National Association of Mental Health, the Post Graduate Hospitals Matrons Association and the World Federation of Mental Health. Then, in 1969, she sat on a national working party with the Secretary of State, Richard Crossman, reviewing government policy on mental subnormality, in the wake of revelations of malpractice at Ely Hospital, Cardiff. Some of the results of this work were seen in the White Paper of 1972 *Better Services for the Mentally Handicapped*. For this, she was awarded an OBE.

For the Bethlem and Maudsley nurses, she established a combined degree course with Brunel University at a time when the number of

79

graduates among British nurses was still very small. She wanted to bring more scholarship and a more 'academic' approach into the nursing profession (F Hare, oral history 1995).

Bethlem's first community psychiatric nurse was appointed by Eileen Skellern, in spite of opposition from some medical staff.

She also encouraged innovation, especially in facilitating work by nurses as behaviour therapists, and in 1973 established, with Professor Isaac Marks, the first course for nurses in adult behavioural psychotherapy.

Her last honour, being made a Fellow of the Royal College of Nursing, came in the middle of her final piece of work, which was to create and plan London's first International Psychiatric Nursing Congress. This gave rise to the Psychiatric Nurses Association. The address of welcome which Eileen Skellern wrote shortly before she died for the delegates to the Congress in the programme of events, summed up themes that she wished to emphasise:

> Since the end of the World War Two there has been a remarkable development of the identification, practising and teaching of new skills by psychiatric nurses. I have been a psychiatric nurse for 30 years out of the 40 years of professional nursing. I entered psychiatric nursing questioning its existence as an art and science. I retired early from the profession, but holding a firm and deep conviction that psychiatric nursing – both art and science – is essential and must be done by nurses who have been suitably educated, based on the real needs of patients and family care in the community, the objective being to effect a cure or alleviate the suffering of patients and relatives alike.
>
> If we do not develop these psychiatric nursing skills we fail not only our colleagues but patients too. We are at a crossroads as important issues are debated, not least the fact that psychiatric nurses must live up to the standard of nursing care they set themselves when first entering this most exciting form of nursing.
>
> Britain's entry into the EEC has placed a question mark over the type of training most appropriate for nurses caring for patients who are mentally ill. Other currently debatable issues include where such patients should be nursed – in hospitals, in community centres or at home; who the caring personnel are – doctors, nurses, social workers, occupational therapists; how the nursing process can best be adapted to psychiatric nursing practice; and what kind of nursing care plans can be devised to meet the individual requirements of each patient. So this is a crucial period for the development of the art and science of psychiatric nursing . . .
>
> The patient's voice is never far away and we are delighted to present the patient's point of view of psychiatric nursing as a culmination of this conference.

Eileen Skellern was a woman who had a personal charisma that compelled attention; few would deny that. We are left with a clutch of published papers, a tape, some photographs and personal recollections. In retrospect, it is sometimes questioned whether her achievements equalled her opportunities. What gaps in effectiveness did the charisma conceal?

A major curiosity is that she did not follow up her trail-blazing early research work when she came to the Maudsley. Not only did she fail to do any further research herself, but she also did little to initiate research projects by others. She did, however, start up the degree programme with Professor Elliot Jacques, and a few research papers started to emerge from the undergraduates and graduates of this course.

During her time in post, she saw to it that the teaching of student nurses on the courses leading to the qualification of Registered Mental Nurse was of a high standard, and, during this period especially, the Maudsley produced trained nurses who were in demand for senior positions throughout the UK and abroad (Everest et al 1979). Yet, on the service side, the hospital continued to be beset with the problems of standards of practice and management competence that are some of the themes of this book. The early nineteen seventies were a restless period when the nurses began to engage in industrial action, in spite of Eileen Skellern's personal efforts to avoid this.

Her relationships with the medical staff, although sometimes warm, were often uneasy. She related best, perhaps, to those psychiatrists of a psychotherapeutic bent who had been psychoanalysed, as she had been. She sometimes emerged from the Medical Executive and other Committees feeling bruised in her struggles with the doctors, whom she rightly perceived as being more powerful, in a situation where nurses were often treated as second-class citizens. Even on the Nursing Committee, she complained that doctors could outvote nurses and change nursing policy. The period of the introduction of the Salmon structure for nursing management in the 1970s made for more stress in a hospital where doctors attitudes were disapproving of the new ideas.

Eileen Skellern is often credited with the introduction of courses for nurses in behaviour therapy, and, while this is true, tribute must be given to Dr Isaac Marks who developed the programmes. What Skellern did do was to stimulate growth in the provision of many courses to develop skills in nurses working in specialist areas – in child and adolescent psychiatry and in mental impairment, for instance – and shorter training sessions to improve the practice standards of all the nurses in the organisation.

The writings of Eileen Skellern, for example the descriptions of the therapeutic community and social rehabilitation (Skellern 1955, 1957, Jones et al 1956, Jones and Skellern 1957), practically all predate her time at the Bethlem and Maudsley. Apart from a chapter in a textbook on the role of the psychiatric nurse (Skellern 1964), there are short writings on topics such as stress, introducing change and being a cancer patient. Her last years were clouded with illness, as the cancer spread and she underwent much surgical intervention. This had the effect of limiting the attention she could give to nursing innovation, and turned her towards being a role model of how to cope with the stress of chronic physical deterioration. As if to compensate for the time lost in illness, she worked phenomenally long hours (Russell and Skellern 1992). Making a virtue of her limitations, empowering others became a vital aspect of her work. She encouraged nurses to train and function as therapists and have their own clinical caseloads (J Wiltshire, oral history 1994). Her fortitude became a great encouragement to other staff with health problems.

So, what is left of the work, from her Maudsley years, that is distinctive? There are few who can remember her practising as a psychiatric nurse, but more who can remember her as a nurse manager. Two of these are Baroness Jean McFarlane and Professor Annie Altschul. In a memorial lecture, McFarlane (1982) explained that, as a professional, Eileen Skellern was not only forward looking, innovative, skilful and knowledgeable, but also careful that her actions were consistent with her values and ethics, hence the importance for her of values classification, i.e. clarifying her own values, which in her case were informed by Christian principles. McFarlane said that the nature of nursing was such that it carried with it values about the human person and the nature of human interaction, and also the scientific values of knowledge and competence. This is important when one considers Eileen Skellern's own emphasis on the use of relationships in nursing and the identity of the nurse:

> If they [the patients] are to be helped as individuals, a human relationship must be formed and it is here that the psychiatric nurse finds her chief role. She does not help her patients so much by the things she does for them as by being the kind of person they need . . . The nurse who remains calm in the midst of disturbance, settles her patients not so much by her actions as by making her presence felt. (Skellern 1964)

Eileen Skellern was, in her management as well as her nursing role, an exemplar of this approach. This emphasis on the individual person and 'being' chimes in well with the existentialist philosophies of her age.

Altschul (1984) took up a similar theme in another lecture:

> Eileen Skellern [was] unmistakably a good practitioner, who should have been entitled to call herself a psychiatric nurse long before a belated course of training bestowed on her officially the right to do so and entitled her to the Whitley Council negotiated remuneration. I am reluctant, however, to view psychiatric nursing purely as an art form, perfected by the performers; though I am attracted to the idea of judging the practice of psychiatric nursing without reference to the would-be beneficiaries. Psychiatric nursing might even be judged without reference to the actions of the practitioners, but rather on the basis of who they are as people . . . If they are mature, well balanced, sensitive, interested in people I would be prepared to regard them as good practitioners, without having seen them in action.

Eileen Skellern was someone people wanted as a friend; she was also a nurse practitioner of national importance.

Table 5.1 Table of Bethlem and Maudsley Matrons

Elizabeth Withers	1633–54	
Jane Johnson	1663–4	
Millicent Matthews	1664–84	
Hannah Matthews	1684–7	
Gartwright Wood	1687–1709	
Mrs Humphrey Pooler	1709–13	
Mrs Benjamin Brockden	1713–15	
Mrs James Male	1715–24	
Rachel Wood	1724–52	
Diana Hodges	1752–65	
Mary Spencer	1765–93	
Mary White	1793–8	
Eliza Bradbury	1798–1815	
Elizabeth Forbes	1815–40	
Henrietta Hunter	1840–52	
Sarah Eager	1852–54	
Emma Dunn	1854–69	
Elizabeth Wright	1870–91	
Alice Kough	1892–1905	
Edith Meikle	1905–12	
Harriet Deakin	1912–14	
Gladys Bettinson	1914–16	
Sarah Hearder	1916–37	
M.I.H.Skene	1937–45	
Margaret Robinson	1945–63	
Eileen Skellern	1963–80	Superintendent of Nursing/Chief Nursing Officer
Juliette Wiltshire	1981–6	Chief Nursing Officer
Julia Brooking	1987–9	Chief Nursing Adviser/Senior Lecturer
Ben Thomas	1991–	Chief Nurse Advisor/Director of Quality

References and further reading

Andrews J (1991) *Bedlam Revisited: A History of Bethlem Hospital c1634–c1770.* Unpublished PhD thesis, University of London.

Altschul A (1984) Psychiatric nursing: does good practice need good principles? *Nursing Times*, July 11 and 18: 36–38, 49–51.

Commissioners in Lunacy (1852) *The Report of the Commissioners in Lunacy to the Secretary of State on Bethlem Hospital.* London: Spotiswoode and Shaw.

Everest R, Richards E and Hanrahan M (1979) What happens to Maudsley nurses? A follow up study. *International Journal of Nursing Studies*, **16**: 253–266.

Jones M and Skellern E (1957) Social rehabilitation: a joint project of patients and staff. *Nursing Mirror*, 23 August.

Jones M, Pomryn BA and Skellern E (1956) Work therapy. *The Lancet*, **CCLXX** (6918): 343–344.

McFarlane J (1982) Nursing values and nursing action. *Nursing Times*, **78**(28) 109–112.

O'Donoghue EG (1914) *The Story of Bethlehem Hospital from its Foundation in 1247*. London: T. Fisher Unwin.

Russell DH and Skellern M (1992) Eileen Skellern House. *History of Nursing Journal Royal College of Nursing*, **4**(2): 82–84.

Skellern E (1953) *Report of an Investigation Carried out 'To Study, Report and Make Recommendations on the Practical Application to Ward Administration of Modern Methods in the Instruction and Handling of Staff and Student Nurses'*. RCN Research Report. London: Royal College of Nursing.

Skellern E (1955) A therapeutic community. *Nursing Times*, **51**(16): 426–428, **51**(19): 533–535, **51**(21): 593–594, **51**(23) 642–643, **51**(25): 688–689.

Skellern E (1957) From custodial to therapeutic care. *Nursing Times*, **53**(8): 209–211 and 220–221.

Skellern E (1964) The role of the psychiatric nurse. In Ackner B (ed.) *The Handbook for Psychiatric Nurses*, 9th edn. London: Baillière Tindall and Cassell.

Walker N and McCabe S (1973) *Crime and Insanity in England*, vol. 2. Edinburgh: T. and A. Constable.

William Hogarth.
A Rake's Progress
(1733-4)
VIII The Madhouse

Richard Dadd.
Contradiction: Oberon
and Titania. 1854-58

Isaac Oliver. Lady Eleanor Davies (1590-1652) prophetess and patient

British School. Nathaniel Lee (c1649-1692) dramatist and patient

Anonymous. Margaret Nicholson (c1750-1828) housemaid, needlewoman and patient

Richard Dadd. Charles Neville, first Head Attendant at Bethlem, appointed 1853

Charles Fréchou. Dr W. Charles Hood, Resident Physician at Bethlem 1852-1862

Epitaph, of my poor Jack, Squirrel.

Here are the remains of my poor little Jack,
Who, with a little fall; almost broke his back—
And I myself was the occasion of that—
By letting him be frighten'd, by a Cat—
I then picked him up, from off the floor;
But he, alas! Never danced a hornpipe more:
And many a time, have I laugh'd, to See him So cunning;
To Sit and Crack the nuts I gave him So funny;
Now in remembrance of his pretty tricks—
I have had him Stuff'd, that I might not him forget—
And So he is gone; and I must go, as well as him;
And pray God, Send I may go, but wi the little Sin;
So there is an end, to my little dancing Jack.
That will never more, be frighten'd, by a Cat—
Died Sunday
Morning   James Hadfield—   Bethlem
July 23.1826.   Hospital

James Hadfield (c1771-1841) soldier and patient. Poem and painting on his pet squirrel

*Louis Wain (1860-1939)
artist and patient.
Sweetness Coyed Love
into its Smile. 1930s*

Bethlem Royal Hospital, 1995

A multi-disciplinary team at The Maudsley Hospital, 1984.
1 Jean Rainey, social worker. 2 Thelma Pryce, SEN. 3 Gary Winship, student nurse.
4 Dr Michael Reveley, locum consultant. 5 Dr Ian Oswald, registrar. 6 Susan Ritter, ward sister.
7 Al Williamson, social worker. 8 Jamie Christison, staff nurse. 9 Padmal De Silva, psychologist.
10 Stephen Redpath, nursing assistant. 11 Dr Francis Winton, registrar. 12 Dr Sue Davison,
senior registrar. 13 Olga Grant, occupational therapist. 14 Heather Deadman, staff nurse.

*R*ules for the workplace

*N*one of the three women in the previous chapter had an inclination to write work routines for others, but such routines have been a long-standing feature of Bethlem life. In the Archives at Bethlem today there is a unique range of Rule Books, written anonymously at the behest of the Bethlem Governors. The books stretch back to the seventeenth century, and list the tasks that staff were expected to perform. These books also illustrate the development of ideas about how patients ought to be treated and represent what was thought at the time to be desirable. The rules outlined what the Governors officially expected of their staff, although, in the Court of Governors, some divergence was noted from time to time between the rules and the realities of staff behaviour. Nevertheless, the rules occupied a central place in providing a framework for the organisation of patient care and established boundaries for day-to-day activities. By the division of tasks between different grades of staff, relationships were defined and responsibilities delineated. The rules covered routine and order, surveillance and discipline. They showed where power lay and indicated the limits of action beyond which sanctions might be imposed or disciplinary actions taken. Many of the rules seem to have originated as a response to particular problems or criticism, and, as time went on, the number of regulations increased. They are of two types, the first being general rules for the institution as a whole, and the second specific orders for named grades of staff.

For the purposes of this chapter, the documents are considered in three groups. There are examples from the seventeenth and eighteenth centuries when the hospital was at Moorfields, examples from the nineteenth century when the hospital was at Southwark, and further examples from the twentieth century, from Southwark and Beckenham, stopping in 1935 with the end of this collection of documents.

Before looking at the contents of the Bethlem Rule Books, it is useful to consider another document – The Order of the Hospitals of Henry

VIII and Edward VI 1557. The Order of the four royal London hospitals, namely St Bartholomew's, Christ's, Bridewell and St Thomas's, does not mention Bethlem, but seeing that Bethlem at the beginning of 1557 was under the management of Christ's Hospital, and then from September 27, 1557 under that of Bridewell, we can assume that The Order applied also to Bethlem. The short document detailed the charge given to each of the officers of the hospitals, of which the ones most concerning us are those to the Matron, the nurses and the keepers of wards.

Matron was to have the oversight of all the women and children within the hospital, and she was especially answerable for discipline and reporting back to the Governors. Her duties included supervision of laundry, proper bedding, stock-taking, cleaning, the appearance of nurses, the particular nurse responsible for the patient, night rounds and records of admission.

The nurses and keepers were to be of virtuous behaviour. Their 'charge' included directions on observation, management, cleanliness, occupation, chastity, order at night, reporting faults and punishment.

Bethlem was only a small part of this larger collection of institutions, and, being specialised, with far fewer patients, The Order cannot have applied in all details, but it nevertheless gives some idea of the general ethos and principles on which the hospitals were organised.

The seventeenth century

Shortly after the opening of the Moorfields hospital, an early set of general rules for Bethlem was laid down:

> *An Abstract of Orders of Court made the 30th of March 1677, for the good Government of the Hospital of BETHLEM.*
>
> *I. That the Bell be rung at Sun setting every evening, Summer and Winter: and that all persons do depart, and that afterwards no Persons be admitted in, but Quality or Governors.*
>
> *II. That no Servant go out of the Hospital till half an Hour after ringing of the Bell; nor stay out after Eight from Michaelmas to Lady Day, nor after Ten from Lady Day to Michaelmas; and that but one half of them be out at one time.*
>
> *III. That the Back Gate at London Wall shall always be kept shut, except extraordinary Occasions of bringing in Beer, etc. and that no Person shall come in to see the Lunaticks that way.*
>
> *IV. That no Person, except Governors, shall be permitted to see the Lunaticks on Sundays.*
>
> *V. That no Person do give the Lunaticks Strong Drink, Wine, Tobacco, or Spirits: Nor be permitted to sell any such thing in the Hospital.*
>
> *VI. That such Lunaticks as are fit, be permitted to walk in the Yard till*

Dinner-time, and then be lock'd up in their Cells; and that no Lunatick that lies naked, or is in a Course of Physick, be seen by any Body, without Order of the Physician.

VII. That no Servant, or other Person whatsoever, shall take any Money given to the Lunaticks, to convert the same to their own Use, but the same to be kept for the Lunaticks, till recovered, or laid out for them in the mean time, as the Committee thinks fit.

VIII. That no Officer or Servant shall beat or abuse any Lunatick, nor offer any Force to them, but upon absolute Necessity, for the better governing of them.

IX. That no Person do presume to ask any Person for Money, till such Person's Charity be first put in the Poor's Box; and that what afterwards shall be given to such Servant, be put by him into the Servants Box, to be distributed among them, pursuant to an Order of Court for that purpose.

X. That some of the Committee go weekly to the said Hospital, to see the Provisions weighed; that the same be good, and rightly expended. That the Men Servants shall attend the Delivery of the Diet to the Lunatick Men, and the Women Servants to the Lunatick Women ...

Although the rules reflected the preoccupations of the time (four rules mention visiting or access), many of the topics they covered are perennial for psychiatric institutions – staff hours of duty, the financial rewards for services rendered, security, patients' feeding and occupation, their safety, especially from sexual exploitation, the custody of patients' monies, substance abuse and the use of physical coercion. This is a formidable collection of controversial areas, and it is not surprising that this preliminary exercise in establishing ground rules had to be supplemented by more guidance. In fact, it was only four years before sexual exploitation became a subject of scandal and needed severe measures (see Chapter 12).

The eighteenth century

The first Bethlem job descriptions were set out in 1736 for specific members of staff, including the Steward, Porter, Matron, Nurse (first appointed 1693), Basketmen, Cook and Gallery Maids. Here are some for those working closely with the patients. They all start 'The Care Duty and Trust of the [name of post] of Bethlem Hospital'.

Of the Matron.
    To attend and assist at Bathing and Bleeding the Women.
    To look after the Maids and see that they do their duty.

Of the Nurse.
    To attend carefully on the Patients especially when weak.
    To give an account to the Doctor of the condition of each Patient.

To administer the medicines prescribed.

To Shift the Women both Curable and Incurable once a week.

Of the Basketmen.

Two are to cut the Bread Butter and Cheese by turns, the other to take care of the Beer.

All to distribute the Provisions and Beer to the Patients.

To clean the cells, galleries, chequer and stairs on the Men's End.

To shift the Men Patients once a week.

To attend on the Committees.

To go on Messages and with letters as Ordered by the Committee, Treasurer, Clerk or Steward.

To attend and assist the Men Patients at Bathing, Bleeding, Shaveing and taking their medicines.

To take care of the keys of the gates after ringing the bell by turns, and on every Sunday and after ten in the Summer and nine in the Winter every night to deliver the keys to the Porter.

Of the Gallery Maids.

To distribute the Provisions to the Women Patients.

To help wash and iron the linen of all the Patients.

To clean the Cells, Gallerys, Chequer and Stairs of the Women's end, also the Committee Rooms and the Stairs and other parts in the Middle of the House.

The duties of the Matron were limited to two short instructions, which is somewhat surprising seeing that the post had already been in existence over a hundred years. This eventually appeared to the Governors to be unsatisfactory, so when Diana Hodges, wife of the Steward, resigned as Matron in July 1765, the duties were expanded and combined with those of the former nurse:

The Duty of the Matron.

That she shall be absolute mistress of hiring the Gallery Maids, who shall be approved of by the Committee, and of discharging them with the consent of the same, when ever she finds them negligent in their duty, wanting in care or otherwise misbehaving towards the Patients.

That she shall go round the house every day on the Women's side before ten o'clock, but on Tuesday before nine, to see that the Patients are regularly shifted and sheeted as they ought to be ... (More follows on linen and laundry).

That she shall go into the Stove Room in the winter time by 8 o'clock to see that the fire is lighted, and shall then order the patients proper for that place to be carried there as soon as they conveniently can, and shall complain to the Steward if she finds the gallery maids or basketmen negligent therein.

That she shall see that the patients in general are taken care of and kept as clean as their complaints will allow, and that such of the patients as are low spirited or inclinable to be mopish be obliged [sic] to get up, and that they be turned out of their cells, the doors locked, that they may not creep back again to their beds.

That she shall take particular care of the sick, and see that they are moved into the infirmary if judged necessary by the Physician and there taken care of.

That she shall take particular care of such women patients, as are lewdly given, be confined to their cells, and no persons suffered to come to them but in company with one of the gallery maids.

That she shall acquaint the Physician when ever any of the patients (without particular sickness) take to their beds.

That she shall distribute the patients in their proper cells, that each gallery maid may have a proper number of such hands as are fit to work to assist her, and employ such of the patients at their needle as are capable, when not otherwise busied, rather than let them walk idle up and down the house shewing it to strangers and begging money.

That she shall bring into the Committee Room such patients of the women as are discharged well.

That she shall take care that the straw on which the patients are laid is changed when damp or dirty.

As in the previous age, there was a preoccupation with laundry, bedding and cleanliness, but there was now also a concern for the care of the depressed, the sexually disinhibited and the physically sick, an awareness of the usefulness of occupation and a rudimentary appreciation of the need for comfort, in the shape of warmth and dryness. At the same time, the regulations for the office of Basketman were defined as follows:

The Basket Men on the Men's side

That they shall rise at 6 in the Summer time and at 7 in the Winter, to light the Fires in the Stove Room, Surgery and Infirmary, Carry down their patients as soon as possible and then set about cleaning their galleries and shall take away such provisions as be found every morning.

That they shall receive the linen and other necessaries brought in with the Patient by their Friends, and shall keep Account in writing that they may be delivered up when the Patient is discharged, or if torn that the pieces may be returned to shew that they have not been purloined.

That they shall suffer no strong Beer or other Liquors to be brought in for the Patients on any account but through the Steward's apartment.

That they shall confirm every good rule made long ago but now much neglected, not to suffer 'Prentice boys, idle girls and Jews on a Saturday to stay long in the house and loiter away their time and shall turn them out if they behave improperly'.

The disparaging mention of Jews may be distasteful to us nowadays, but it bears witness to early difficulties concerning ethnic minorities living near the hospital. Other warnings were also drawn up to prohibit the bringing in of tea, wine or strong beer by the friends of patients, and to threaten the servants on pain of discharge from fetching, retailing or

(71)

The Duty of the 2 Basket Man on the Women's Side.

THAT he shall light the fire in the stove-room and assist in carrying the women thither.

That he shall assist the Gallery Maids in bathing, bleeding, shaving and giving the Patients their medicines, and also in removing the straw and cleaning the cells and galleries.
See Order Qurt 20th June 1765

That no gratuity be accepted by him on any pretence whatsoever, on pain of being discharged and rendered incapable of holding his office in future.
See Order 21st Nov. 1770

That the feet of every Patient in chains or straw, be carefully examined, well rubbed and covered with flannel every night and morning during the winter season; and if necessary, that immediate notice be given to the Surgeon.
See Order 22d Jan. 1778

From the General Orders concerning Bethlem Hospital, 1778

accepting money for such commodities. All these rules came in the wake of the great riots and disorders during the Christmas, Easter and Whitsuntide holidays in 1763–4, which had necessitated the employment of constables to be stationed in the galleries to suppress the disturbances.

The duties were once again revised in 1778 to ensure that the basketmen and gallery maids cared for the patients' feet: 'That the feet of every Patient in chains or straw, be carefully examined, well rubbed and covered with flannel every night and morning during the winter season; and if necessary, that immediate notice be given to the Surgeon.' Later that year, the court ordered that, to guard against patients' wounds and sores being unnoticed, on admission every patient be stripped and examined by the respective basketmen or gallery maid in the presence of the patient's friends. It was already the practice that the patient who was being discharged, either sick or incurable, was stripped and examined by the basketman to whose care he had been entrusted, to see that the patient was clean and free from vermin. The two basketmen on the women's side remained intimately involved with the care of female patients, but the responsibility for the care seems to have shifted onto the maids: 'That he [the Basketman] shall *assist* the Gallery Maids in bathing, bleeding, shaving and giving the Patients their medicines, and also in removing the straw and cleaning the cells and galleries.'

The list of General Orders recapitulated a specific order of April 27 1769, which enjoined that the gates of the hospital should be constantly shut and that no person should be permitted to enter without a ticket signed by one of the Governors. This order largely brought to an end the horrors of open visiting, which were a scandal for so much of the eighteenth century.

The nineteenth century

The fresh version of the Rules in 1818, while drawing substantially on earlier versions by then over fifty years old, moved in the direction of greater and more explicit control by the Governors of the senior staff, and by the senior staff of the more junior servants.

The Matron was to reside in the hospital, giving her whole time to the organisation, and not sleeping away from the hospital without permission. She was to be between thirty and forty years old when first employed, and, although she could be married, she was not to have any family. This was in direct response to the problems the Governors encountered with the Matron Mrs Forbes, whose maid had been looking after a child in Matron's lodgings, whom, it was alleged, Mrs Forbes had conceived by a man friend sometime before. She had also been criticised by Urbane Metcalf (1818), an ex-patient, for going off on holiday with a patient. This explains the Governors' concern that she should give her whole time to the organisation. Other aspects of this affair are discussed in Chapter 12. The Governors had been very concerned about the behaviour of resident officers and servants. The Matron was to control the female keepers, as they were then called, and ensure they knew the rules and orders, for the infringement of which she might report them to the Committee. Matron would also ensure that the able patients assisted the washerwomen in boiling the dirty linen.

The keepers, too, were to be more controlled. It was directed that they were to dine together with the Porter and all the servants at the same table. They were to fetch coals to the wards to warm the patients, rather than taking the patients to the stove room. The male patients were also to be shaved twice a week: every Tuesday and Saturday. The keepers were advised to pay 'humane attention' to the patients. This may have seemed necessary in the wake of the outcry two years earlier about James Norris who had been chained to the wall for fourteen years. The picture of daily life on the wards at this period is filled out by the keeper, James Smyth (Anon. 1823) in *Sketches in Bedlam*:

> *They [the patients] breakfast at 8 in the summer, and in the winter at half past eight. They dine daily at one, sup at six, and retire to bed at 8, when they are locked up. Each patient has a separate room. The bedsteads are of iron, with a common sacking bottom; the bedding a good flock mattress, a pillow, 3 blankets, a pair of sheets and a rug. The sheets are regularly changed every fort-night or oftener if necessary. In the basement gallery where the disorderly patients lie, there are no sheets, and they sleep on straw, which is changed every morning if requisite . . .*
>
> *The cold, warm and shower baths are in constant use. The warm bath frequently, as well for purposes of cleanliness as for medical application . . . This is Howlett's patent bath, heated by steam . . . No keeper has authority to put a patient in confinement without first acquainting the superintendent who enquires into the circumstances.*

By 1837, the Charity Commissioners reported that additions had been made to the duties of male and female keepers, which were partly restrictive, partly liberating. They were directed to be in the hospital punctually at ten o'clock every night, but they were sometimes granted leave, when the assistant keepers would cover their duties. Assistant keepers were developing a wide role as follows:

> *The assistant-keeper is to help in the garden, to carry the provisions to the galleries on the male side, and the dinners to the galleries on the female side; to assist in watching the patients employed in the garden, to cleanse the rubbish from the grounds of the hospital, and generally to perform such duties as may be required without side the galleries, and occasionally within the galleries, during the absence of the keepers with leave.*

This sort of catch-all job description could have been useful for what was, in practice, a poorly paid training position, clearly designed to pick up menial aspects of work that keepers might not want to do.

The problems that the Governors experienced with Mrs Hunter, the Matron, in 1847 were reflected in a new list of duties, trying to exert yet more control. It was explicitly stated that she was to be under the control of the President, Treasurer, Committee and Bethlem Sub-Committee. Quite how this was to work is difficult to imagine, but there was a determination that no loop-holes were to be left. We do not know precisely what misdemeanours occurred that made it necessary to ban Matron from connection with other lunatic asylums or dealings with patients' relatives. The friction between Mrs Hunter and the Apothecary led to a requirement for her to keep record books, recording all the instances of restraint or separation, or liberation from restraint, that might take place under her direction. Whatever Mrs Hunter may have thought about this control, it could be seen as a healthy development.

In 1847, the servants too came under more restrictive regulations. In this, they shared the lot of attendants in other asylums, such as Hanwell, Duddleston Hall, Birmingham, and The Retreat, York. At Hanwell, the duties were spelt out for every fifteen minute interval of the day and for different days of the week (Haw 1991). This puts one in mind of the schools, workshops and hospitals cited by Foucault (1975), where disciplinary power was exerted through detailed timetables. Activities do not appear to have been controlled quite as tightly at Bethlem as at Hanwell, but Bethlem had many of the Foucauldian features of institutional life – enclosure in a building, partitioning in cells and hierarchical surveillance. From the Bethlem documents, it reads as if the Governors were making a last ditch attempt to regain mastery of a situation that was running out of control. Servants were not to go on leave without permission in writing, and they had to sign in and out in a book kept by the Porter. They were to give one month's notice of intention to terminate their employment. On pain of dismissal, they were not to carry any hospital property out of the hospital, nor were they to buy and sell articles for the patients or accept any gratuities. There was also more emphasis on the physical care of patients and their environment. The male attendants were to 'Wash, Dress, and Comb the Patients who require such assistance' and take particular care that 'all the Bedding of the Patients, and also the Galleries and Sleeping Apartments are kept perfectly clean, neat, and in good order'. All this was not sufficient to restore good practice to the hospital, for, in 1851–2, a major investigation was required, which resulted in many resignations of senior staff.

Once again, there was a revision of rules, where we can see, in the new duties of the Matron, the new structure and ethos. In 1854, there was an emphasis on control by the Resident Physician, inspections and propriety, but also a new stress on the qualities of the attendants. The following extracts give some of the flavour of this:

> She [the Matron] shall, in common with the Resident Physician, have control over the Female Attendants, and shall uniformly enforce on them the constant exercise of gentleness and kindness in the performance of their duties.
>
> She shall take care that all the Female Attendants be faithful and diligent in the performance of their duties; that they observe the strictest propriety in their language, conduct and demeanour, and that there be neither waste nor mismanagement in any part of the hospital under her charge.
>
> She shall cause every Female Patient becoming dangerous or annoying to others, and not to be soothed by calmness or persuasion, to be quietly removed, and the circumstance to be immediately communicated to the Resident Physician, who alone shall have the power of imposing restraint or seclusion.

Many more sets of rules were issued in the nineteenth century, for example again in 1862, 1866, 1868 and 1891. The last set were more elaborate than their predecessors, showing increasing regimentation of the nurses, attendants and servants. This was not wholly negative, as it showed an increasing awareness of the management problems arising in the care of disturbed patients that are familiar to nurses today. The 1891 duties follow the patients' day through, hour by hour, laying down the range of activities proper for staff and patients. At 7 am the patients were let out of their bedrooms, and washing and dressing commenced. The attendants also started the morning cleaning and organised the stores and the break-fasts. After that:

> *At 9 a.m. All the Patients selected for employment shall be ready to go with the several Attendants and Servants under whose care they are to be occupied; and the sick in the infirmaries and in the wards shall be ready for the morning visit of the Resident Physician.*

> *At 10 a.m. The Attendants shall endeavour to get those Patients up who are still in bed, unless otherwise directed; and shall induce them, when practicable, to take such exercise in the galleries or airing-courts as the Medical Officers shall suggest.*

> *At 11 a.m. The Attendants shall have now completed the cleansing and proper arrangement of their several departments, and shall be neatly dressed.*

The instructions continue for the rest of the day and the night, and there were also duties for particular days. Sundays were for attendance at Chapel and rest from work; Monday afternoons were for visiting between 2 and 4 o'clock every other week; Tuesdays were for taking to the store room articles made by the patients and receiving a fresh supply of work. There was also weekly bathing, and, for the men, shaving three times a week, except for those with suicidal tendencies.

The attention needed by disturbed patients was apparent. Patients were not allowed to gain possession of the gallery or gate keys, and attendants were particularly warned about patients escaping. The suicidal patients were to be watched with extra care, and changes in the appearance and conduct of patients were to be reported. Only razors with special protective shields were to be used for patients in the wards or by the attendants themselves, who were permitted to shave only in their own rooms, behind locked doors! Wards were not to be left without a named attendant being in charge. Refractory patients might be removed to a bedroom or padded room, but there should always be enough staff to accomplish duties with such patients with ease and safety. Whistles were issued so that attendants could summon assistance from their colleagues.

For all the deadening routines prescribed, there was nevertheless a noticeable swing to a more patient-centred approach. The authors of the

Rule Books also started to look more broadly at the needs of the patient. One of the general duties read:

The Attendants shall devote the whole of their time during the day to the Patients, and shall execute with care and diligence all the directions they shall from time to time receive respecting their treatment, medicine, food, dress, occupation, exercise and amusement.

The twentieth century

A copy of the Rules for the Head Attendant of the male wards for September 1911 shows a renewed concern for the supervision of staff and a need for regular observation and inspection of their work. There were responsibilities for recruiting staff, instructing them in their duties, assigning placements with regard to cover, checking on their performance, allocating leave and supervising the ending of their employment. The Head Attendant checked standards by being present at admissions, bathing, entertainments and the administration of medicines, as well as teaching fire drill. He had charge of stocks of 'strong clothing', garments used for restraining patients. Perhaps the most significant item was an explicit statement of the attendant's responsiblity for an individual patient: 'On the admission of each Male Patient, he [the Head Attendant] shall see that he is placed under the special charge of one of the Attendants, who shall be responsible for his care.'

The Matron's duties for 1916 follow those of an earlier date and have similarities to those of the Head Attendant. It was said that she should be responsible for seeing that the Sisters and nurses kept the lists of suicidal patients up to date and, for this purpose, inspecting the lists once a week. This confirms the continuing concern about patients' suicidal intentions, which had preoccupied staff for many years.

Bethlem was at Beckenham, Kent, when the next set of Rules and Orders was issued in 1932. The general rules affirmed the authority of the Physician–Superintendent over all employees, requiring that staff attend services in the Chapel, and stressing that all nurses and servants should render a punctual and cheerful obedience to the orders of their superior officers. As if this was not enough, no nurse above the age of 30 years was to be engaged. The duties assigned for the various hours outlined the pattern of afternoon activities. After dinner, at 1 p.m., Garden Duty commenced, with walking parties in the grounds accompanied by nurses:

Nurses detailed shall be properly dressed and ready punctually to accompany the patients into the garden. Male nurses will wear the uniform hat. Charge Nurses shall have posted two nurses, where supervision is most needed, who shall ascertain that all garden gates are securely fastened before any patient is permitted to enter the garden.

They shall then count out the patients and verify the total with the numbers given by the nurses who have been counting from the wards. On their return, they must be certain that all patients are accounted for in their respective wards.

The Charge Nurses shall induce patients, when practicable, to take exercise whilst in the garden as the Medical Officer shall suggest.

In the damp weather the patients shall not be permitted to lie on the ground, and in very hot weather they shall be placed in the shade.

Staff remaining in the wards had to busy themselves in hair-cutting, tidying rooms and lockers, general dusting, preparing the teas and accompanying patients to treatments and occupational therapy. After that there was tea for the patients at 4.30 p.m., amusements and reading at 5 p.m., supper at 7 p.m. and then, half an hour later, preparation for bed, clothes taken away, bedroom doors 'fastened' and lights switched off. The resident staff had to retire at 10.30 p.m. and switch their lights out by 11 p.m. The care of the suicidal was elaborated to include more checking. The responsibilities seem onerous, especially as there is no indication of the maximum number of patients the nurse might be expected to observe at the same time:

Every nurse shall be provided with a book when on duty in which shall be a list of suicidal or dangerous patients. This book shall on no account be out of his or her possession when on duty, nor shall it be taken out of the hospital. He or she shall sign the parchments relating to these patients, and when given cautionary tabs which accompany these parchments shall carry them with care, as the nurse, whilst holding these tabs, is held responsible for constant observation of these patients. Should nurses be called upon to leave the ward, they shall hand these tabs to the Charge Nurse in an unobtrusive manner.

For an irreverent version of this procedure, see Chapter 9, where Samuel Beckett gives his interpretation of what the nurse should do.

Three other rules show some attitudes of the times:

(a) the nurses shall not discuss or give an opinion with regard to the illness of the patient [that was doctors' business];
(b) attendance at lectures and practical instruction by the medical staff and Sister Tutor was compulsory [training was part of one's duty];
(c) the Matron must be registered as trained in general nursing, and mental nursing, or hold the certificate of the Royal Medico-Psychological Association [physical nursing comes first].

The final set of duties of this collection are those for the Senior Male Nurse and the Matron in 1935. The title 'Attendant' has at last been dropped in favour of Male Nurse. Although the actual duties have changed very little since 1932, one is struck by the almost military restriction and control kept over the post-holder. The Senior Male Nurse was a uniformed official who had to live in the prescribed residence on site, from which he was never to be absent overnight without permission. All his duties were to be regulated by the Physician–Superintendent, whose permission would be needed to move nurses from one ward to another. He must not talk to patients' friends, and could only have the pass key that gave entry to the portions of the hospital for male patients, and the key to his own offices.

At least the Senior Male Nurse did not have the irksome duty that the Matron had of being responsible for the general discipline of the kitchen staff, dining-hall maids and laundry maids during their off-duty hours. In practice, we are told by Vicki Hayward (1980/82), this meant Matron looking out of her window after 11 p.m. at night to see if any lights were still on after 'lights out', and then telephoning the residences to get this misdemeanour corrected. Possibly even more unsettling for the Matron was the new rule that she must apply in writing for her job on an annual basis, and be subject to re-election by the hospital's General Committee. How careful Miss Hearder, by then Matron for nineteen years, must have had to be not to offend her superiors!

After this, the supply of collected documents dries up, influenced perhaps by the upheavals of the war and the amalgamation of hospitals. More detailed procedural documents were produced in the 1950s to cover the nursing routines in treatments such as continuous narcosis and continuous baths. These were within the context of the Standing Orders for Ward Sisters/Charge Male Nurses that gave the general framework and that were still in force in the 1960s. After that, consequent on the implementation of the Salmon structure, detailed job descriptions were written for every grade of nurse, and these were often revised. From then on, the changes in these sorts of document about nursing have been much more rapid than before. Further research might usefully uncover job descriptions or job specifications that would illuminate the changes of the second half of the twentieth century.

References and further reading

Anon. ('A Constant Observer') (1823) *Sketches in Bedlam*. London: Sherwood, Jones and Co.

Bowes Sir Martin and Hill Sir Rowland (1557) *The Order of the Hospitals of K. Henry the VIIIth and K. Edward the VIth*. London (no publisher given).

Foucault M (1975) (translated by A. Sheridan 1977) *Discipline and Punish*. London: Allen Lane.

Haw C (1991) John Connolly's Attendants at the Hanwell Asylum 1839–1852. *Royal College of Nursing, History of Nursing Journal* **3**(1): 26–58.

Hayward V (1980/82) *Bethlem Royal Hospital from its Beginning in 1930, Nursing Recollections.* Unpublished material in the Bethlem Archives.

Metcalf U (1818) *The Interior of Bethlehem Hospital.* London (published by the author).

Strype J (1734) *A Survey of the Cities of London and Westminster . . . Written at First in the Year MDXCVIII.* By John Stow. London: A. Churchill.

*P*atients – mostly notorious

*T*he people in this chapter were individuals who had led colourful or dramatic lives in the public eye before they were admitted to Bethlem. They have been selected largely because their stories were better recorded and more accessible than others. These patients had drawn attention to themselves either by writing or painting, or otherwise by criminal acts. Their lives within the walls of Bethlem have not always been recorded in the detail one might have wished, as case records do not give much detail before the mid-nineteenth century, but there is enough information to give an impression of care in different ages.

This particular group of patients have all been dead for some considerable time, their admission periods covering from 1636 to 1930. Some other twentieth-century patients, such as Claire Marc Wallace and Antonia White, who have written about themselves are considered in Chapters 2 and 9. It would not be acceptable to talk about the individual histories of other recent patients, on the grounds of confidentiality. This was a problem that agitated the Governors in 1823 when James Smyth published potted histories of many patients who were currently still living. His book was rightly thought of as scandalous at the time, but now, at a distance, it can be seen as valuable source material about life within Bethlem, written by one who was obviously in close contact with the wards. The Bethlem Governors fulminated against the book, saying it was false and erroneous, although they did not give details. They also thought the work was indecent, inhuman, offensive, disgusting, disgraceful, inexcusable and improper. Material from the book is used for the sections on Margaret Nicholson and James Hadfield.

The patients are presented in chronological order, spanning almost three centuries. While not being representative of all patients, they comprise both women and men, distressed with a variety of states – delusions, paranoia, dementia and substance abuse; their behaviour ranged from

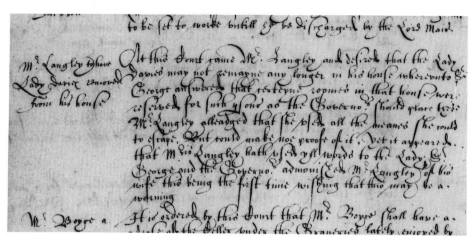

Minute of the Court of Governors meeting – 16 August 1637

being compliant and sociable, to being aggressive and isolated. The patients of the whole hospital, although living in different wards, get to know something about each other. Some patients attract attention and become well known to the other inmates. Those described here were among the most notable, some of whom attracted many visitors from the outside world.

Lady Eleanor Davies, 1590–1652

As a young lady, Eleanor Touchet, daughter of Lord Audley, impressed people with her intellectual gifts. She made a distinguished marriage in c.1608 to Sir John Davies, the Attorney-General for Ireland, by whom she had two children. It was only after about fourteen years of marriage that her gift for foretelling future events began to become noticeable. She prophesied that her husband would die in three years. This he obligingly did, so she was able to marry a second time, on this occasion to Sir Archibald Douglas. Eleanor, now Lady Douglas, had already started writing her mystical commentaries on the biblical book of Daniel, in which she found predictions of events in English life, such as the death of King Charles I, prefigured in the story of King Belshazzar's feast.

> *A hand appears, lo in his sight, as he did drinke the wine,*
> *Upon the wall against the light it wrote about a line*
> *In presence of his numerous Peers, not set an hour full,*
> *In loyns nor knees had he no might, chang'd as a ghastly skull.*

100

This, she thought, also described the end of Charles I, who died on the scaffold. In 1633 she petitioned King Charles I and published some of her prophecies in Holland. For this she was tried at Whitehall, and, as the Privy Council thought her to be mad, they confined her for two years in the Gate-House at Westminster.

The year following her release, Eleanor Davies stayed in Lichfield. There she engaged in direct action in support of her prophecies. She gathered around her a group of women at the Cathedral who challenged the established seating arrangements by sitting in the 'wrong' places. Eleanor was also critical of the Laudian reforms, whereby the communion table was fenced off and reverenced as an altar, so she defaced the new altar hangings by pouring hot tar and wheat paste on them; she also sat on the Bishop's throne and declared herself Primate and Metropolitan Bishop. For this seemingly 'mad' and outrageous behaviour, she was committed to Bethlem on the December 17 1636.

At Bethlem, Lady Davies was placed, not on a common ward, but in the house of the Steward, Mr Langley, where she became the occasion for disagreements. On August 16, 1637, the Court of Governors minute reads:

> At this Court came Mr Langley and desired that the Lady Davies may not remayne any longer in his house whereunto Sir George [Whitmore, the President] answered that certeyne roomes in that house were reserved for such persons as the Governors should place there. Mr Langley alleadged that she used all the meanes she could to escape. But could make noe proofe of it. Yet it appeared that Mistress Langley hath used ill words to the Lady. Sir George and the Governors admonished Mr Langley of (sic) his wife this being the first time wishing that this may be a warning.

In January 1638, the Governors felt it prudent to restrain her spending, so they limited her to twenty shillings a week for her diet and necessaries. The next month, Lady Davies came to their attention again when it was reported that the Langleys, coming home from the tavern 'very farre gone in drincke', very much disturbed the Lady. At this time, Langley was also busy petitioning the Privy Council to have Lady Davies removed to another building. The upshot of these events was that Langley was suspended from office, and Lady Eleanor moved from the Steward's house, although only for a short while. The Privy Council transferred her in April 1638, for what reason we know not, to the Tower of London, a place used for the imprisonment of those who were a threat to society.

In the early part of her stay in Bethlem, she was not always ill at ease. She wrote to her daughter, Lucy saying:

> for this place, thoughe princes persecute etc I want not therein: a greater on my side accompanied with prayers of his people. Bedlems gatehouses birds bulles which may imprisone put there; but honore and truthe cannot put out of countenance.

101

After her discharge, in her petition to the House of Commons, she was more critical, complaining that she could not 'goe forth to receive the Sacrament unlesse she would take itt there in the house of such restlesse cursing to bring the cup of blessing'. She complained that she had been stripped of all her possessions and that Bethlem was like 'hell – such were the blasphemies and the noisome scenes'. She resented the stigma associated with admission, in that it would 'make her ever incapable of anie complaint but ever held or taken to be person non compos mentis to the perpetuall blott and infame of her familie and posteritie'.

Eleanor Davies must have been a taxing patient to care for, bearing in mind her forceful projection of fixed bizarre ideas. As she was of noble birth and a 'person of honour' in the eyes of the Privy Council, she was thought to merit more privileged treatment than were the common people, although she lacked the means to pay for her care. She left Bethlem still with sufficient spirit to continue campaigning for recognition of her prescience.

There have always been differing views on Eleanor Davies, her person and her message, and it would seem that she must remain an enigma. In her own time, Sir John Lambe made an anagram of her name, Dame Eleanor Davies, to form the phrase 'never soe mad a ladie' (Cope 1992); on the contrary, Dr Peter du Moulin thought her 'learned above her sex, humble below her fortune, having a mind so great and noble, that prosperity could not make it amiss, nor her deepest adversity cause it to shrink.' (Ballard 1752). In the twentieth century, Roy Porter (1987), drawing on Christopher Hill (1984), has seen her as the victim of 'psychiatric abuse' occasioned by her lack of diplomacy concerning the fall of Charles I. This rather assumes that she was sent to Bethlem after her petition to King Charles I and the publication of her prophesies, whereas Cope (1992) has since demonstrated that it was after her strange behaviour in Lichfield that she was detained in Bethlem. Whether or not her confinement constituted abuse, it is clear she was a disturbing lady to have at large in society. Cope sees her as an example of an early feminist, who focused on the wrongs she herself had suffered and identified a host of irrationalities in English law and society with regard to women. Ideas that support this theory were expressed in tracts which she penned from 1625 onwards.

In later life, her stream of enigmatic prophecies and treatises continued to pour out, but they were destined to be ignored by both Charles I and Oliver Cromwell. Eleanor Davies died in 1652 and was buried with her first husband. Just five years before her death, her tract, *The Gatehouse Salutation* showed her looking back on her confinements in symbolic and surprisingly positive terms. Bedlam became the real Bethlehem, where the Virgin Mary (Eleanor herself) was undergoing labour (imprisonment), but in the expectation of entering heaven when the promised Jesus should come again. She wrote:

So Gates and Prison Doors be no
more shut,
The King of glory comes, your
souls lift up.

Nathaniel Lee, circa 1649–1692

Nat Lee was not of aristocratic lineage like Lady Eleanor but was the son of a Doctor of Divinity who held the livings of several parishes. After being educated at Westminster School, Nathaniel went to Trinity College, Cambridge. This handsome young man 'of ingenious conversation' attracted the attention of the Duke of Buckingham, who brought him to London, where he tried to establish a career as an actor. Yet it was as a dramatist that he found fame, being primarily noted for his heroic tragedies, which were filled with passion and extravagance. *The Rival Queens* (1677) was his most successful drama, this being frequently revived in Britain and America well into the nineteenth century. The play told of the jealousies of the wives of Alexander the Great, ending with the first wife stabbing the second wife and Alexander being poisoned. In a Dedication to the printed version of the play, Lee spoke of his youthful life of hot hours burnt in night revels, of how he acted in animal spirits without reason and then drowned in day-dead-sleep. Early on, he gained a reputation for heavy drinking. When staying with the Earl of Pembroke at Wilton House in Wiltshire, he remained longer than he was welcome, in what the butler thought was an attempt to drain the cellar.

Later critics, knowing of Lee's decline into madness, tended to find in his plays evidence of an unbalanced nature, laced with frenzy and morbidity, but they also praised his extravagant audacity and extreme sensual vigour. Another play Lee wrote was *Caesar Borgia* (1680) in which there was a description of a madman such as he may have seen when he visited Bethlem before being admitted:

He reasons well: his eyes their wildness lose:
He vows the keepers his wronged sense abuse
But, if you touch the cause that hurt his brain,
Then his teeth gnash, he foams, he shakes his chain,
His eyeballs roll, and he is mad again.

Lee took his place with that talented band of Restoration dramatists that included Wycherley, Etherege and Otway, as well as the more famous Dryden, with whom he collaborated. He also worked with the composer Henry Purcell. In 1684, Lee's play *Constantine the Great*, was produced, and after that he was said to have lost his reason. Dr Tyson admitted Nat Lee to Bethlem on the November 11 1684, and he remained on the books there until April 23 1688, although Ham (1931) describes his confinement there as intermittent. Lee's fellow playwright Wycherley, who had always thought of Lee as a little mad, wrote a poem addressing Lee in Bethlem that refers to the rigours of treatment there by starvation and the whip, not to mention being exhibited as a madman:

> *You, best because you starv'd, fell mad before,*
> *Now Starving, does your Wits to you restore; . . .*
> *You did, before that you were mad, engage*
> *With Numbers, and in your Poetic Rage,*
> *Lash'd (as your Keeper you) the madder Age; . . .*
> *And now, the Rabble to thee does resort,*
> *That thy Want of Wits may be their Sport.*

To add to these indignities, Wilkes reports that his head was shaved, presumably to allow for blistering: 'He had a fine head of hair, which, when he missed in his lucid intervals, he often regretted, it having been necessary to shave him in his madness'.

Ned Ward, the journalist, who was among the visitors to Bethlem, wrote of Lee's red nose and love of claret, a weakness for drinking being a feature of Lee's disorder. When he was more lucid, Nat Lee busied himself in Bethlem writing a play in twenty-five acts. John Dryden, visiting Lee in Bethlem, heard how another visitor had observed that it must be easy for Lee to write like a madman. Lee was said to have replied, 'No Sir, it is not so easy to write like a madman: but it is very easy indeed to write like a fool.' Another recollection of Bethlem is in Lee's aphorism: 'They said I was mad: and I said they were mad: damn them, they outvoted me' (quoted in Porter 1987, Byrd 1974, Frye 1963). Whatever the source of this quotation, which I have been unable to find, it fits well with the theme of the madness of the whole of mankind, to which Wycherley referred when he reported Lee's complaint 'that he ought no more to be in Bethlem for Want of Sense, than other Mad Libertines and Poets abroad, or any Sober Fools whatever'.

Nat Lee's stay in Bethlem was paid for by the Royal Palaces' Board of Green Cloth, which acted as a court of jurisdiction 'within the verge', i.e. within twelve miles of the King's household. Lee was ultimately released by the intervention of the Duke of York, to return to his old haunts, where he lived on a pension of twenty shillings a year from the Theatre Royal. Return to the community did not mean a resumption of his career, for he produced no more new plays, although some of his earlier work appeared in print. Bout drinking continued intermittently. The repeated links between wine and death in his play *The Rival Queens* read like a premonition of Lee's own end:

> *The rage of wine is drowned in gushing blood.* (Act IV Scene 2)
>
> *Hephestion having drunk too largely*
> *At your last feast, is of a surfeit dead.* (Act V Scene 1)

Alexander, the hero, himself dies a slow death from a poisoned cup of wine.

Lee met his death in 1692 at the age of about forty-three. Wilkes recounted the sorry end:

> *Misfortunes and drink were the occasion: he was under the regime of a milk diet for the last week of his life; but getting one evening out of his physician's reach, he drank so hard, that he dropped down in the street, and was run over by a coach. His body was laid in a bulk near Trunkit's, the perfumer's at Temple Bar, till it was owned.*

Nathaniel Lee was buried at St Clement Danes in the Strand, London.

Margaret Nicholson, 1734–1828

In 1991, the Royal National Theatre, London, performed a play by Alan Bennett called *The Madness of George III* (turned into a film, *The Madness of King George*, in 1995). The play opened with the historical encounter of Margaret Nicholson with the King of England. 'Peg' Nicholson, as she was later called, was to become one of the foremost characters of Bethlem in her time, attracting many visitors on account of her celebrated crime.

A native of Stockton-on-Tees, Margaret Nicholson had spent much of her life in service, as an upper servant to the aristocracy. While in one of her employments, she had an affair with a valet, with whom she was said to have 'misconducted herself'. Perhaps it was this, or her approaching madness, that led her to be in rather reduced circumstances. From 1783, when she was 49, she had been residing at the house of Mr Fisk, a stationer in Wigmore Street, London, where she made a living by taking in plain needlework. Mr Fisk later said that she was 'very odd at times'. In 1786, she sent a petition to the King, which was found to be on the theme of tyrants, usurpers and pretenders. Ten days later there occurred the event that shaped the rest of her life. A contemporary report (quoted in *Sketches in Bedlam*, Anon. 1823) read:

> *On the 2d of August 1786, as the King (George III.) was alighting from his chariot at the garden entrance of St. James's [Palace], a woman, very decently dressed, in the act of presenting a petition, which His Majesty was receiving with great condescension, struck a concealed knife at his breast; which happily he avoided by drawing back. As she was making a second thrust, one of the yeomen caught her arm, and, at the same instant, one of the King's footmen wrenched the knife from her hand. The King, with great temper and fortitude, exclaimed, 'I am not hurt: take care of the poor woman; do not hurt her'.*

THE KING'S LIFE ATTEMPTED, AUG? 2,1786.

Margaret Nicholson attacking King George III

Later Margaret Nicholson said it was all a mistake, and that she just happened to have a dessert knife in her pocket, that she drew out instead of the petition which she meant to deliver to His Majesty. However, this dubious excuse was undermined by her incredible testimony, in which she claimed 'that the crown was hers; she wanted nothing but her right; that she had great property; that if she had not her right, England would be drowned in blood for a thousand generations'. She was arrested and examined by Dr Thomas Munro of Bethlem. Because her crime was treason, she was brought before the Privy Council who, not surprisingly, decided that she was insane and sent her to Bethlem.

On arrival, the Steward invited her to dine with him and some company, which she did, remaining perfectly composed, except for saying that she expected the King to visit her. A contemporary broadsheet took up the story:

> At six o'clock she was conducted to her cell, which had been previously furnished
> with new bedding etc for her reception; a chain was put round her leg, and
> fastened to the floor. While this was doing she was perfectly composed and took no
> notice of it. On being asked by the Steward if the chain hurt her leg as it should
> be altered if it did? she replied 'No, not at all'. Mr Coates [the King's Messenger]

was reminded by her to bring the paper, pen and ink which he had promised her, as she meant to write some of her friends by him; they were brought, and although Mr Coates stayed an hour, she did not attempt to write anything.

Lord Sidney for the Privy Council asked that the Governors 'cause the most strict and proper care to be taken of her'. The Governors in turn, ordered that no person whatever be permitted to see her, except in the company of a Governor. For the next six months, they saw her every week on Saturdays to check on her general state, and, for the rest of the time, she was confined to her room.

Then in August 1787, the Bethlem Sub-Committee Minute Book records that King George III sent a verbal message, via an Under-Secretary of State, saying that he was rightly sensible of the great care and attention that had been observed by the Governors of the hospital, and, having been informed of her still continuing distracted state, he would wish her to be accommodated in any manner consistent with the rules and regulations of the hospital. The consequence was that Peg Nicholson was accepted as an 'incurable' patient, entitled to stay in Bethlem for the rest of her life. After almost four more years in Bethlem, it was decided that she need no longer be kept confined in her cell by a chain.

James Smyth in *Sketches in Bedlam* (Anon. 1823) gave an account of her in Bethlem thirty-six years later when she was showing no signs of insanity beyond an occasional irritation, which he regarded as justified. At the age of 82, she:

appears perfectly tranquil and contented; she very seldom speaks, has totally lost her sense of hearing, nor would the discharge of a cannon at her ear in the least disturb her. Snuff seems to be her favourite luxury, of which she takes a great quantity, and seems to enjoy it with a peculiar satisfaction. She has contracted a singular aversion to bread, and never can be induced to eat any. The cause of this antipathy is unknown, but she is allowed gingerbread and biscuits, which she eats with good appetite, in moderate quantities. Tea is also allowed her, and she has besides, the exclusive privilege of living apart from all the other criminal patients, in a ward appropriated as a nursery for the aged and infirm, and such as are quiet and harmless. She enjoys a good state of health, is regular, cleanly and attentive to her little concerns, and is desirous to render herself useful, so far as her great age will permit.

Such material is the stuff of nurses' progress notes and, apart from the language and period detail, could have been written at any time in the past hundred and fifty years. It is pleasing to note that Margaret Nicholson was allowed some comforts in her old age at Bethlem, where she survived to the age of 94 years.

James Hadfield (c1771–1841) soldier, silversmith and patient

James Hadfield, circa 1771–1841

Like Margaret Nicholson, James Hadfield was famous for an attack on King George III, but one made years later in 1800. From 1793, Hadfield had been a soldier in the 15th Dragoons regiment, and, at the Battle of Lincelles, had received several sabre wounds to the head and had his arm broken by a musket ball. The head injury was so severe that it affected his brain, causing intellectual disturbance. This led to his discharge from the army on grounds of insanity, as he had delusions about the imminent end of the world. From 1796, James Hadfield worked at his trade as a silversmith in the city of London. One day when he was walking in the fields, he was accosted by a religious fanatic, Bannister Truelock, who persuaded him that the Messiah was about to come out of Truelock's mouth, and that, if the King was killed, all obstacles to the progress of their religion would be removed. Hadfield was to be the chosen instrument for the accomplishment of the great design. On May 14, 1800, Hadfield tried to destroy his eight-month-old baby son 'for the benefit of mankind'. He also felt that he must sacrifice himself for the salvation of mankind, but, as he did not wish to be guilty of suicide, he hoped that by appearing as a criminal, his life might be taken away by others.

So Hadfield took himself to Drury Lane Theatre on May 16, 1800, armed with a pistol loaded with gunpowder, and leaden shots, slugs and bullets. Hadfield later recounted how, when the doors of the theatre pit were opened, the crowd made a rush forward, and a young woman cried out 'Oh, sir! the handle of your umbrella is running into my breast.' It was in fact the butt end of the pistol. Once inside the theatre, as James Smyth reported:

> *His Majesty had scarcely entered his box, when in the act of bowing with his usual condescension to the audience, a pistol was fired by Hadfield, who sat in the pit on the second row from the orchestra. The ball struck the roof of the royal box, just at the moment when the Queen and princesses were entering. His Majesty with great presence of mind, waved his hand as a signal to dissuade the royal party from making their immediate appearance, and instantly standing erect, raised his right hand to his breast, and continued bowing for some minutes to his loyal subjects . . . After the first moments of astonishment had subsided, some musicians from the orchestra seized Hadfield, and dragged him over the pallisadoes into the music room.*

Bearing in mind the events of the French Revolution and the fate of their royal family, any attack on the sovereign was of great national concern. Although Hadfield was arraigned for high treason, his trial was discontinued when his defence lawyer convinced the judge and jury that violence to the brain had caused incurable insanity. There were many witnesses to Hadfield's previous abnormalities. The upshot of the trial was that he was sent to Bethlem.

Nothing more is heard of him until about two years later, when he punched another patient, Benjamin Swain, on the head. Swain tumbled over a form and fell to the ground dead (J Simmonds in Minutes of the House of Commons Select Committee). It was popularly supposed that Hadfield had murdered Swain, although the hospital later denied this. Rather surprisingly, Hadfield managed to make his escape from the hospital, getting as far as Dover before he was arrested. After a spell of fourteen years in Newgate prison, he was returned to Bethlem, where his life continued less eventfully. Writing in about 1823, Smyth describes him as symptom-free, but a grumbler and fault-finder, yet he was not without compensations for his confinement:

> *Though his manners and language are those of a vulgar, low-bred fellow, he is cleanly in his person and regular in his habits; knacky and ingenious in his amusements. He makes handsome straw baskets, which he is permitted to sell to visitors, and for which he obtains from 3s. 6d. to 7s. 6d. each. He receives a pension from the government of 6d. per day in consideration of his former military services.*

He retained his interest in the outside world, as is seen from the Bethlem Sub-Committee minute of 1826: 'James Hadfield applying for liberty to hold communication with a Female through the Railings, the permission was refused on account of the great indecency of his conduct on former occasions'. Nevertheless Hadfield was allowed some freedom in his activities, for we hear that he kept birds and cats, also sold poems and spent his money on tobacco. Here is a poem that he wrote on a pet squirrel:

> *Epitaph, of my poor Jack, Squirrel.*
>
> *Here are the Remains of my poor little Jack,*
> *Who, with a little fall; almost broke his back*
> *And I myself was the occasion of that*
> *By letting him be frighten'd, by a Cat*
> *I then picked him up, from off the floor;*
> *But he, alas Never danced a hornpipe more;*
> *And many a time, have I laugh'd, to see him so cunning;*
> *To Sit and Crack the nuts I gave him So funny;*
> *Now in Remembrance of his pretty tricks*
> *I have had him Stuff'd, that I might not him forget*
> *And So he is gone; and I must go, as well as him;*
> *And pray God, Send I may go, but withe little Sin;*
> *So there is an end, to my little dancing Jack*
> *That will never more be frighten'd, by a Cat.*

There was one more moment of glory when Hadfield became the principal character of interest at Bethlem. After the death of Margaret Nicholson in 1828, he became the patient to attract most visitors, but, to Hadfield's deepest chagrin, his popularity was quickly snuffed out the following year with the arrival of Jonathan Martin, the York Minster incendiary.

The hospital kindly bought Hadfield a wig in 1833, presumably to help cover the war wound on his head. After his death in 1841, the surgeons were able to establish at the autopsy that this wound had caused internal damage, such as would have caused severe mental disorder.

110

Richard Dadd (1817–1886) artist and patient, shown while painting
Contradiction: Oberon and Titania 1854–58

Richard Dadd, 1817–1886

Thirteen years after Hadfield's death, another homicidal patient arrived in Bethlem. The difference was that while Hadfield only attempted the murder, Dadd succeeded in carrying out the crime. Born in Chatham, Kent, the son of a chemist, Richard Dadd was educated at the grammar school in Rochester. As he showed some aptitude for drawing, he continued his studies at the Royal Academy Schools in London, where he won several prizes. William Frith, another artist, remembered him as 'a man of genius that would assuredly have placed him high in the first rank of painters'. Dadd had early success and exhibited some of his work,

111

most memorably the fairy paintings of 1841–2. Then, in company with Sir Thomas Phillips, he travelled extensively in Europe and the Middle East, sketching and collecting visual memories, which he was to use later.

During the latter part of his travels, he began to experience mental disturbance, believing that some people were possessed by evil spirits. In particular, he thought that his father was actually the Devil. Dadd invited his father to go with him to Cobham in Kent, where after supper at an inn, they went for a walk in Cobham Park. Next day, the father's body was found stabbed to death. Meanwhile, Richard Dadd had set off for France, where he attempted to kill another person.

Eventually Bethlem, which was functioning in part as the state criminal lunatic asylum, admitted him in 1844. At the time of Dadd's admission, the criminal patients had individual sleeping rooms, just under eight by ten feet in size, and, apart from the wash rooms, they had access only to the long corridor and the exercise yard. The wings for such patients were unprepossessing, as described in *The Quarterly Review* (vol. 101, pp. 361–362) a few years later in 1857:

> *They consist of dismal arched corridors, feebly lit at either end by a single window in double irons, and divided in the middle by gratings more like those which enclose the fiercer carnivora at the Zoological Gardens than anything we have elsewhere seen employed for the detention of afflicted humanity.*

Fortunately for some of the criminal patients, those of the 'better class' were transferred to ordinary but secure wards, with large airy rooms, books and pictures, in the same year as the above article appeared. Dadd was favoured by being given materials and space to develop his art. During his time at Bethlem, Dadd painted two master works, 'Contradiction: Oberon and Titania, 1854–58' (private collection) and 'The Fairy Feller's Master-stroke, 1855–64', which can be seen in the Tate Gallery, London. He also did a series of watercolours entitled 'Sketches to Illustrate the Passions', and portraits of the Head Attendant, Charles Neville (although this might have been painted at Broadmoor), and a man, possibly Dr Charles Hood, the Physician–Superintendent. The latter made some entries in the case records that describe Dadd's behaviour. The following extract was written ten years after Dadd's admission:

> *March 21st 1854. For some years after his admission he was considered a violent and dangerous patient, for he would jump up and strike a violent blow without any aggravation, and then beg pardon for the deed. This arose from some vague idea that filled his mind and still does so to a certain extent that certain spirits have the power of possessing a mans body and compelling him to adopt a partic-ular course whether he will or no. When he talks on this subject and on any other at all associated with the motives that influenced him to commit the crime for which he is confined here, he frequently becomes excited, in his manner of speaking,*

and soon rambles from the subject and becomes quite unintelligible. He is very eccentric and glories that he is not influenced by virtues that other men pride themselves in possessing – thus he pays no sort of attention to decency in his acts or words, if he feels the least inclination to be otherwise; he is perfectly a sensual being, a thorough animal, he will gorge himself with food till he actually vomits and then again return to the meal. With all these disgusting points in his conduct he can be a very sensible and agreeable companion, and shew in conversation, a mind at once well educated, and thoroughly informed in all the particles of his profession in which he still shines . . .

Another entry reads:

1860 Jany.10. – No alteration in this man's symptoms have occurred since the last note was made in the No.1 case book. He still employs himself daily with his brush, but he is slower in completing any work he takes in hand. He associates very little with other patients, but is generally civil and well behaved to them. His mind is full of delusions.

Richard Dadd stayed at Bethlem until the criminal patients were transferred to the new hospital at Broadmoor, Berkshire, in 1863–4. Charles Neville, the Head Attendant, went with him to a new post there. Broadmoor was to be Dadd's home for the rest of his life, and it was there that he died of consumption in 1886 at the age of 69.

It is greatly to the credit of Charles Neville, Charles Hood and the rest of the staff at Bethlem that, in spite of earlier difficulties in the management of homicidal patients, they were able to facilitate the development of Richard Dadd's superb artistry, even in the face of his unprepossessing behaviour.

Louis Wain, 1860–1939

Another artist patient, Louis Wain, began his career as an art teacher at the West London School of Art, before moving on to work as a journalist on *The Illustrated London News*. His interest in cats led him to take positions on committees such as the Society for the Protection of Cats and Cats' Home, Our Dumb Friends League Receiving Shelter for Stray Cats and the National Anti-Vivisection Society, and eventually he became the President of the National Cat Club.

Louis Wain was a black-and-white draughtsman and oil painter, drawing and painting a variety of subjects, including landscapes, flowers and birds. Gradually, he came to concentrate on animal portraits, in particular caricatures of comic cats occupied in a wide range of human activities, for example cats reading, playing cricket and going to the theatre. He became well-known for these amusing cats, and they were frequently reproduced in annuals, in children's coloured toy books, in cinema cartoons and on picture postcards.

After a period of suspicious behaviour in 1924, when he thought his sisters were robbing him and when he threw one of them out of their house, the doctor was called. He diagnosed dementia. Aged 64, Louis Wain was admitted to Springfield Hospital, Tooting, London, where he was thought to be schizophrenic, although the real diagnosis must remain now a matter of conjecture. By the intervention of Ramsay Macdonald, the Prime Minister, he was transferred to Bethlem, which was thought to provide a more salubrious environment. There Wain gave expression to some delusional ideas, thinking that spirits had filled him with electricity and that he had magic powers of healing by the laying on of hands. He talked extravagantly on science, health and politics. Certain factors, such as the loss of his wife, his sister's illness, his failure in financial matters and a street accident, were thought to have combined to provoke an onset of mental illness late in life. There was also the fact that public taste was changing and there was less interest in his work.

At Bethlem, Louis Wain appeared quaintly old-fashioned in dress and manner, more suited to the nineteenth century than the twentieth. He became something of a recluse, staying in his own room, where he collected many items, such as old newspapers, which he refused to throw away. Initially, he did not find it easy to establish relationships with the male nurses, but his confidence gradually grew and he became more cooperative, also mixing with the other patients and laughing at the behaviour of two doctor-patients who disliked each other. His concern for patients' welfare is shown in a letter to his doctor (in Dale 1968):

> *26th October 1928, 7 Room 2 Gallery.*
>
> *Dear Dr . . .,*
> *In the central Dining Hall today a patient sitting next to me from our gallery showed that indeterminate condition of a sudden pull at my coat and talk under breath to sit down. As the present uncertain winds bring the change of temperature on the uncertain cases, I judged it advisable to shout in his ear Be Quiet! and Wake up! as sharply as possible. This aroused him into quiet. He was badly steamed while at 6 months scullery work and this has had the condition of recovery made a matter of time as all the morning movements upset him and his difficulty now is to eat his good meal. His name is . . . I talked to the chief of the Hall about it so he will know the condition and the result of the few words. My own condition is a constant improvement by constant work and I am enabled to know what is best to be done.*
>
> *Yours sincerely,*
> *Louis Wain*

Most important to him still was the opportunity to work hard at drawing and painting, as he had done all his adult life, although he sometimes had to make do with whatever crayons were available, and he was not allowed a pencil sharpener. His sisters visited him and collected works he had finished to take away and sell. One Christmas, the staff asked him to contribute something to the ward decorations, so he painted on the ward mirror a scene of cats in a gleeful mood facing each other across a Christmas pudding.

Following a review of his condition, he was transferred to Napsbury Hospital on May 30, 1930, as the old Bethlem at Southwark was closing before the move to Beckenham. Louis Wain lived out the declining years of his old age at Napsbury until, at the age of 79, he died.

References and further reading

Lady Eleanor Davies

Ballard G (1752) *Memoirs of Several Ladies of Great Britain*. Oxford: W Jackson.
Cope ES (1992) *Handmaid of the Holy Spirit; Dame Eleanor Davies, Never Soe Mad a Ladie*. USA: University of Michigan Press.
Hill C (1984) God and the English Revolution. *History Workshop*, **17**: 19–31.
Porter R (1987) *Mind-Forg'd Manacles*. London: The Athlone Press.

Nathaniel Lee

Byrd M (1974) *Visits to Bedlam*. Columbia: University of South Carolina Press.
Frye N (1963) *Fables of Identity: Studies in Poetic Mythology*. New York: Burlingame: Harcourt, Brace and World.
Ham RG (1931) *Otway and Lee*. USA: Yale University Press.
Lee N (1713) *The Works of Nathaniel Lee*. London: R. Wellington.
Lee S (1917) *The Dictionary of National Biography*. vol. XI: 805–9. London: Oxford University Press.
Porter R (1987) *Mind-Forg'd Manacles*. London: The Athlone Press.
Wilkes T (1759) *A General View of the Stage*. London. J Coote.
Wycherley W (1706) *Miscellany Poems*. London: Jeffrey Wale.

Margaret Nicholson

Anon. (1786) *Authentic Memoirs of the Life of Margaret Nicholson*. London: Ridgeway.
Anon. (1786) *High Treason Committed by Margaret Nicholson*. A Broadsheet. London (no publisher given).
Anon. ('A Constant Observer') (1823) *Sketches in Bedlam*. London: Sherwood, Jones and Co.
Hunt W (1882) Margaret Nicholson. In *The Dictionary of National Biography*, vol. XIV: 467–468. London: Smith, Elder and Co.
Macalpine I and Hunter R (1969) *George III and the Mad-Business*. London: Allen Lane.
Walker N and McCabe S (1973) *Crime and Insanity in England*, vol. 2. Edinburgh: T. and A. Constable.

James Hadfield

Anon. ('A Constant Observer') (1823) *Sketches in Bedlam*. London: Sherwood, Jones and Co.

Select Committee on the Provision being made for the better Regulation of Madhouses (1816) Minutes of Evidence, First Report. London: House of Commons.

Walker N and McCabe S (1973) *Crime and Insanity in England*. Edinburgh: T. and A. Constable.

Richard Dadd

Allderidge P (1970) Richard Dadd (1817–1886): Painter and Patient. *Medical History*, July: 308–313.

Allderidge P (1974) *Richard Dadd*. London: Academy Editions.

Allderidge P (1974) *The Late Richard Dadd*. London: The Tate Gallery.

Louis Wain

Dale R (1968) *Louis Wain, The Man Who Drew Cats*. London: William Kimber.

Parkin M (1983) *Louis Wain's Cats*. London: Thames and Hudson.

*K*eeping order

*E*nsuring that patients and staff conformed to what society considered to be acceptable standards of behaviour has been so problematic throughout the centuries that it seemed to merit consideration in a chapter of its own. The use of varying methods of restraint of patients has been the cause of bitter complaints from the patients themselves, of difficulties experienced by the staff, and of criticism from the managers, if the methods were not carried out as ordered. It is sometimes forgotten that up to at least the nineteenth century, restraint was considered to be an integral part of a cure. Samuel Hadwin of Lincoln Lunatic Asylum (1841) wrote:

> *Restraint forms the very basis and principle on which the sound treatment of lunatics is founded. The judicious and appropriate adaptation of the various modifications of this powerful means to the peculiarities of each case of insanity, comprises a large portion of the curative regimen of the scientific and rational practitioner; in his hands it is a remedial agent of the first importance, and it appears to me that it is as likely to be dispensed with, in the cure of mental diseases, as that the various articles of the materia medica will altogether be dispensed with in the cure of the bodily.*

Keepers, attendants and nurses are not much mentioned in Bethlem reports on restraint, but they were the people who bore the responsibility for the carrying out of this part of the treatment. Restraint has been an activity that has occupied considerable amounts of time for nurses and their predecessors, and, in view of the lack of rapid cures for mental disturbance, this seems likely to continue, as Hadwin predicted. The reason usually given for the use of restraint in the nineteenth century was 'to prevent injury', and that did not just mean injury to the patient himself, or to the general public, but injury to the staff themselves. If caring for the mentally disturbed was to be an acceptable occupation, violence had to be controlled.

117

In this chapter we consider the ways in which order was kept among the patients, ranging from whipping and starvation to mechanical restraint and isolation, moving on to the use of padded rooms, seclusion, and the giving of sedating medication. Next we move on to ways of keeping order among the staff, covering censure and encouragement to improve, making rules and disciplinary procedures which could lead to dismissal.

Order among patients

The earliest Bethlem example of controlling the behaviour of a patient comes from Sir Thomas More in 1533. Thomas More lived at one time very close to Bethlem in the city of London, so had opportunity as a local resident to take an interest in the activities of the hospital. He wrote that the patient had been treated in Bethlem by beating and correction, but that, having come to himself, he had been set at liberty. The effects of the treatment proved to be only temporary, and the old fancies in his head reasserted themselves. His particular form of disturbed behaviour took place in church. During the Holy Communion, while the devout women were kneeling bowed low in prayer, the ex-patient would sneak up behind them and throw their skirts over their heads:

> wheruppon I [Sir Thomas More] beyng advertysed of these pageauntes, and beynge sent unto and requyred by very devout relygyouse folke, to take some other order wyth hym caused hym as he came wanderyng by my dore, to be taken by the constables and bounden to a tre in the strete byfore the whole towne, and there they stryped hym with roddys therfore tyl he waxed wery and somwhat lenger. And it appered well that hys remembraunce was good inough, save yt it wente about in grasynge tyll it was beten home. for he could than very well reherse hys fawtes hym selfe, ans speke and trete very well, and promyse to do afterwarde as well.

Although we have no descriptions of whipping actually inside the hospital, this account serves well enough to let one grasp the principle, which appears to be that, when a patient has been beaten, he is less likely, either from exhaustion or pain, to behave unacceptably or assert his strange ideas. What is worth noting is not so much the details of striping with rods, but the viewpoint the incident displays. The reaction to unpalatable behaviour is violent and, to us, might seem inappropriate for the offence as described. Yet this was a brutal society, which would eventually see the political execution of the author of this passage, who had himself initiated the beating. The prescription for the patient was much the same in the community as in the hospital. We do not find so much of the social toleration of madness that Michel Foucault imagined was common in the Middle Ages. As Andrew Scull (1993) says, 'Where the mad proved troublesome, as we shall see, they could expect to be beaten or locked up; otherwise they might roam or rot.'

Deprivation of food was another traditional method of restraint, which would be effective in producing a similar weariness and languor, such as More mentions. Mad Tom in the early ballad, besides singing of the whipping and chains at Bethlem, witnessed to the 'wholesome hunger plenty'. It should not have altogether surprised the Governors who visited in February 1631 that the patients had only small scraps to eat, and that, on a previous Sunday, there had only been four pounds of cheese between twenty-five or thirty patients. While this situation was perhaps justly ascribed to the veniality of the staff, the pardonable aspect of their sin lay in the fact that it was considered useful to keep the patients on short commons. The popular view of hunger as a corrective to unwanted behaviour, particularly idleness, was expressed by John Bellers (1696): 'The Sluggard shall be cloathed in Raggs. He that will not work shall not eat.' Later, in 1786, Joseph Townsend wrote, 'Hunger will tame the fiercest animals, it will teach decency and civility, obedience and subjection to the most perverse.'

Mechanical restraint in the modern mind is associated with chains and strait-jackets. Bethlem has a long and varied history in the use of these types of device, stretching from the early days to the mid-nineteenth century. In 1403, iron chains and manacles were part of the inventory, and they continued in use for over four centuries more.

John Haslam, the Bethlem Apothecary (1809), recommended the use of metallic manacles for the hands, as there could be friction of the skin for long periods without excoriation. Ligatures should be avoided, but one leg iron could be used. A strait waistcoat could stop the patient harming himself, but it irritated in hot weather. It could also be uncomfortably tight, if so done up by the keeper, and a patient could not brush off flies that were troubling him. The Steward's Account Books and Treasurer's Cash books of eighteenth-century Bethlem show the frequent puchase of waistcoats: for example in 1786, Mrs Hannah Williams was paid £4 10s 6d for 'Ticking for Strait Waiscoats and Making Blanket Gowns'.

Dr Thomas Monro (1815) thought 'gentlemen' should have strait waistcoats and not irons or manacles, which were nevertheless useful for chaining other classes of patient to the walls. Haslam, in 1817, in spite of considerable public opposition, was still advocating the use of metallic manacles. Other sorts of chaining were possible, as in the case of James Norris, who appears in an illustration with a harness, which by a system of iron bars kept him close to the wall.

Isolation frequently accompanied mechanical restraint. Haslam wrote:

> *In the most violent state of the disease, the patient should be kept alone in a dark or quiet room, so that he may not be affected by the stimuli of light or sound, such abstraction more readily disposing to sleep.*

Violence by patients was sometimes answered by violence by staff. A case in point was James Norris, mentioned above, who, before he was chained, had an outburst, and a keeper approached him with a shovel. Somehow in the ensuing scuffle the patient's arm was broken, but this was not held to be the keeper's fault.

Locked doors seem to have been for centuries a principal method of keeping order. Patients were routinely locked in their cells at night, which served not only to confine the patient, but also to prevent access by undesirable intruders.

Patients were also subject to restraint by being deprived of articles with which they might do themselves harm. In 1767, the Governors ordered that 'no patient in this hospital be permitted to have in his cell any box with a lock or key and that the Basketmen and Gallery Maids do immediately search all the patients and their cells for any razors pens knives or other offensive instruments of that kind and that they do secure the same to prevent the patients doing any mischief to themselves or others therewith'. Nor were the visitors allowed to bring in knives or instruments of any kind.

'Co-ercion' was distinguished by Haslam (1815 in Report from the Committee on Madhouses in England) as a type of restraint, but here the patient was 'driven' rather than confined. For instance, if the patient would not go to the bath, he was driven, or compelled, and co-erced to go into the bath. Given the small number of keepers, one wonders how this was achieved.

In France and Italy towards the end of the eighteenth century, there were moves to abandon the use of chains and fetters for restraint, led by Vincenzo Chiarugi at the Hospital Bonifacio in Florence (1774–88) and Pinel with his Chief Keeper Pussin at Bicêtre and Salpêtrière in Paris from 1893 onwards. In England, this development is linked to the innovations of William Tuke at The Retreat in York from 1796 onwards, making emphasis on moral management with mildness and humanity, and less recourse to mechanical restraint. The Retreat, however, did not practise complete non-restraint at the beginning of the century, and, in fact, Jepson the Apothecary invented a new form of strait-jacket and other forms of restraint. Throughout England, restraint started to go out of fashion with the advent of 'moral treatment'.

Mrs Forbes, the new Bethlem Matron in 1815, by degrees set about freeing all the females under restraint and producing a clean comfortable atmosphere. Such was her success that in 1839 only 3.53%, i.e. 11 out of the total 311 patients, were being restrained. Within a year or two of this, reformers such as Dr John Conolly at Hanwell, Dr Charlesworth and Robert Gardiner Hill at Lincoln declared support for the abolition of personal restraint. At Bethlem, although practices had changed dramatically since the period 1750–70, when the records showed every patient as under restraint, there was a reluctance to abandon it completely. In 1848, Drs E.T. Monro and A. Morison said 'that it is sometimes necessary is too evident, but it should always be avoided if possible, and its only legitimate use is protection; its use is recognized by acts of Parliament, which have directed that every resort to it should be accurately recorded; its abuse lies at the door of those who are so wanton or negligent as to abuse it'. Nevertheless, in 1851, it was proudly reported to the Governors of Bethlem that no mechanical restraint had been used throughout the year.

Padded rooms were in use in 1845 and remained so, and there was a new padded room lined in 1880. This was not considered as 'restraint' and was not so often reported.

The burden on the keepers was increased by moral treatment, for the task of preventing patients harming themselves or others was to be accomplished through supervision by the keepers themselves. John Conolly of Hanwell Asylum said, 'we rely wholly upon constant superintendence, constant kindness, and firmness when required' (Clark 1869). In spite of the rhetoric against restraint, Hanwell continued to use dresses of strong material, strong blankets and the shower bath as means of control. However, it was still a difficult remit for the attendants, and the change was not easily accepted. Although Conolly had an ideal picture of the benevolent attendant as a friend, adviser and protector of the patient, he found (1863) that the reality was very often that attendants were 'the torment of the physician's life, constantly counteracting all that he wishes'.

The Bethlem Governors were pleased in 1853 that chains, belts, leg-locks and handcuffs were no longer thought to be indispensable. Patients under restraint were reported as averaging 2% between 1841 and 1850, and none at all between 1851 and 1869.

The old habits of restraint had been driven underground but were to re-emerge. In 1871, a man had his hands confined nightly for two weeks to prevent him doing himself serious injury. The Commissioners in Lunacy report for 1879 noted that four men were wet-packed, one man and three women dry-packed and one man confined by strong clothing at night. Wet-packing was a procedure whereby the patient was wrapped in a wet sheet from which water had been wrung out. The patient was laid on his side in bed, wrapped also in a blanket and covered with several thicknesses of blanket tucked around him up to his chin (Medico-Psychological Association 1885). Dry-packing was a similar immobilising procedure, whereby a sheet was wrapped around the patient's body and arms, sewn up from feet to neck with stout thread and secured to the bedstead with webbing to prevent movement (Santos and Stainbrook 1949). The restraining practices, having been re-established, were reported frequently by the Commissioners, who visited twice a year. They described what they saw, or said what was written in the report books, so it is unlikely that this was the entire extent of restraint used. The following reports illustrate the types and growing incidence of restrictions:

1880	*Gloves used in 2 cases to prevent destruction or injury.*
	1 patient wet-packed on 3 days for 3–4 hours at a time.
1881	*1 patient dry-packed for 3 nights for 6 hours each.*
1882	*2 women restrained for 5 hours, 3 women twice for 12 hours.*
1883	*1 man restrained for 2 days for surgical reasons.*
	1 female twice wet-packed for 6 hours.
1884	*1 gentleman restrained by closed sleeves. 2 other patients restrained on account of violence or self-destruction.*
1885	*2 ladies restrained by gloves, 1 by a side arm dress, 1 wetpacked.*
	2 gentlemen wetpacked for 4 hours, 1 drypacked, 1 wore a side arm dress.
1886	*8 men, 7 women restrained with gloves, 2 with side arm dress, 1 dry-packed.*
1887	*32 patients wore gloves. 30 patients slept in side-arm dresses, covering 276 hours (including 89 hours for 1 suicidal male).*

The next year, the Medical Superintendent felt obliged to justify these practices in a letter to the *Lancet*. Further control was instituted by the Lunacy Act of 1890, which provided for the keeping of daily registers of the use of mechanical restraint, and required that in every case a certificate had to be signed by a doctor stating the means, duration and reason for it. It would be good to record that the use of restraint then declined, but the practices were persistent, as a few samples show:

1900	*2 males wore gloves 83 times for a total of 568 hours.*
	1 female wore gloves 8 times for a total of 113 hours.
	2 females had prolonged baths for a total of 50 hours.
	Many females wore exceptionally strong dresses.
1910	*8 patients restrained on 136 occasions – 595 hours in all.*
1920	*5 ladies mechanically restrained 318 times for a total of 1434 hours.*
1929	*2 ladies restrained on 11 occasions for a total of 62 hours to prevent injury.*

Thereafter, the Annual Reports tell us nothing about mechanical restraint, but that is no proof that its use was discontinued.

The Maudsley Hospital, from the beginning – according to the official reports – occasionally isolated a patient in a separate room but did not regularly seclude or use strong clothing. Yet Sister Florence Glass, who was a Night Sister at the Maudsley, recalled the use of strong suits, continuing up to the 1950s. This has been corroborated by other staff employed at that period.

Alternative methods of restraint were sought out by patients, who were almost as likely to be disturbed by their fellow patients as the staff. In

1873, the Annual Report said: 'Haematoma auris' [popularly called a 'thick ear'] has occurred once on each side of the house, and in both in restless, excitable cases that were very likely to have got struck or injured by some other patient, as a reward for their restless worrying. One was a case of general paralysis, and the other a woman with acute mania.' This taking of the law into the patient's own hands was not commonly reported, so one cannot assess its significance or otherwise.

Seclusion, if defined as isolating a patient in a room from which he has no means of egress, was a procedure with which Bethlem had long familiarity. Patients were locked in their rooms for long periods. How else in 1730 could four officers and six servants, with help only from the night-watchman control two hundrd and forty-two patients? 'Seclusion', as a word, started to appear in official documents from 1851 onwards. The Annual Reports from 1845 record the use of the padded rooms by night and occasionally by day, for clamorous, violent or unruly patients. Temporary isolation for the 'effect of tranquilising' continued even during the rule of Dr Hood, when the use of other modes of restraint was abolished. Later the Commissioners in Lunacy started to quantify the use of seclusion, for example in 1868: two men secluded for five hours, twelve women for thirty-three hours. In 1880, a patient who had been secluded for three and a half hours died of epilepsy when no attendant was present. This led to the rules for frequency of observing secluded patients being printed and a copy hung in every attendant's room. Another example from 1892 was of one woman being secluded for one hundred and eleven hours spread over twenty-three occasions. Later examples from the Commissioners' six monthly reports, showing an eventual decline in use of this procedure, were as follows:

1900 *9 patients secluded on 59 occasions for a total of 233 hours.*
    11 patients secluded on 56 occasions for a total of 367 hours.
1910 *3 patients secluded on 79 occasions for a total of 293 hours.*
    16 patients secluded on 371 occasions for a total of 1016 hours.
1920 *2 patients secluded on 60 occasions for a total of 104 hours.*
    1 patient secluded on 6 occasions for 5 hours on each occasion.
1929 *'No use of mechanical restraint or seclusion has been resorted to.'*

Apart from a reiteration in 1938 that no seclusion was used, the Annual Reports cease to comment on this topic. Yet it remained a possibility if authorised by the Medical Officer, as evidenced by the nursing instructions of 1955, which note that seclusion, meaning 'the confinement of a patient in a single room with a locked door, between 7 a.m. and 7 p.m.', must be recorded for report to the Board of Control.

Seclusion as a method of restraint has been tenacious, for, although it had been almost discontinued by the early 1970s, it never quite disappeared and soon experienced a revival. Detailed operational procedures were drawn up to help nurses and doctors, and monitor the application, with a view to protecting the rights of the patient. An example of this is in the Bethlem and Maudsley *Manual of Clinical Psychiatric Nursing Principles and Procedures* (Ritter 1989). The discussion section of Chapter 34, 'Seclusion', concludes thus: 'Seclusion is therefore a treatment to be used with the utmost caution and with scrupulous attention to the civil liberties of the patients and to the mental health law governing the administration of treatment without consent.'

The ebb and flow of the use of differing methods might be conjecturally explained by the changes in types of patient admitted, for instance the larger numbers of less behaviourally disturbed neurotic patients in the 1960s. Although a more detailed historical analysis is still awaited, the chosen methods were inevitably influenced by what was considered socially palatable.

One of the complaints of Michel Foucault against 'moral treatment' was that it replaced the 'great confinement' of the eighteenth century by a new 'moral imprisonment'. The mad were treated as children, to be restrained by the installation of guilt and self-control. At The Retreat in York, Samuel Tuke taught the therapeutic power of fear, which he thought was 'of great importance in the management of patients'. Theorists of an earlier period espoused the use of fear; for instance, Thomas Willis (1672) thought that curing the madman needed threats and keeping him in awe of medical staff and servants; Richard Mead (1751) advocated harsh words, threats and fear. Even Dr William Battie (1758), the Bethlem Governor, asserted the value of bodily pain and fear in treatment. In the eighteenth century, it was not mental patients alone who were ruled by fear. Flogging was a frequent occurence in the public schools. Hunter, the headmaster of Lichfield, whose pupils included the great Samuel Johnson, whipped his boys unmercifully to inculcate a knowledge of Latin.

It was not only physical reprisals that the patients had to fear, but also sanctions in the form of loss of privileges. In 1809, John Haslam wrote: 'Where the patient is in a condition to be sensible of restraint, he may be punished for improper behaviour, by confining him to his room, by degrading him, and not allowing him to associate with the convalescents, and by withholding certain indulgences he has been accustomed to enjoy'.

In the mid-nineteenth century, Bethlem attendants organised the transfer of troublesome patients from the more pleasant wards to the Basement Wards, where the conditions were primitive. The badly behaved were thereby excluded. Even in the 1960s, nurses sometimes threatened patients who made suicidal attempts with transfer to the feared, locked ward for disturbed patients.

In the popular mind, ECT has often been seen as punitive, possibly linked to its original purpose in controlling abnormal behaviour in schizophrenia. This method of inducing fits by electrical induction, developed by Cerletti and Bini in 1938, which came to be known as ECT, had become, with electronarcosis, the most widely used of treatments at the Bethlem and Maudsley by 1949–51. Although it continued to be used for catatonic states, ECT was, after the introduction of phenothiazines, used almost exclusively for treating depressive or cyclothymic illnesses. The treatment appeared unattractive to some who received it or observed its consequences in memory deficit, headache, confusion or retrograde amnesia. Nevertheless, for some patients, ECT could be life-saving, provide relief from symptoms, and control the incapacities arising from depression.

Apart from electrical 'treatment', the use of hypoglycaemia in insulin therapy, and neurosurgery for mental disturbance, could also be seen as being, at least in part, an instrument of restraint (Hunter 1956). Arguments about the legitimacy and practicalities of answering undesirable behaviour by 'time out', or giving small electric shocks as aversion in the course of behaviour therapy preoccupied the hospital ethical committees in the 1970s and 80s. Electric shocks, however small, were thought by many to be unpalatable, but 'time out' achieved a certain currency, notably in the treatment of children.

Medical measures for achieving the restraint of patients were not necessarily so visible to the visitor as was the use of mechanical means, but they could achieve similar effects. Sedation through the administration of opiates or alcohol had its critics. Thomas Tryon, a merchant of London, who described some of the practices of Bethlem in 1689, condemned the giving of 'sleepyfying things' and 'stupefactive Medicines'. He thought that these medicines gave the patients stupefying dreams and so increased the madness. More preferable were the practices of Dr Battie (1758) who advocated the use of wine or vinous spirits to calm the patients, and incidentally to give them some pleasure.

The traditional medical 'anti-phlogistic' measures, popular in the eighteenth century, of bleeding, blistering, purging and vomiting were applied with the intention of lowering the turbulent spirits and thus making the patients more amenable, as discussed in Chapter 4.

The use of sedating medication continued in the nineteenth century with the administration of conium, digitalis, antimony and chloral.

In the twentieth century, the use of paraldehyde and chloral hydrate was practised until well after the introduction of the phenothiazine group of drugs (major tranquillizers) in the 1950s. So although chemical restraint is not a modern initiative, it is only in recent developments that sedation and relief of symptoms have been so effectively combined. This, in fact, poses slightly more problems for the nurse who wishes the doctor to

125

prescribe tranquillisers for her patient. Is the removal of symptoms the dominant aspect, or is it because the carers need a more restful time? A special problem for Maudsley nurses was once the emphasis on a lengthy initial assessment of patients, who were kept unsedated. Richard Hunter, writing in the *Lancet* in 1956, disapproved of chemical restraint, because it came in the way of proper mental nursing, which was based on 'sustained kindly understanding and contact'. Maudsley nurses would not have all agreed. In 1973, the Maudsley junior doctors supported them by writing reprovingly in the *Hospital Gazette*, 'Emphasis on diagnosis by mental state has sometimes made prolonged social control of disturbed patients necessary, when they could have been sedated and adaptive relationships made easier'.

There also remain other considerations. Is the level of sedation going to be such as will still allow the patient to function to his optimum standard? What about the long-term effects of medication? Would some form of confinement or even mechanical restraint be equally useful? Which method is going to show most respect for the patient as an individual, entitled to choice and quality care? What are the lessons of history?

Order among staff

The keeper must himself be kept. If he be not watched and punished, an asylum is likely to be little beyond an alternation of reciprocal violence between the prisoner and the gaoler (Samuel Nicoll 1828).

The Governors of Bethlem have, over the centuries, been much exercised about keeping control of the keepers, especially when the personal interests of the staff were at variance with the best interests of the patients. The first indications of conflict came in 1346, at a time when the hospital was said to be staffed by a master, brethren, proctors, attorneys, servants and domestics. Bethlem had asked for help from the City of London in the management of its affairs, and the City had delegated Aldermen to give assistance. Some members of the hospital were punished for disobedience, first privately in the chapter house and then publicly in the hall of the hospital, the Aldermen sitting on each side of the Master to see correction administered (Talbot 1969, from City Letter Book 1346). Unfortunately, the nature of the disobedience or the type of punishment is not disclosed.

At the first public inquiry in 1403, it was clear who the culprits were. The hospital losses, damage to property and extortion were attributed to the Porter and his wife. Income from legitimate sources had not satisfied them, so they turned to commerce, embezzlement of the hospital's effects and extortion of goods and money from patients. This did not go unpunished, for Peter Taverner, the Porter, was deprived of his position and ordered to make restitution of the goods he had removed.

In 1437, similar problems occurred, involving the destruction and removal of hospital property. The hospital was sufficiently supplied with charitable donations to provide rich pickings. The office of Keeper attracted men of note, including Dr Helkiah Crooke, the King's physician, appointed in 1619, who was able to profit from the hospital without much input. He, too, was eventually removed from office, amidst threats of prosecution for his misdemeanours.

Regarding servants and inferior officers, little is known until the seventeenth century. The Governors' minutes remain preoccupied with Bridewell, the larger of their responsibilities, not mentioning Bethlem much until the institution of a weekly Bethlem Committee and a Grand Committee for both hospitals at the end of the century. The Governors' lack of interest in Bethlem was accompanied by a lack of supervision, with unfortunate results. They attempted to correct matters by censure of wrong-doing, exhortations to improve, making rules for right conduct, as shown in Chapter 6, the occasional demotion and more frequent dismissals. Stealing from the poors' and servants' boxes were common faults of basketmen, but there were other examples of deviant behaviour:

1637	*A maid servant dismissed for vicious gossiping.*
1657	*Anthony Dadsworth, basketman, dismissed for abusive carriages and misbehaviour.*
1675	*Rowland Woolly, basketman, a person of evil fame and dishonest conversation, dismissed.*
1681	*Edward Langden and William Jones, basketmen discharged for making a patient/patients pregnant.*
1727	*Sarah Wright, nurse, convicted of profiteering but not dismissed.*
1774	*William Dodd, Porter and ex-basketman, dismissed for drunkenness.*
1781	*Watkin Walters found to have sold patients clothes, offered demotion but declined and was dismissed.*

The recital of these disheartening facts leads one to suspect that sometimes only a low quality of care was available. The above dossier is amplified by the statistical information compiled by Andrews (1991), illustrating the transience and unsuitablity of some staff. From 1633 to 1700, over one third of the recorded basketmen were discharged from their posts. Over half of the basketmen served for less than three years. From 1700 to 1777, a fifth were discharged for abuses committed, and the average length of service was slightly shorter than previously. The maid servants seem to have been in trouble less often and stayed longer.

John Haslam (1798) explained some of the difficulties that keepers met with, for instance in applying mechanical restraint, and ordered that it be done in the presence of other patients to avoid abuse. It 'prevents the wanton exercise of force, and those cruel and unmanly advantages which might be taken when the patient and keeper are shut up in a private room'. This worked in another way too, for the protection of the keeper. Haslam reported that instances were not rare where the patient had overcome the keeper, sometimes causing his death. This is a rare reference in the literature to the death of staff at the hands of patients. In the eighteenth century, because of the temperate manner in which he was forced to live, the patient was sometimes stronger than the keepers, for whom it was common 'to indulge in a diet and beverage, which induce corpulence and difficulty of breathing' (Haslam 1809).

It makes a little relief from this gloomy narrative to recall that a small number of basketmen stayed on for many years with apparently unblemished records, achieving promotion either at Bethlem or elsewhere, for example William Day as Governor to the Lunatic Hospital in Manchester (1773) and Thomas Dunstan to a promotion at St Luke's, London (1781).

The staff of Bethlem had a reputation for brutality in the public eye in the eighteenth century, and, while this may not have been always as well deserved as the exaggerated gossip implied, it must be acknowledged that the conditions of their work were such as disposed them to become brutalised. The servants lived in close proximity to the patients, working long hours for small pay. They were poorly educated and often unmarried. They were perpetually involved in coercing patients into patterns of behaviour that were thought necessary for the institution to function. It is a wonder that the disorderly behaviour was not even more prevalent. Even Urbane Metcalf (1818), the ex-patient so eager to complain, put forward (apart from the gross charge of a murder by Keeper Blackburn) only fairly trivial accusations against the staff. The disadvantages of the keepers' positions were offset by an expected security of employment, unless one was grossly badly behaved, which alas many were.

Gradually, from about the early nineteenth century, the pattern changed, with different types of treatment and higher expectations of staff. Control of staff activities, as mentioned in Chapter 6, was achieved by an increasing elaboration of the rules of behaviour and by the management trying to operate a 'total institution', legislating for almost all aspects of staff and patient lives. Even at the end of the nineteenth century, nurses were confined to institutions by their hours of duty, which were commonly eighty-nine hours per week. Sporadic reports were made to the Court of Governors about attendants who had been dismissed or disciplined. One is again at the mercy of the vagaries of reporting practice. After a long period of silence about dismissals, there were more reports made towards the end of the century:

1871   1 Attendant discharged for neglecting Watchman's duty.
1882   1 Attendant rough with patients discharged.
1887   1 Charge Attendant discharged for intemperance.
1890   1 Attendant discharged for disobedience to orders, one for outstaying his
*   leave, and one, previously cautioned, for speaking improperly to a patient.*
1894   1 Nurse (female) dismissed for corresponding with a male patient.
1896   Some dismissals for neglect of duty, – carelessness allowing a patient to
*   escape, misconduct when out with patients, and disobedience to orders.*
1899   5 males discharged as unsuitable after an initial probationary period.

Probation seemed to have been a useful innovation, for notes about dismissal thereafter declined, although there were occasional unfortunate events, for example in 1912: 'Attendant dismissed – left store cupboard open and patient acquired the means to commit suicide'.

There were sometimes, for example in 1881 and 1894, complaints of rough usage by the attendants. One patient died of internal injuries in 1887 after a scuffle with the night attendants. Complaints against staff of rough handling were never regarded as substantiated, but, in 1896, the Commissioners, while suspecting considerable exaggeration, feared there was some foundation in fact and recommended close supervision of the ward staff. Difficulties for independent visitors in establishing precisely what had taken place remained considerable, yet the reports they made undoubtedly provided an invaluable contribution to monitoring hospital practices.

The ward staff were left in no doubt of the intended accent on discipline, which was listed as the first of the duties of the attendant, in the *Handbook for the Instruction of Attendants on the Insane* (Medico-Psychological Association 1908). Discipline was to be understood:

1) *As it is imposed on the attendants – that is his duty to the asylum and his fellows;*
2) *As he should impose it on his patients – that is his duty to his patients.*

In the twentieth century, there is little in the Bethlem records about staff disciplinary problems, as, with a larger staff establishment, cases were not commonly brought to the Board of Governors but dealt with by the various officers of the hospitals. Difficulties for the Governors in keeping order among nursing staff tended to centre on unrest about pay, which is discussed in Chapter 11. Detailed disciplinary procedures were eventually developed in the late 1970s, which codified management's response to unsatisfactory behaviour and laid out the system of warnings and suspensions leading up to final dismissal. In this, the rights of staff as well as management were safe-guarded, with provision for representation and appeal. Today the behaviour of trained nurses remains subject to national regulation, yet, alongside the principles laid down, there is scope to develop a wide range of disciplinary interventions. One might hope that improved job satisfaction, better conditions of employment and increased financial reward have produced staff who are not so prone to exploiting the organisation for personal ends.

References and further reading

Andrews J (1991) *Bedlem Revisited: A History of Bethlem Hospital c1634–c1770.* Unpublished PhD thesis, University of London.

Battie W (1758, reprinted 1962) *A Treatise on Madness*, and Monro J *Remarks on Dr Battie's Treatise on Madness.* London: Dawsons.

Bellers J (1696) *Proposals for Raising a College of Industry of All Useful Trades and Husbandry.* London: Sowle.

Clark J (1869) *A Memoir of John Conolly MD.* London: Murray.

Conolly J (1863) In Annual Meeting of the Association of Medical Officers of Asylums and Hospitals for the Insane. *Journal of Mental Science* **IX**(45): 439.

Foucault M (1965) (translated R Howard). *Madness and Civilisation: a History of Insanity in the Age of Reason.* New York: Random House.

Hadwin S (1841) *The Times*, January 25.

Haslam J (1798) *Observations on Insanity.* London: F. and C. Rivington.

Haslam J (1809) *Observations on Insanity*, revised edition. London: Hayden.

Hunter RA (1956) The rise and fall of mental nursing. *Lancet*, January 14: 98–99.

Mead R (1751) (translated by T Stack). *Medical Precepts and Cautions.* London: Brindley.

Medico-Psychological Association (1885) and (1908) *Handbook for the instruction of attendants on the insane.* London: Baillière and Co.

Metcalf U (1818) *The Interior of Bethlehem Hospital.* London (published by the author).

More T (1533) *The Apologye of Syr T. More, Knyght.* London: Rastell.

Nicoll S (1828) *An Enquiry into the Present State of Visitation in Asylums for the Reception of the Insane and into the Modes by which Visitation May Be Improved.* London: Harvey and Darton.

Report from the Committee on Madhouses in England. (1815) London: House of Commons.

Ritter S (1989) *Manual of Clinical Psychiatric Nursing Principles and Procedures.* London: Harper and Row.

Santos EH and Stainbrook E (1949) A history of psychiatric nursing in the nineteenth century. *Journal of the History of Medicine and Allied Sciences*, IV: 48–74.

Scull A (1993) *The Most Solitary of Afflictions. Madness and Society in Britain 1700–1900.* New Haven and London: Yale University Press.

Townsend J (1786) *A Dissertation on the Poor Laws by a Well Wisher of Mankind.* London: Dilly.

Tryon T (1689) *A Treatise of Dreams and Visions. To which Is Added, a Discourse of the Causes, Natures and Cure of Phrensie, Madness or Distraction.* London: Sowle.

Tuke S (1813) *Description of the Retreat, an Institution near York for Insane Persons of the Society of Friends*. London: Dawsons of Pall Mall, facsimile of 1813, reprinted 1964.

Willis T (1672) *De Anima Brutorum* (translated by S Pordage as *Two Discourses concerning the Soul of Brutes*). London: Dring.

*T*he public eye

*I*n the first chapter of this book, we noted that the historical image of Bethlem had been shaped in a theatrical way. Bethlem came to be presented through the medium of short scenes, in which the patients acted out the contents of their private worlds, interacted with staff and bemused the visitors. The public perception of the hospital has been formed partly by the published findings of Inquiries, by protest documents and by the writings of staff who concentrated on the positive aspects of Bethlem life. Alongside these is an astonishing range of literature on Bedlam as an institution and as an idea.

In this chapter, we consider the image of Bethlem as fashioned by dramatists, journalists and novelists. The dramatists and journalists selected were all working in central London less than a handful of miles from Bethlem, which, in their time, was open for the world to visit. The novelists, although coming later, also had personal contacts with Bethlem. Of these, only the journalists can be thought of as making any claim to factual reality, and even they were often writing more with entertainment and literary effect in mind. Yet it is striking how often these imaginative works reflect the historical evidence found elsewhere. These writers communicate their ideas of how the practices of Bethlem were perceived and extend our perceptions about the plight of the mentally disturbed and their treatment. This literature has been a significant factor in the development of Bethlem, for the day-to-day life of the patients and employees is influenced by how the public sees them. As Henry James (1915), the novelist, wrote 'it is art that makes life'. The fictions and reports about the past, while sometimes exaggerating the defects of the institution, have led to reaction and modification and are worthy of attention not least for their own artistic merits.

It is not possible here to do more than sample sections of the literature about Bethlem, and, for the purposes of this chapter, we will have to content ourselves with illustrations from Jacobean dramatists, shuddering with fearful delight at the lunatics; eighteenth-century journalists laughing, jeering and lamenting at the human spectacle; and twentieth-century novelists on becoming mad and making a way through to survival or death.

Bedlam on the Jacobean stage – as seen by Shakespeare, Dekker, Webster, Fletcher and Middleton

The plays in this section illustrate various topics, such as Bedlam in the community, madmen's behaviour and its control, sexual disinhibition in disturbed individuals, types of mad people and their entertainment, keepers' reports on their charges, and the character of a keeper.

In the space of eighteen years, from 1604 to 1622, there was a remarkable explosion of theatrical representations of madness and the madhouse on the London stage. Much of this is thought by Reed (1952) to have been based on actual observation, as he believed that Jacobean comedy was, as a rule, documentary as well as theatrical. At least two of the plays explicitly depict scenes in Bethlem, the only public madhouse in England at the time, while other plays have groups of Bedlamites in exotic imaginary locations.

This preoccupation with madness by a group of London playwrights was given impetus, unsurprisingly, by William Shakespeare, especially in his plays, *Hamlet* (1601) and *King Lear* (1604). In the former we see Ophelia, the prototype mad girl, sadly deranged by love, while in the latter we have Edgar, the courtier, feigning madness, pretending to be the well-known character and ex-Bethlem beggar, Tom O'Bedlam. Edgar graphically describes putting on the disguise of a degraded madman, roaming about frighteningly in the community (Act II, Scene 3). Edgar makes his plans to escape from his enemies:

> *I will preserve myself; and am bethought*
> *To take the basest and most poorest shape,*
> *That ever penury, in contempt of man,*
> *Brought near to beast: my face I'll grime with filth;*
> *Blanket my loins; elf all my hair in knots;*
> *And with presented nakedness outface*
> *The winds and persecutions of the sky.*
> *The country gives me proof and precedent*
> *Of Bedlam beggars, who, with roaring voices,*
> *Strike in their numb'd and mortified bare arms*
> *Pins, wooden pricks, nails, sprigs of rosemary;*

And with this horrible object, from low farms,
Poor pelting villages, sheep-cotes, and mills,
Sometime with lunatic bans, sometimes with prayers,
Enforce their charity. – Poor Turlygod! poor Tom!

Shakespeare outlined some features of mental disturbance shown by ex-Bethlem patients in the community – threatening behaviour, exposure of the body and masochism – and focused on how the condition and resulting poverty brought the sufferer to an almost animal-like state, which evoked both fear and sympathy.

The first actual representation of Bethlem on stage came in 1604 in *The Honest Whore,* a play by Thomas Dekker. Act V Scene 2 was set in an apartment at Bethlem Monastery, which was being run by a Friar and some servants. It had been at least over half a century since the real Bethlem had been a monastery, but it was not unreasonably depicted as a place where there had been assignations and clandestine marriages. The complex plot included both unjustified imprisonment and feigned madness. The unruly, violent madmen, who had been kept hungry, were treated by chaining up and whipping. Father Anselmo described them to a visiting courtier:

There are of mad men, as there are of tame,
All humoured not alike: we have here some,
So apish and fantastic, play with a feather,
And, though 'twould grieve a soul to see God's image
So blemished and defaced, yet do they act
Such antic and such pretty lunacies,
That spite of sorrow they will make you smile:
Others again we have like hungry lions,
Fierce as wild bulls, untameable as flies

To the theme of man degraded to the level of animals is added the unde-niable conviction that the madmen are entertaining, and that, of course, was why they were shown on the stage. To illustrate this, we are given a stretch of wild, jolly, bantering conversation, which works up to a fight:

3rd Madman: *Give me some porridge.*
2nd Madman: *I'll give thee none.*
3rd Madman: *Give me some porridge.*
2nd Madman: *I'll not give you a bit.*
3rd Madman: *Give me that flap-dragon.*
2nd Madman: *I'll not give thee a spoonful. Thou liest, it's no dragon, 'tis a parrot, that I bought for my sweetheart, and I'll keep it.*
3rd Madman: *Here's an almond for parrot.*
2nd Madman: *Hang thyself!*
3rd Madman: *Here's a rope for parrot.*
2nd Madman: *Eat it, for I'll eat this.*

3rd Madman:	I'll shoot at thee, an thou't give me none.	
2nd Madman:	Wu't thou?	
3rd Madman:	I'll run a tilt at thee, an thou't give me none.	
2nd Madman:	Wu't thou? do an thou darest.	
3rd Madman:	Bounce!	*[Strikes him.*
2nd Madman:	O – oh! I am slain! murder, murder, murder! I am slain; my brains are beaten out.	
Friar Anselmo:	How now, you villains! Bring me whips: I'll whip you.	
2nd Madman:	I am dead! I am slain! ring out the bell, for I am dead.	

The madmen seem firmly established in their roles of provocateur and victim. They are controlled in the traditional mediaeval way by inflicting pain as punishment. If they had been at Bethlem in a later age, they might have been able to hope for an earlier and more compassionate intervention than that made by Friar Anselmo.

This comedy was followed three years later (1607) by another comedy by Thomas Dekker, this time in collaboration with John Webster, called *Northward Ho*. The title was derived from the cry of the boatmen on the river Thames, calling out for trade. Jack Bellamont, the principal character, an old, white-haired poet, was on his way to Ware with some young gentlemen for some sport. While passing through Bishopsgate, they decided to stop off and visit Bedlam. In Act IV, Scene 3, the gallants met the keeper, Master Fullmoon, and asked to see some of the mad folks. The inmates they met were a musician, beside himself for love of an Italian dwarf, and a bawd (procuress), who had been frightened out of her wits by a fire. Musicians and girls affected by their relationships with men were thought especially vulnerable to madness, or lunacy, and the keeper's name reflected the connection with the moon, the supposed cause of these conditions. We find out little about Master Fullmoon, except that he was easily bribed into admitting a new inmate and putting him under restraint, although the man was perfectly sane. The play showed only a couple of the patients, of which the Bawd in particular illustrated one of the accompanying features of madness, which was that the 'madcaps' were often sexually disinhibited and obscene in conversation. This might have been thought amusing both for the visitors and, at second hand, for the masses at the theatre. The Bawd willingly entertained the visiting gallants:

Bellamont:	But what say you to such young gentlemen as these are?
Bawd:	Foh! they, as soon, as they come to their lands, get up to London, and like squibs that run upon lines, they keep a spitting of fire and crackin till they ha' spent all; and when my squib is out, what says his punk? foh, he stinks!

[Sings.

Methought, this other night I saw a pretty sight,
Which pleased me much, –

135

A comely country maid, not squeamish or afraid
To let gentlemen touch:
I sold her maidenhead once, and I sold her maidenhead twice
And I sold it last to an Alderman of York;
And then I had sold it thrice.

This play paraded the sexual disinhibition of the mentally disturbed in a way that today would be found distasteful. It is to be hoped that carers can find ways to protect the patients from exploitation and offer an environment where patients can be safe from showing themselves in a way that they might later on regret.

John Webster wrote a play without Dekker five years later (1612), this time a tragedy, *The Duchess of Malfi*, which had considerable success and still enjoys revivals. This is the malicious reverse of the farcical entertainment in *Northward Ho*. The madmen here had been sent to the Duchess, who was held in captivity by her tyrannical brother, to terrorise her into madness. The action of this episode was formalised into a frightening ritual. Eight madmen are described, who sing a noisy, gloomy song, which is followed by a competitive conversation and a wild dance. This is sometimes called the anti-masque. There is also the beginning of some differentiation of types of mad people, with occupation linked to complaint. Ridicule of the professions is a main vehicle of satire in these parts of Jacobean plays. A servant introduces the madmen:

Servant: *There's a mad lawyer; and a secular priest;*
        A doctor that hath forfeited his wits
        By jealousy; an astrologian
        That in his works said such a day o'the month
        Should be the day of doom, and, failing of't,
        Ran mad; an English tailor craz'd i' the brain
        With the study of new fashions; a gentleman-usher
        Quite beside himself with care to keep in mind
        The number of his lady's salutations
        Or 'How do you' she employ'd him in each morning;
        A farmer too, an excellent knave in grain,
        Mad 'cause he was hinder'd transportation:
        And let one broker that's mad loose to these,
        You'd think the devil were among them.
Duchess: *Sit, Cariola. – Let them loose when you please,*
        For I am chain'd to endure all your tyranny.

                Enter Madmen.

   Here by a Madman this song is sung to a dismal kind of music.

    O, let us howl some heavy note,
    Some deadly dogged howl,

Sounding as from the threatening throat
Of beasts and fatal fowl!
As ravens, screech-owls, bulls, and bears,
We'll bell, and bawl our parts,
Till irksome noise have cloy'd your ears
And corrosiv'd your hearts.
At last, whenas our quire wants breath,
Our bodies being blest,
We'll sing, like swans, to welcome death,
And die in love and rest.

Once again, there is the persistent bestial imagery, with a menagerie said to be cacophonous until the approach of death. This could be one of the most macabre horrifying presentations of patients in Jacobean drama, contrasting as it does with its model, the pleasing courtly masques of gods and goddesses popular at this period.

Almost every list of causes of mental disorder that we encounter includes love or lust in some form. The heroine, Alcinda, in the next play was assumed to be mad, because of her passionate behaviour. *The Pilgrim*, a comedy by John Fletcher, was produced in 1621. Act III Scene 6 was set in a madhouse, where the madmen could be seen in their cells. The place was staffed by a Master and two keepers, the senior one of whom made reference to a patient called Mad Bess, who would have been recognised by the audience as Bess O'Bedlam, the female counterpart of the legendary Tom O'Bedlam. The scene opened with an exchange between the two keepers that is rather like one nurse giving a report to another. The dialogue included the question of who had the monopoly on madness or sanity – was it the madmen or their keepers?

Enter two Keepers,

1 Keeper: *Carry Mad Bess some meat, she roars like thunder;*
   And tie the parson short, the moon's i' th' full,
   He has a thousand pigs in's brains. Who looks to the prentice?
   Keep him from women, he thinks he has lost his mistress;
   And talk of no silk stuffs, 'twill run him horn-mad.

2 Keeper: *The justice keeps such a stir yonder with his charges,*
   And such a coil with warrants!

1 Keeper: *Take away his statutes;*
   The devil had possessed him in the likeness
   Of penal laws; keep him from aquae-vitae,
   For if that spirit creep into his quorum,
   He will commit us all. How is it with the scholar?

2 Keeper: *For anything I see, he's in his right wits.*

1 Keeper: *Thou art an ass! in his right wits, goodman coxcomb?*
   As though any man durst be in's right wits, and be in here:
   It is as much as we dare be, that keep 'em.

The first keeper, who is obviously in charge, and free to abuse the second keeper, covers some of the topics that are standard for carers today – observation, dietary intake, limitation of movement or otherwise, occupation and segregation. One might wish to have had some expansion of these themes. The dialogue does not display the keepers in a good light. The first keeper is reluctant to accept information from the second keeper and concentrates on giving directives – not the behaviour we would expect from a modern team leader.

Themes such as the expressing of sexuality and the doubts about who is sane and who mad surface again in Thomas Middleton's tragedy, *The Changeling* of 1622. The madhouse in this play was being run by a doctor, Alibius, and his man, the steward/keeper Lollio, who looked after two wards, one for madmen and one for fools, the whole being thought of as a school for lunatics. In this play, we have the most fully worked-up representation of a keeper on the stage for this period. Lollio is a humorous character, in some ways an archetype of the venal servant. His ready wit puts something of an acceptable gloss on the less attractive qualities – his overfamiliarity with his master, his itch for financial gain, his sadism and his lechery. However, there is reason to respect him for his skilful manipulation of unruly situations. Lollio, rather than the doctor, takes the lead in interviewing the relative and making the initial assessment when the new patient is admitted. The madmen are frequently shouting out, acting out their fantasies as birds or beasts, the while singing, howling, braying or barking, or preparing to dance for the nobility. Lollio remains in charge, no matter whether he has to control two wards at once or cope with the sounds of hungry, agitated crying at mealtimes. In Act I Scene 2, Lollio and Dr Alibius stand outside the madhouse, listening to the shouts from within:

Madman 1:   *Put's head i' th' pillory, the bread's too little.*
Madman 2:   *Fly, Fly, and he catches the swallow.*
Madman 3:   *Give her more onion, or the Devil put more rope about her crag.*
Lollio: *You may hear what time of day it is, the chimes of Bedlam goes.*
Alibius: *Peace, peace I say, or the wire [whip] comes!*
Madman 3:   *Cat whore, cat whore, her permasant, her permasant!*
Alibius: *Peace I say; their hour's come, they must be fed, Lollio.*

Bethlem was the model used by all these London dramatists. They depicted a highly disturbed community, where the madmen were largely ruled by fear of the whip and the keepers were as much engaged in anti-social behaviour as were the inmates. Yet, in spite of the depiction of the degradation of the madhouse community, the public was compulsively attracted to a world where fantasies could be acted out and the division between the normal and the abnormal was blurred. It may be thought to represent the last phase of Bethlem's mediaeval period. Certainly, attitudes had changed by the time of the visits of the journalists in the next section.

Ned Ward and Mary Midnight have outings to Moorfields

In this section, the two accounts of visits to Bethlem at Moorfields show contrasting attitudes: the first is high-spirited and satirical, and caricatures the patients, while the second account explores the pathos and predicament of patients seen as victims of society.

Ned Ward, who was said to keep a public house near Bethlem, wrote for a journal called *The London Spy*, in which he published satirical pieces humorously exposing the vices of the age. He wrote a lengthy article about Bethlem in 1699, regaling his readers with details of the strange madfolks' activities and also the reprehensible behaviour of the visitors. The whole tale was dominated with Ward's views and pronouncements on the visit, which make one feel at some distance from whatever the reality of the situation might have been.

He started with a discourse on the 'noble Pile of Building', a magnificent structure and a stately edifice not much more than twenty years old, thinking that it must be a sign of a 'mad Age'. One would have expected this sort of building to be erected for persons of quality and not for poor wretches. This he found an ostentatious piece of Vanity by the City Fathers who commissioned it.

In spite of the elegant facade, one saw, on entering, a vision of Hell and heard the uproar of the damned. Ward went on to catalogue the madmen, from whom he singled out seven men and five women, some of whom were wandering freely about the galleries, and some of whom were confined, but could be seen in their cells through wicket peepingholes in the doors. No staff were mentioned. There were encounters on the male side with a drunkard or two, a lecher, a depressed musician and a grotesque, who, although confined, 'entertained' the visitors:

> We then moved on till we found another remarkable figure worth our observing, who was peeping through his Wicket, eating of Bread and Cheese, talking all the while like a Carrier at his supper, chewing his Words with his Victuals, all that he spoke being in Praise of Bread and Cheese; Bread was good with Cheese, and Cheese was good with Bread, and Bread with Cheese was good together, and abundance of such stuff; to which my Friend and I, with others, stood listening; at last he counterfeits a sneeze, and shot such a mouthful of Bread and Cheese

amongst us, that every Spectator had some share of his kindness, which made us retreat; he calling after us Masters, Masters, some went back to hear what he had to say, and he had provided them a plentiful Bowl of Piss, which he cast very successfully amongst them, crying, in a laugh, I never give Victuals, but I give drink, and you're welcome, Gentlemen.

The laugh is decidedly with the patient at the visitors' expense. Apart from the patients who suffered from what Ward described as the 'noble sins of drinking and whoring', there was one who had trouble suppressing his conscience and another who wittily took up Ward's theme of liberty. The visitors have sacrificed some of their liberty by being locked in with the madmen, only to find the inmates boasting of possessing more freedom of speech than the visitors have outside:

We Madmen have as much privelege of speaking our Minds, within these Walls, as an ignorant Dictator, when he spews out nonsense to a whole parish. Prithee come and live here, and you may talk what you will, and nobody will call you in question for it: Truth is persecuted everywhere Abroad, and flies hither for Sanctuary, where she sits as safe as a Knave in a Church, or a Whore in a Nunnery. I can use her as I please, and that's more than you dare do.

On the female side of the hospital, apart from some foul-mouthed old women, we meet only an adulterous woman, who keeps reliving her marital problems:

The first that we looked upon stood straddling with her back against the Wall, crying, Come John come; your Master's gone to 'Change [Stock Exchange]. I believe poor Fool's afraid of forfeiting his Indentures. Did you ever see the like? Why, sure you won't serve your Mistress so, John, will you? Hark, hark, run you Rogue, your Master's come back to Shop. Yes, you shall have a wife, you old Rogue, with seven hundred pounds, and be married six Years, and not get a Child! Fly for shame, out upon't! A Husband for a Woman, a husband for the Devil! Hang you, rot you, sink you, confound you. And thus at last she run raving on into the highest Degree of madness.

Ward rounded off his account of this visit to Bethlem by observations of visitors, who include whores and lechers pairing off. He wrote that this opportunity for 'sport' was a great conveniency to London, and that one could be satisfied if one did not mind picking up the pox at the same time. So having brooded about who was mad, who was free and the place of sexual morality in all that, the visitors left the 'piss-burned Prison' that was Bedlam and went off to a cook-shop to satisfy their bodily appetites with lunch.

In the next account, unlike earlier texts, the patients have names and more personal identification. Mary Midnight reported in *The Midwife, or The Old Woman's Magazine* how she went to the Moorgate Coffee House on February 2, 1750, where she met up with an old gentleman who started

140

to talk to her about love and proposed a visit to Bethlem nearby. Once there, they met on the stairs some well-dressed ladies and gentlemen, who teased Mary about her boyfriend and his intentions, and then they passed on to the rooms above where they met a patient called Hannah:

> *After we had disengaged ourselves from these fashionable gentry, I turned aside to speak to a young woman, who was so far recovered, as to be intrusted with her liberty. The good old gentleman hearing me ask her several questions, joined us, and the poor unhappy Creature told us her case with an air of seriousness that confessed her Sincerity, and the Flood of Tears that testified the Truth.*

There followed the story of Hannah, a well-to-do country girl who was crossed in love. She married a man who turned out to be a bigamist only interested in her money, and, when the man had acquired control of the money, he deserted her. When Hannah had come to that point in her narrative:

> *she wept bitterly, and then attempted to give us some account of her Father, but was interrupted by one of the Keepers who perceiving her greatly agitated with passion ordered her to her apartment.*

Mrs Midnight was indignant at hearing of this girl's sufferings, thinking that there ought to be a law against artful fellows taking advantage of a girl with impunity.

Mary Midnight and her amorous escort were later accosted by a madman who had known Mrs Midnight socially before his illness. He identified himself as Will Wimble, the second son of a wealthy father who did not provide for him in his Will. The son had become impoverished and on being arrested for debt, he 'lost his senses'. Mary Midnight was made uneasy by this encounter, partly because Will had been within her circle of acquaintance and also because he appeared disturbed. He said:

> *The Sun don't give half the light it used to do, and the Moon is perpetually in a cloud: there are but six of the seven stars to be seen, and one of those has got the green sickness –*
>
> > *But why should we quarrel for Riches*
> > *Or any such trifling toys,*
> > *A light heart and a thin pair of breeches*
> > *Goes thorough (sic) the World brave boys.*
>
> *Here the poor creature began to rave, which one of the Keepers perceiving, immediately took hold of him. The sudden Transition from incoherent Madness to solid Reasoning, which this occasioned in him really surprised me; and I was no less pleased to see with what dexterity he endeavoured to conceal from me his confinement. He whispered sometime with the Keeper, then shook him by the hand; and, as he was coming towards us, called to him to walk about and not be uneasy, for they had Time enough to go home. When he had joined our Company,*

141

he did not forget to intimate that the Person who laid hold of him was a Countryman, whom he had brought there to shew him the Place, for he was a mere Bumpkin. Poor Will carried the Farce so far as to offer to treat me with a Glass of Wine, and attempted to go out for that Purpose, but was stopped by the Porter. This affected him prodigiously, and he raved to a Degree not to be described; but when he saw the People come about him, and found that he must submit, he made a Bow, and walked off.

Mary Midnight had to abandon her visit at that point, because she was so deeply affected.

In these passages, we have read of more enlightened programmes of management than we have come across before. The keeper in the first episode intervened to segregate the patient when she became agitated. In the second section, the keeper controlled the agitation by a simple holding technique and allowed the patient to negotiate with him for an extension of visiting time. When this proved too much for the patient, the keepers were assembled, and the knowledge of their presence was enough to enable the patient to regain some self-possession and disengage himself from the disturbing situation. Some of these methods are still useful today.

Incidentally, Mrs Midnight was a nom de plume that concealed the identity of Christopher Smart, the celebrated poet and journalist, who undoubtedly visited Bethlem. It was particularly poignant in that what he saw was like a preview of his future. Increasingly weighed down by drunkenness, debt and melancholy, and in spite of memorable poems like *Jubilate Agno* and the *Song of David*, he went downhill in the course of several admissions to madhouses (not including Bethlem) and finished his life in a debtors prison at the age of forty-nine.

Samuel Beckett and Antonia White have nightmares about surviving mental illness

Having considered some works by dramatists and journalists, we move to novelists, this time in the twentieth century. Both novelists, while drawing attention to the horrors of hospital life, find more time than previous writers to comment on the practices and attitudes of nurses.

Samuel Beckett, novelist, poet and playwright (*Waiting for Godot*), came to London at the age of twenty-eight in 1934 to seek treatment from Dr Bion at the Tavistock Clinic for his anxiety and depression. While the psychotherapy was in progress, Beckett also worked for three years on his novel *Murphy*. He had an Irish friend in London, Dr Geoffrey Thompson, who was doing post-graduate psychiatric training at Bethlem. This gave

Beckett the chance to come to Bethlem, where he walked in the grounds, visited the wards and played chess with Dr Thompson. Beckett himself acknowledged that he used Bethlem as a point of departure for his novel *Murphy*, which had as its setting a sanatorium for the mentally ill, called the Magdalen Mental Mercyseat. This is a comic, satirical book, in which seething near the surface are themes such as sexuality, punishment and death.

Like Beckett, Murphy the hero had recently come from Ireland to London, where he had been living in a flat in West Brompton. He fell in love with Celia, a prostitute, but got most pleasure from sitting naked, tied to his rocking chair. A friend, Ticklepenny, told him about a job that was available at the Magdalen Mental Mercyseat. There Murphy met two members of the Clinch family, Mr Thomas ('Bim') Clinch, the Head Male Nurse, and Mr Timothy ('Bom') Clinch, a Charge Nurse:

> *Bim Clinch had no fewer than seven male relations, lineal and collateral, serving under him, of whom the greatest was Bom and perhaps the least an aged uncle ('Bum') in the bandage-winding department, as well as an elder sister, two nieces and a by-blow on the female side. There was nothing old-fashioned or half-hearted about the nepotism of Bim Clinch, there was no more resolute and successful pope to his family in the south of England, and even in the south of Ireland there were still some who might have studied his methods with profit.*

Bim Clinch, who engaged Murphy, was described as a 'huge red, bald, whiskered man of overweening ability and authority in his own department', but his weakness was that he had a fancy for Murphy's friend 'not far short of love'. Ticklepenny did not reciprocate this, as he had a fascination for Murphy. Bim's twin brother, Bom, was known as a sadist who encouraged his staff to take it out on the patients. Those patients who managed to avoid submission during the day where labelled as 'uncooperative' and were 'liable to get hell at night'.

Bim's introductory monologue to Murphy on the ward routines concerned what the new nurse must do:

> *He would be expected to make beds, carry trays, clean up regular messes, clean up casual messes, read thermometers, write charts, wash the bedridden, give medicine, hound down its effects, warm bedpans, cool fevers, boil gags, sterilize when in doubt, honour and obey the male sister, wait hand and foot on the doctor when he came, look pleasant.*
>
> *He would never lose sight of the fact that he was dealing with patients not responsible for what they did or said.*
>
> *He would never on any account allow himself to be affected by the abuse, no matter how foul and unmerited, that would be poured out upon him. The patients seeing so much of the nurses and so little of the doctor, it was natural that they should regard the former as their persecutors and the latter as their saviour.*
>
> *He would never on any account be rough with a patient. Restraint and*

co-ercion were sometimes unavoidable, but must always be exerted with the utmost tenderness. After all it was a mercyseat. If singlehanded he could not handle a patient without hurting him, let him call the other nurses to his assistance.

He would never lose sight of the fact that he was a creature without initiative. He had no competence to register facts on his own account. There were no facts in the MMM except those sanctioned by the doctor. Thus to take a simple example, when a patient died suddenly and flagrantly, as was sometimes bound to happen even in the MMM, let him assume nothing of the kind when sending for the doctor. No patient was dead till the doctor had seen him.

He would never on any account neglect to keep his mouth shut. The mercies of the Mercyseat were private and confidential.

Murphy identified strongly with the patients whom he esteemed, particularly Mr Endon, a passive, withdrawn schizophrenic who became the object of Murphy's affections. After a while, Murphy was assigned to look after Mr Endon, because of the patient's suicidal intent. There was a system of passing responsibility for the observation of the patient from nurse to nurse in the form of a 'tab':

A 'tab' was a patient 'on parchment' (or 'on caution'). A patient was put on parchment (or on caution) whenever there was occasion to suspect him of serious suicidal leanings. The occasion might be threats uttered by the patient or it might be simply the general tenor of his behaviour. Then a tab was issued in his name, specifying in all cases where a preference had been expressed [for] the form of suicide contemplated. Thus: 'Mr Higgins. The bellycut, or any other available means.' 'Mr O'Connor. Venom, or any other available means.' 'Any other available means' was a saving clause. The tab was then passed on to the male sister, who having endorsed it passed it on to one of his male nurses, who having endorsed it was from that time forward responsible for the natural death of the bastard in question.

At the Magdalen Mental Mercyseat, the chief duty of the nurse was to check on the patient every twenty minutes, because the hospital reckoned that only the most skilful patients could commit suicide in less time than that.

This daytime ritual was paralleled by the system of night checking. The nurse had to visit every patient at regular intervals of twenty minutes throughout the night. It took ten minutes to inspect the ward, then there was a pause and the nurse started again. This procedure was satisfactory unless someone had cut his throat or otherwise required attention, which disturbed the routine and for which there was no provision. The way the nurse carried out the round was as follows:

The nurse had merely to depress a switch before each door, flooding the cell with light of such ferocity that the eyes of the sleeping and waking opened and closed respectively, satisfy himself with a glance through the judas that the patient looked good for another twenty minutes, switch off the light, press the indicator and pass.

The indicator was most ingenious. The indicator recorded the visit, together with the hours, minutes and seconds at which it was paid, on a switchboard in Bom's apartment.

Some nurses did not bother to do all the checking, but just pressed the indicators. Murphy managed for a while until he got drawn into a game of chess with Mr Endon and gradually became drowsy. When he came to, he found Mr Endon missing. The patient had been drifting about the ward, pressing the light switches and the indicators. The switchboard recorded that one patient had been visited at regular intervals of ten minutes from 8 pm till shortly after 4 am, then for nearly an hour not at all, then six times in the course of one minute, then no more. This caused Bom some consternation next morning and baffled him for the rest of his life.

Murphy put Mr Endon to bed and, kneeling beside him, took his head in his hands to kiss him. At that moment, Murphy realised that Mr Endon was not aware of him. So in the dawn, Murphy left the ward, returning to the male nurses home, where, in a kind of accident, he was gassed in his room. With his death, the tragicomic story moved towards its end.

In this novel, Beckett has highlighted some themes in mental hospital life, for instance the dominance that a family of employees can establish, which was not unknown even at Bethlem. Beckett singled out for ridicule the stupefying routines that stifled initiative and the rationale for which was not always easily apparent. Some of the procedures described bear a marked resemblance to those used at Bethlem in the first half of the twentieth century (see the 1932 rules in Chapter 6). Beckett had little to say about the patients whom he characterised as melancholics, paranoids, hypomanics or schizoids, who sometimes played games but mostly just hung about. The topic that comes out most strongly in the novel is the often covert sexual agenda that influences what happens between staff and staff, and staff and patients. The central narrative is a cautionary tale about Murphy the nurse becoming overinvolved with Mr Endon the patient, and the dire consequences. This is a problem that generations of mental nurses have been warned about and with which they still frequently need help.

Antonia White's account of Bethlem has not the comedy of Beckett, being in the main a lightly fictionalised version of her own terrifying experiences. In her novel *Beyond the Glass* she wrote of events at Nazareth Royal Hospital, drawing on what happened to her in 1922–3 at Bethlem. She explicitly owned that her life was the raw material for her novels, with the caveat that writing autobiography and writing fiction were very different. While Clare Marc Wallace (see Chapter 2) wrote a straightforwardly autobiographical book about hospital life, Antonia White wrote this more highly structured novel, with themes such as seeing and

Antonia White (1899–1979) novelist and patient c1924

perceiving, glass and mirrors. Nevertheless her daughter said that this novel was the least fictional of all the fiction she wrote. Antonia White spent ten months in Bethlem.

In *Beyond the Glass*, Antonia White provided a patient's view of the Nazareth Royal Hospital and the course of a mental illness, ranging from the initial solitary time in a cell to convalescence and discharge. While not all the narrative was negative in tone, the hospital could sometimes seem rough and uncaring. She described the first phase of the illness of the book's heroine, Clara:

> *Months, perhaps years, later, she woke up in a small bare cell. The walls were whitewashed and dirty, and she was lying on a mattress on the floor, without*

146

sheets, with only rough, red-striped blankets over her. She was wearing a linen gown, like an old-fashioned nightshirt, and she was bitterly cold. In front of her was the blank yellow face of a heavy door without a handle of any kind. Going over to the door, she tried frantically to push it open. It was locked. She began to call out in panic and to beat on the door till her hands were red and swollen. She had forgotten her name. She did not know whether she was very young or very old.

The story continued to tell how sometimes she was taken out of her cell, covered with a brown serge dressing gown, to queue up to have her hair plaited or have a bath. Once she tried to run away and was dragged back by the nurses, along a passage decorated with wax flowers under cases and engravings of Queen Victoria and Balmoral. Worse still was the arrival of a procession of nurses and a young man with a funnel and a basin, to force-feed her. Sometimes she was in the padded cell, a small six-sided room, where the walls were padded with thick bulging panels of grey rubber. The door had a small red window, through which a face watched her and laughed. There were also occasions when Clara was mechanically restrained in a wooden manger clamped to the floor. She found she was wearing a curious white garment, very stiff and rough, which came down over her hands and feet, and she was kept in the manger by means of a stiff canvas apron over the top, like a piece of sail-cloth, fastened with studs and metal eyelets. One of her difficulties was understanding the nurses:

She was frightened of the nurses. Sometimes they were rough and called her 'naughty girl': sometimes they were friendly and said 'good girl'. But she could not discover what it was that she did that made them say 'naughty' or 'good' though she was very anxious they should not be angry.

The book charted Clara's long slow progress back to normality, although there seemed little connection between the treatment and the improvement. She gradually started to interact with the nurses, having varying feelings about individuals. Jones, with the red-hair and green eyes, she liked. Smith, with the fair hair and blue eyes, she feared. Jones gave her magazines. Smith rapped her over the knuckles with her hospital keys. Jones gave her a kiss. There was one Irish nurse called Kathleen who found a point of contact with her by sharing a recitation of the Litany of Our Lady. Yet, as in so many accounts of ward life, attention centred on the personality of the Sister, in this case Sister Ware, fat and middle-aged with a severe expression, a person whom Clara did not like but made great efforts to please. Sister Ware placed a strong emphasis on being good, tidy, obedient and appreciative. Clara rightly perceived that these were the social skills vital to her achieving discharge.

The other patients she met could be terrifying and tried to attack her when she was out in the asphalt exercise yard, but she was encouraged to have conversations with them, and this, in time, led to a realisation that the other patients were mad. In due course, her scope of activities broadened to include croquet in the garden and writing to her father, and then progressed to a period of leave and ultimately discharge home.

Antonia White pinpointed the monotony of hospital life, the repetitive activities of the day, the bird-like meaningless twitter of the inmates at mealtimes and the insensitive conversations of nurses and doctors. She stressed the problems that Clara had in relating to other patients who were also quite disturbed, but above all the problems Clara had of understanding the treatment, values and culture of the institution. Like many mentally disordered patients before and after her, Clara had to struggle to conform to hospital norms that required different behaviour from that which she had previously been used to in her ordinary social milieu. Yet somehow, in spite of it all, recovery was possible.

The author herself made a slow recovery from her encounter with what she called 'The Beast', after which she lived on with her vivid memories to write this, her last novel.

Literature continues to feed back into life and play its part in the evolution of clinical services. A few years after the publication of the novel, Juliette Wiltshire, a young English nurse with time on her hands in a one-horse American town in the middle of nowhere, read the experiences of Clara and her nurses. She was so stirred by them that they came to form part of the motivation which led her to take up psychiatric nursing. In time she became the Chief Nursing Officer of the Bethlem and Maudsley, where she promoted the use of therapeutic relationships and teamwork, striving vigorously for improved patient care. Improving care is the subject of the next chapter.

References and further reading

Beckett S (1938, reprinted 1973) *Murphy*. London: Pan Books.

Chitty S (1985) *Now to my Mother*. London: Weidenfeld and Nicolson.

Dekker T (1604) *The Honest Whore*. London: V.S. for John Hodgets.

Dekker T and Webster J (1607) *Northward Ho* (ed. Reverend Alexander Dyce 1857). London: G. Routledge and Sons.

Fletcher J (1621, reprinted 1840) *The Pilgrim*. London: Moxon.

James H (1915) Letter to HG Wells. In *The New Penguin Dictionary of Quotations*, eds Cohen JM and MJ, 1992. Harmondsworth: Penguin Books.

Middleton T (1622, reprinted 1653) *The Changeling*. London: H. Moseley.

Reed RR (1952) *Bedlam on the Jacobean Stage*. Cambridge, MA: Harvard University Press.

Shakespeare W (1889) *The Works of William Shakespeare*. London and New York: Frederik Warne and Co.

Smart C (1751) A Survey of Bedlam. *The Midwife, or The Old Woman's Magazine*, 1750–1: 215–262.

Ward E (1699, reprinted 1706) *The London Spy*, pt 111: p. 57. London: B. Bragg.

Webster J (1612–13) *The Duchess of Malfi* (ed. Reverend Alexander Dyce 1857). London: G. Routledge and Sons.

White A (1954) *Beyond the Glass*. London: Eyre and Spottiswoode.

*T*he 'Golden Bank' – Victorian Bethlem

*A*t no time is the ferment in the processes of historical change better illustrated at Bethlem than in the dreams and contradictions of the Victorian period. Attempts to progress and make 'improvements' in hospital life reached a climax in the golden age of Dr W. Charles Hood (1852–62), fell off somewhat in the troubled years of Dr George Savage (1878–88), but strengthened again in the calm glow of the Edwardian age.

In the first part of the nineteenth century, Bethlem was severely shaken by two Inquiries into ill-treatment of patients, which resulted in the exodus of many high-ranking members of staff. The first of these Inquiries, in 1815–16, had the effect of initiating a whole variety of alterations to improve Bethlem. Here are a range of examples. The mechanical restraint of patients by chains and manacles declined in usage, although it did not fully disappear until 1851. Wooden floors were substituted for stone paving. New workrooms and parlours were equipped, and also a library. The wards were given pianofortes and games, as well as materials for handicrafts. Gas was introduced to the hospital in 1850, and the use of knives and forks established in the following year. Professional education made its appearance with the taking in of medical pupils. Bethlem was proud that the experiences of their physicians could add much to professional studies. It was thought that the post mortem examinations of patients were highly interesting to the student. This followed in the wake of the French enthusiasm for 'opening up corpses', led by Bichat, who was influenced by Pinel (Foucault 1963).

A more energetic adoption of the 'moral treatment' of the age came to Bethlem after the Inquiry of 1852. Charles Hood, Medical Superintendent of Bethlem, wrote in 1855, 'The humane and enlightened

150

principles which now guide us in the moral and medical treatment of insanity may be said to have been recently discovered, and we may therefore look forward to many improvements being introduced.'

Although we may think Hood, in the wake of Pinel and Tuke, a little late in arriving on the scene of reform, the above statement was nevertheless an expression of the attitudes towards enlightenment and progress that were to characterise Bethlem well into the twentieth century. As late as 1947, Dr D. Whittaker said that the current regime at Bethlem was a direct continuation from Hood's day. Dr Hood was the first physician required to be resident, and, during his first few years, many advances were made.

Herbert Butterfield, the twentieth-century Cambridge Professor of History, inveighed strongly against the Whig interpretation of history. By this he meant 'to emphasise certain principles of progress in the past and to produce a story which is the ratification if not the glorification of the present'. In this approach, the Whig historian could look back at catastrophe and 'see only the acquired advantages and the happy readjustments'. Although historians may nowadays look critically on this approach, it was in just this vein that Charles Hood tackled his task of writing the Bethlem Annual Reports.

Dr Hood, when aged only twenty-eight, arrived at Bethlem in the wake of the major disaster of the Inquiry of 1852, in which the findings of the Commissioners in Lunacy were deeply critical of the hospital. As the first resident physician, he tackled his task of introducing change with alacrity, producing a programme of physical alterations and organisational improvements that would contribute to the 'moral and hygienic welfare of the patients'. He wanted Bethlem to become a place open to whatever the medical fraternity wished to know, in the interests of science and for the benefit of humanity. The image of Bethlem was being raised. The Annual Reports to the Governors of the 1850s reminded them that Bethlem was a noble Charity, one of the oldest charitable institutions for the reception of the insane in Europe, and that staff were carrying out the great designs of the munificent endowment. The Governors' interest in Bethlem's place in the world was not entirely altruistic, as they had to consider how they should be running Bethlem in an age that saw the multiplication of County and private Asylums, exposing the hospital to competition for patients. Bethlem was situated in central London, rather than the country, and sought to be aligned with the great hospitals of the capital, rather than the County asylums. There was a renewed emphasis on curing patients by enlightened moral medical treatment. The middle years of the century were a time of public confidence and prosperity in the UK, with London at the centre of a federation of colonies worldwide. Wages were increasing, and trade and industry developing in an expanding economy, as London became the financial capital of the world. This success was symbolised in the Great Exhibition of 1851. It was time for Bethlem to become an exemplar of success in treatment and care of patients, functioning to the highest standards of the day.

To some extent, the attempt to make reality match the vision was successful. The ten years Dr Hood spent at Bethlem saw an attempt to engage respectable, humane and intelligent attendants, the adoption of a comprehensive ward reporting system, additional rooms for the sick and infirm, improved occupations and recreations, and better domestic arrangements, especially the removal of the massive iron bars that still darkened some of the bedroom windows. Charles Dickens, writing as a journalist, praised the latter improvement in the journal *Household Words* when he wrote, 'The light has been let into Bethlem: it gives light to the flowers on the wards: it sets the birds singing in their aviaries: it brightens up the pictures on the walls.' Apart from the buildings for the criminal patients, Dickens found much to admire, especially in the thoughtful and energetic Medical Superintendent, and much to marvel at in the 'quickness and completeness of the change made by a reversal of old superstitions on the treatment of insanity'. Dickens summed it up by saying 'The star of Bethlem shines out at last.'

One of the chief improvements was dispensing with the outward signs of restraint, substituting the presence of attendants for the 'revolting instruments of mechanical coercion'. Perhaps we would have expected this to have been done after the scandal of James Norris, who was discovered in 1815 to have been chained to the wall with little possibility of movement for fourteen years. Some progress in releasing the patients was made by Mrs Forbes, the Matron, but restraining practices were persistent. From a daily average of over thirteen patients under restraint in 1840, the use of mechanical restraint began to decline, and eventually, in 1851, it ceased. Nevertheless, the pride and awed sense of achievement in the staff at making this change were palpable, even in the Annual Reports. The Governors were told that 'iron circlets, which had previously been used as manacles, [were] converted into stands for the irons employed in ironing the linen; and it strongly reminded us of the descriptions of the golden age, when spears were beat into pruning hooks, and battle-axes into plough-shares'. The religious imagery was not accidental. Charles Hood was known to invoke the blessings of God on the life of the hospital.

Other developments included patients being allowed to walk outside the hospital, under the care of nurses and attendants, eventually spending days at Kew Gardens, going on steam-boat trips or visiting the National Gallery, the Zoological Gardens or the Smithfield Cattle Show.

A kind of 'halo' seems to have developed around Charles Hood. In October 1859, George Sala, a journalist from *The Illustrated London News*,

A women's ward in 1860 at Bethlem, Southwark

and his friend went to Bethlem to be shown around by the kindly and benevolent Dr Hood. Although he kept them waiting, they were soon deep in admiration of the artistic ornamentation of the patients abode, which was a source of solace and delight, provided by the courtesy of Dr Hood, 'this kind and wise labourer in the field of mercy'. Dr Hood was portrayed as positively saintly. Mr Sala wrote 'he comes to soothe and heal; and we all know that he is on his Master's business, that he is doing that which shall be done to him on the great day of reckoning'. He was also said to be a good Samaritan, and Bethlem was fortunate to have a man of such education and refinement. Illustrations of the male and female galleries appeared in *The Illustrated London News* magazine the following year.

The bulk of the upgrading of the wards was aimed specifically at making the environment suitable for the impoverished middle classes. By 1857, Hood had established preferential admission policies for educated people in straitened circumstances. The Annual Reports betray considerable social snobbery in the tone of remarks about pauper patients. Charles Hood argued that the educated classes were often unable to pay for lengthy stays in private asylums, yet suffered the pain of being forced to associate with paupers of every grade. Curates and governesses, for instance, could

A men's ward in 1860 at Bethlem, Southwark

not afford private asylums, yet had the close proximity of parish paupers at the dining table and in the airing ground. Dr Conolly at Hanwell (quoted by Dr Hood in the Annual Report 1854) was also alert to the problem of the impecunious educated middle classes.

Hood sometimes seemed to equate social class differences with behavioural differences, which, in this hospital setting, may have been linked more to mental disturbance than class. He planned to overcome his difficulty at the hospital partially by segregation. He wrote, 'It is evident that the homicidal and suicidal, the maniacal and the melancholic, the noisy and the dirty, must be separated from those who are tranquil, cleanly, well disposed, and perhaps only partially insane, or under some harmless delusion.' The contrasts were, to his mind, highlighted by the male criminal patients, whom he divided into three distinct classes: firstly, those who were afflicted by insanity, but educated and refined, and secondly those who were little educated but harmless, inoffensive and controllable. These two classes were said to regard with horror a third class of men coming from prison, who were the most debased characters, whose associates had ever been of the worst description and who often only feigned insanity and used large amounts of blasphemous and indecent language.

The 'Golden Bank' was the prison slang name that the criminal patients gave to Bethlem. It must have seemed a heaven-sent refuge, compared with their alternative fate of being transported on convict ships to Australia. It was this 'worst class of moral offenders' who seem to have most enjoyed the comfortable quarters, generous diet and comparatively indolent life at Bethlem.

In the Hood era, Bethlem began to admit fewer of the parish paupers who had come to Bethlem free of charge for a year before being sent on to County Asylums. The problem of the criminal patients was only solved when they all departed for the newly built Broadmoor Hospital. Dr Hood was remembered long after his time for being the one who was instrumental in having the criminal patients removed.

Other improvements of the Hood age were the arrival of flower beds, grass plots, more books, bowls, skittles, open fire-places, cocoa-nut matting, carpeting and wooden bedsteads. Evening activities of dancing and singing were supplemented by weekly Bible classes, led by the Chaplain, for the good of the patients' souls. All these benefits were in addition to the ordinary moral treatment (humanity, kindness and occupation), and were backed up with a generous diet, wine, laxatives and morphia in grain doses at bedtime to procure sleep.

Much of this was accomplished during the first six years of Dr Hood's residence, leaving some room for consolidation. When the Commissioners in Lunacy came in 1861, they were able to praise the establishment:

> The Patients on the Curable and Incurable Lists at the time of our visit yesterday, were, without exception, tranquil and orderly, and their personal condition was satisfactory. The Dinner, which we saw comfortably served, was of excellent quality, and ample in quantity. The Wards and Rooms generally, and the Beds and Bedding throughout, were clean, and in their usual good order. The ordinary Galleries are enlivened by a great variety of subjects of interest, which the Patients appear fully to appreciate. We have much satisfaction that the Patients of both sexes expressed themselves in terms of gratitude for their kind treatment.

Charles Hood approached the end of his time at Bethlem feeling that he had received much friendship, goodwill and cheerful support from his colleagues, and he particularly praised the hearty and zealous aid of the attendants and nurses. In his last report, he grew lyrical: 'We have been mercifully spared from any accident or act of violence. No epidemic has raged, nor has suicide surprised or shocked us. A great amount of harmony has prevailed among the inmates, and each ward has independently represented much of the sociability of a large family.'

This all begins to sound like a golden age. Perhaps for Bethlem at that time the 'Golden Bank' was not too exaggerated an epithet. But was it real, and, if so, was it sustainable?

Only a year after Dr Hood left, the Medical Officers of the Asylums and Hospitals for the Insane were hotly debating the condition of Bethlem at their Annual Meeting in London. Some doctors said that Bethlem was a gloomy, dreary, desolate place in the Lambeth marshes, unsuitable for the treatment of recent insane cases, in spite of Dr Hood's efforts. Others said it had excellent accommodation. Yet others complained that the Bethlem medical officers lacked the energy to set up a medical school; further doctors suggested that Bethlem needed to be moved to the country. It seems that it was becoming difficult to sustain the myth of the 'Golden Bank' without the presence of the myth-maker.

Mechanical restraint had temporarily disappeared at Bethlem during the time of Charles Hood, to be replaced by increased use of seclusion in the padded room. Dr Autenreith, some time before 1828, had invented a strong room, padded all round, in which the most furious of lunatics might be let loose without doing harm to himself. The temporary isolation was thought to be tranquillising, although Hood had acknowledged that prolonged solitary confinement could become painful and intolerable to many patients. The padding of the rooms at Bethlem was rather rigid and unbending, but this was deemed necessary to prevent either the destruction of the material or it becoming saturated with urine. Even mechanical restraint had not gone for long, for, in 1871, we hear that a man had his hands confined nightly for a fortnight to prevent doing himself serious injury. More details are given in Chapter 8.

New methods of chemical restraint were entering the national scene too – bromides (1857), chloral (1869), paraldehyde (1882) and, later, barbiturates (1903) (Hunter 1956).

The Governors noted in 1869 that the less favourable cases confined in the basement needed to be brought more enlivening influences. The opportunities for neglect or abuse arising from segregating the more disturbed below stairs had been a factor leading to the Inquiry of 1852, and this appeared still to be practised. Had Dr Hood been more successful in editing out and concealing from the world those with bad behaviour than had been realised?

Then, in 1870, there were what was described as 'slanders' regarding bad treatment, and it was necessary for the Governors to consider having inquests on all who died. Some patients died from causes related to their mental state, as well as physical illness, and there were always some patients who killed themselves, ungrateful as that might seem in such a benign establishment. The problem of the suicidal patient was ongoing and of no little magnitude, when one considers that, in 1869 for instance, 140 out of the 246 inpatients were thought to have a suicidal tendency. The occasional suicide in hospital, while regrettable, seemed a customary hazard, but when the numbers rose to at least three a year as, in 1873,

1887 and 1898, the authorities began to feel uncomfortable. There was also some sensitivity about the suicide rate in 1879, when the comment was made that Bethlem received suicidal patients from 'private asylums who have been watched night and day, never being left for an instant. Such cases with us are not watched so much, and the irritation of suspicion is removed and many such cases get well'.

There were always patients who did not recover. Apart from those accepted for permanent residence and listed as 'incurables', there were many who reached the end of the allowed year of treatment and were discharged uncured. This was as high as 42.5% when Dr Hood arrived, and, although the percentage had declined 27% when he left, this may at least in part be caused by some selectivity in admissions, as it was known that the prognosis was better if the patient had not been ill for more than six months before coming into hospital. It is difficult to resist the impression that, although the environment and regimes had become more humane and the patients more refined, the underlying management problems with the mentally disturbed remained the same in spite of a modification of approach.

Improvements continued after Dr Hood's departure to be a Lord Chancellor's Visitor in Lunacy:

1863:   *Poetry reading and singing in church were started.*

1863:   *Some patients were taken on trips to the seaside.*

1863–4:   *The criminal patients departed for Broadmoor.*

1867:   *50 patients went to Brighton for 2–3 weeks.*
            A garden attendant was employed to look after the pleasure grounds.

1868:   *Some of the galleries were wall-papered.*

1869:   *It was recommended that when bathing the patients that the water be changed for each person.*
            Bed-time need not be as early as 8 o'clock for private patients.

1871:   *Blinds and valances were installed in the sleeping rooms.*

1873:   *There were many patients outings to Crystal Palace, and to the Convalescent Section's summer fete at Witley.*

1874:   *More hot water heating expanded the use of rooms.*
            A racquet court was installed.

1876:   *Changes in the system of night-watching meant that every patient was visited at least twice a night, in addition to the special list of patients who were visited every hour, or more frequently if necessary.*
            It was agreed that the double seated toilets should be changed to single seated.

1878:   *The patients' day was changed from 6am-8pm to 7am-9pm. (This stopped the attendants going out to the public house in the evenings.)*
            A regular supper for the patients was introduced, consisting of bread, cheese and beer for the men, and bread, butter and cocoa for the women.
            There was a weekly singing class, led by a junior doctor.
            Trough bedsteads were to be phased out, in favour of low bedsteads which were thought better than mattresses on the floor.

1880: *Facilities for tennis were made available.*
1881: *A gallery was carpeted. Cabinets and ornamental furniture were added.*
1883: *Electric lighting was introduced.*
1884: *A special attendant was engaged for the suicidal.*
1889: *A circulating library was provided*

Yet, in the same years as all these laudable changes were introduced, Bethlem had undergone a covert change of direction, which went back to dehumanising the patients and destroying the good effects of the Hood era. From 1868, the use of seclusion increased; 1871 saw the reintroduction of mechanical restraint after twenty years. The troubled years when Dr George Savage was Medical Superintendent (1878–88) encompassed embarassments with the press over forcible feeding, litigation from a former patient and loss of public confidence in the hospital. Dr Savage was not averse to the employment of many sorts of mechanical restraint, and their use escalated. Nor did he support the popular open-door policy, and in these matters he was out of step with the times. Bethlem was, he thought, unlike most asylums in that it did not have large numbers of chronic cases but an everchanging population of acute cases, some of whom were very violent. Bethlem's affairs became the subject of unwelcome correspondence in *The Times* newspaper, where not only the use of restraint, but also the death rate of 14.4% in 1887, was brought forward as an example of unsatisfactory management. The Commissioners in Lunacy had also expressed dissatisfaction. Dr Savage resigned at the height of the controversy about restraint. The woes of the Bethlem patients over the previous decade came to contribute to the emergence of the Lunacy Act of 1890, which made provision concerning the regulation of admissions, mechanical restraint, case books, reports to the Commissioners, patients' rights regarding letter writing and access to the judicial authority.

Such is the mixture of qualities in all men that we should beware of seeing in Dr Hood only virtue and progressiveness, and in Dr Savage only error and retrograde tendencies. Dr Savage was viewed more kindly at the time. He left Bethlem amidst many expressions of esteem, supported by gifts from both patients and attendants. People talked of his rectitude, gift of humour and genius as a teacher, and, when he died, people wrote of his kindness, geniality and sympathy which were said to have made him popular and beloved by all.

In spite of the enormous setbacks to fulfilling the dream of progress to the ideal Bethlem, more 'improvements' continued to be made:

1891: *A Hospital Band was started, with attendants and others as players. It soon became desirable for newly engaged staff to have musical ability.*
1892: *Spring handles were fitted to the doors of the patients rooms to avoid the use of keys at night.*

A women's ward in 1912 at Bethlem, Southwark

1896: *The Recreation Hall was opened.*
1897: *Dances and theatrical performances were given.*
1900: *A Staff Ball was held in the Recreation Hall.*
1902: *The Hospital Orchestra gave concerts.*
1903: *New lavatory basins, pedestal closets and stall urinals were installed.*
1906: *Matron organised musical evenings and card parties for the patients.*
1908: *A teacher of Handicrafts was engaged to give instruction in basket-weaving and mat-making.*
1911: *The Rev. O'Donoghue's History of the Hospital started appearing in the house magazine.*
1912: *Some nurses were trained in massage.*

Although 'improvements' have continued up to this day, the end of the high summer of the Edwardian age and the outbreak of World War I marked the resting point after a remarkable phase of development. Edward O'Donoghue, the Bethlem chaplain/historian, alleged to be of distressing geniality, pointed up the image in the chapter titles of his book – 'Cinderella and the Prince, 'Night', 'Towards the Dawn', and 'Transformation'. In fact, he used two metaphors for the development of

A men's ward in 1912 at Bethlem, Southwark

Bethlem: the pantomime and the butterfly. In the pantomime transformation scene, the imps of darkness disappear and 'landscapes of fairyland rise tier on tier at a sign from the fairy queen'. It appeared to O'Donoghue that the Victorian dream of progress to an ideal environment had reached its apogee in his own time of writing (1911–14), in what he described as an 'earthly paradise':

> *I shall be glad if you will now follow me into some of the wards on both sides of the house, for I want you, first of all, to get a general impression of our present environment. Here, on the eastern side devoted to the neater and more careful sex, you might be in the drawing room of a ladies' club in Piccadilly. There are flowers, pictures, and nick-nacks everywhere; really a lady visitor feels that she must sit down on one of the tempting sofas, and order afternoon tea from one of the pleasant, uniformed maids, while she turns over the pages of an illustrated paper, or a recent novel. If by way of contrast and complement, we cross over to the western wards, we shall find the smoking rooms, the card-tables, and the billiard rooms of a Pall Mall palace. These cavernous arm-chairs would transform Spartans into dreamy lotus-eaters. Perhaps if you looked closely at the windows, you would see how unmistakably they betray their origin and use, but your*

attention is diverted now by a natural history case, now by a gallery of engravings. You cannot, to be sure, call for a liqueur and coffee, but somebody can always find you a cigarette, or some forgotten grains of loose tobacco, for we are all devotees of the mystic weed . . . This comfort, refinement and luxury has transformed these long avenues only within the last twenty years: grub and chrysalis preceded the butterfly.

Yet even O'Donoghue (1914), in the last paragraph of his book, succumbed to a small nagging doubt that perhaps the achievement he had so rhapsodically described was not quite the whole picture: 'I am not even here to say that we have yet resumed the place to which our history and our resources entitle us, at the head of those who have the spirit of devotion and the material and moral equipment necessary for work so delicate as ours.' It would have to wait another decade or so for the Maudsley Hospital to start claiming the crown of excellence.

References and further reading

Annual Meeting of the Association of Medical Officers of Asylums and Hospitals for the Insane (1863) The Reform of Bethlehem Hospital. *Journal of Mental Science*, **IX**(45): 432–441.

Butterfield H (1931, reprinted 1965) *The Whig Interpretation of History*. New York: W.W. Norton.

Dickens C (1857) The Star of Bethlehem. *Household Words*, **16**(386): 145–150.

Foucault M (1963) (translated AM Sheridan Smith 1973) *The Birth of the Clinic*. London: Tavistock.

Hunter R (1956) The rise and fall of mental nursing. *Lancet*, **CCLXX** (6907): 98–99.

O'Donoghue EG (1914) *The Story of Bethlem Hospital from its Foundation in 1247*. London: T. Fisher Unwin.

Pinel P (1806) (translated by DD Davis) *A Treatise on Insanity*. Sheffield: Cadell and Davies.

Tuke S (1813) *Description of the Retreat: An Institution near York for Insane Persons of the Society of Friends*. London: Dawsons of Pall Mall, facsimile of 1813, 1964.

Nurses finding knowledge, a role and a voice – the twentieth century

In this chapter, we consider the emergence of nurses as a recognisable body, coming out of the melting pot of Victorian change, as they began to possess identifiable knowledge and skills as never before. The beginnings of nurse training at Bethlem at the end of the nineteenth century are discussed, and illustrations given of life on the wards in the 1920s, 30s and 40s. We continue with a look at the development of the nurses' role and function in the post-War years, summarising some of the work of the distinguished educator, Annie Altschul. The chapter concludes with showing how nurses became more articulate and aware through their experiences with trade unions.

Nurse training and the beginnings of change

Reading the Annual Reports of Bethlem for the 1880s, one becomes gradually aware of changing attitudes towards attendants with respect of the sort of people they should be and the knowledge and skills that were needed. In 1881, the Governors were pleased that young, strong men had been engaged, while only six years later they were looking for attendants who were 'more refined'. Lady probationers were taken on who wanted to learn about mental nursing and, at the same time, act as lady companions.

Dr George Savage, the Medical Superintendent, in 1885 clearly felt the need to develop the role of attendants and thought that, like junior doctors, they might be given training. He wrote, 'I hope in time to get the attendants to act more the part of caretakers and medical clerks than mere machines, to prevent accident, and I hope during the coming year to meet them from time to time, to give general instruction in the observations and care of the insane.' This seems to have remained largely a pious aspiration, for, three years later, it is observed that doctors were really too busy to find time for systematic teaching, but it was hoped that attendants had improved by constant supervision. A suspicion that there might have been some underlying resistance to a commitment to training is strengthened by noting the somewhat tetchy medical reaction in 1890 to the new Medico-Psychological Association instruction scheme. This scheme had been framed with the intention of more thorough instruction and a subsequent examination of attendants with a view to awarding a certificate. Dr L. Percy Smith objected that 'the practical work of taking care of the patients and treating them with the necessary combination of tact and firmness is not to be learnt from books or lectures, but needs years of life in intimate association with the insane, and moreover there are some attendants whom no amount of teaching will endow with the necessary qualities'.

With attitudes such as these, it is surprising that the attendants felt strong enough to proceed, but some studied for the examination, and, in 1893, two attendants and two nurses qualified for the nursing certificate of the Medico-Psychological Association. Although Bethlem had admitted doctors as pupils for many years before 1843, instruction for attendants lagged behind other places, such as Springfield (1844) and Crichton Royal (1851) in the UK, and Pennsylvania (1843) and Massachusetts (1882) in the USA. Medical discouragement may initially have affected some, for not all who attended the classes put themselves forward for the examination. Another disincentive was that candidates had to submit a certificate of morality and suitability before they were allowed to sit the examination. In 1895, William Slattery, the Head Attendant took a lead, sat the examination and qualified, after which the training scheme never looked back.

Training was based on Medico-Psychological Association's Handbook for the Instruction of Attendants on the Insane, which had five chapters covering: (1) the body, its general functions and disorders; (2) nursing the sick; (3) the mind and its disorders; (4) the care of the insane; and (5) the general duties of attendants. The latter two chapters contained valuable practical advice. Chapter 4 gave instructions on observation of patients, locked doors, refusal of food, occupations and amusements, precautions against suicide and homicide, and the use of force. Chapter 5 covered ward responsibilites, the Lunacy Acts, mechanical restraint, the supervision of patients, reporting on patients, food and medicines, the admission of patients and visiting. The course itself was based on anatomy, physiology and first aid in the first year, and physical and mental diseases and their management in the second year.

It was proudly announced in 1911 that 62% of men and 60% of women on the Bethlem staff had acquired the MPA certificate. It was regretted that so many of the young male attendants left upon qualifying to take up private nursing work. This was an early indication of Bethlem being seen as a place for training and experience rather than long-term employment, an attitude that has persisted throughout the twentieth century. From early on, the pass rate was very gratifying, some candidates qualifying with distinction.

Gradually, the training became an established feature of hospital life. By 1912/13, the doctors were routinely lecturing the nurses on anatomy and physiology in preparation for the Certificate. Training also included massage.

It was not until 1930 that the education and training of nurses was put on a more formal basis, with the appointment of the nurses' own Sister Tutor, Florence Agnes Parncutt, and the recognition of the Nurse Training School by the General Nursing Council for England and Wales. This national body had accepted holders of the MPA certificate for admission to its national supplementary Register of Nurses in 1920. The General Nursing Council also had had an examination of its own since 1922, in which Bethlem had not participated. Sister Parncutt was to combine with the medical staff to give nursing lectures and demonstrations. Her mission was to make the Nurse Training School a prominent feature of the academic side of the new hospital in Beckenham, and produce some of the most efficiently trained nurses in the country. Nurses from then onwards had a choice of whether to sit the examinations of the Royal Medico-Psychological Association or those of the General Nursing Council; these two schemes continued in tandem up to the amalgamation of the two hospitals.

The last years at Southwark and a new start at Beckenham

Bethlem nursing in the 1920s had continued in the traditional way up to the move to Beckenham. Vicki Hayward, arriving to become a student nurse, commented on the daily routine in 1928 when she started at the old hospital in Southwark:

> *Sister took me into the kitchen and pointed to masses of dirty dishes, and said 'wash up!'; then I came down to earth with a bump! These kitchen chores lasted three months and after this I was introduced to a ward. Each kitchen was equipped with a large cutlery box which was always kept locked, the contents of which were listed on the lid; the key at night was handed over to the Sister and after each meal all cutlery was counted; any omissions started a search of rooms*

and wards until all items were accounted for and we were not allowed off duty until they were!

Food was sent up from the kitchens and kept warm in the dining room oven which had a coal fire – the scene, with Sister carving an enormous joint, was rather like 'old England'. Entering the wards was rather like stepping into a hotel reception of the day - parquet floors, thick patterned carpet, antique furniture, palm plants, stuffed birds in glass cases and plenty of flowers, but this extended only to the partition. We had only one domestic per ward and the nurses were responsible for polishing the floors which were bumpered by hand. Willing and able patients helped a lot as there were no electrical aids in those days. We worked a 13 hour day – 7am to 8pm which included half an hour for lunch and 20 minutes for tea on the ward. The 20 minutes allowed for dressing in the morning enabled us to change aprons before lunch. We were allowed 1½ days off and alternate Sundays; with three weeks holiday a year.

Every afternoon we had to repair the patients' clothing and make chemises, by hand, for general use in the wards, with a calico material – I would compare this now to stitching mail-bags.

Although the range of patient activities improved after the move to Beckenham, the nurses in the 1930s still remained preoccupied with many humdrum routine tasks. Vicki Hayward qualified and became a Staff Nurse. She later described the admission procedures at the Beckenham site:

After being informed of a new patient's arrival, who was brought to the ward accompanied by the medical clerk and relatives we reassured our new charge and tried to get them acclimatised to the new surroundings, then the usual procedure was in force. Doctors were informed of the admittance and the patient was medically examined before our duty ended; this was a hard and fast rule. Bath then weight, height etc., were recorded and a list of all personal belongings taken. Eventually all clothes were marked. This was tedious as we had only tape and marking ink – when it came to handkerchiefs we resorted to writing their names on them. Next day medication was prescribed and the doctor interviewed the patient and instructed Sister to make an appointment with the relatives to see him so that they could give the patient's history.

Reports on all patients were written and sent to Matron's office by 5pm daily, and visiting days were Thursday–Saturday and Sunday 2–4pm.

Tyson Ward was for the very disturbed and it was a most difficult unit with lots of attacks on the nursing staff, glass smashing, refusing food which meant that eventually the patient had to be spoon fed and sometimes tube fed. Some were doubly incontinent, throwing anything which came to hand at the nurses and the walls - we were considered incompetent if we let the patients soil their beds. We had to train everyone and take them to the toilet.

This is a fragment of a lengthy account, the rest of which does little to suggest that there was any intellectual stimulation for nurses, and confirms that the main thrust of the work was to maintain the physically demanding round of keeping the patients clean, fed and exercised. There seemed little relationship between the content of much of the training and the skills that were needed.

The Maudsley and Mill Hill Emergency Hospital

The Maudsley Hospital had started in 1923 by requiring all Sisters and Staff Nurses to hold a certificate of general hospital training. Lectures and demonstrations were instituted, enabling staff to obtain the MPA certificate and registration by the General Nursing Council. Teaching was carried out in the early years by an Assistant Matron, but a Sister Tutor was later appointed. A good reputation for training was established quickly, the examination pass rate was high and there was no shortage of applicants for the courses. A feature was the rapid promotion of doubly trained nurses, who on completing the mental nursing course, soon achieved desirable posts elsewhere. After the first ten years, 27 of the 30 doubly trained nurses still in employment were holding posts as Matrons or Assistant Matrons. Some nurses came from abroad to take the training. An early problem was to find space for those who wanted to stay on after completing the mental nursing course.

With the coming of World War II, the Maudsley Hospital was dispersed, apart from some outpatient work, either to Sutton in Surrey, or to the Mill Hill Emergency Hospital in north London, which had been set up specially for War casualties. From August 1939, Mill Hill was opened with four hundred surgical beds and two hundred psychiatric beds, mainly for neurotic soldiers who had returned from the Front. At this hospital, nurse training continued apace and was said to be of paramount importance. Doctors lectured nurses on psychiatry, general medicine, hygiene, anatomy and physiology, and also dicussed individual cases and gave day-to-day instruction.

While information about the practice of nursing in the early days of the Maudsley is hard to come by, there is fortunately an anonymous document of 1943 that outlines the opportunities for involving nurses in active treatment at Mill Hill. A new spirit was in the air as intelligent women elected to use nursing to carry out their war service obligations. They nursed the soldiers who had become mentally disturbed during the fighting. The procedures used at Mill Hill were agreed and put into practice through cooperation between the senior nursing and medical staff. An anonymous document (in the Bethlem Archives) on *Nursing and Treatment* described the orientation of a new nurse over a week, after which the nurse became a Junior Nurse on a ward:

166

She is shown how to make observations and the pertinence of these observations is controlled by the discussion of her notes with the Doctor. The notes concentrate on personality assessment – a description of a patient's general activities, appearance, talk, mood, intelligence, etc., the data are obtained by seeing and listening, not by prying or asking . . .

The nurse's difficulties in answering patients' questions or in dealing with the patients' attitudes are taken up, and standard replies or action indicated. These replies are put on record and kept in the ward so that a body of experience is available to the nurse in future. Ideally the doctor is always available to the nurse in difficulty, but where this is impossible the senior sister and the recorded answers are always there. A patient, for example, may come to a nurse and say – 'Nurse, if there is nothing wrong with my heart, why is it pumping so hard?' Because this question has occurred frequently before, the nurse is in the position to deal with it reasonably and consistently, and by so doing she is considerably augmenting the doctor's therapeutic efforts.

After one year the nurse becomes a senior nurse. The formal lectures continue for examination purposes, but in the hospital unit the nurse gives current reports on a small ward for which she is responsible. These reports take the group point of view – how one man is fitting in, – how disruptive is another man's attitude – what is the state of morale. Furthermore, at the direction of the doctor, the nurse will undertake a special study of one or two patients. The study is within the limits of ordinary patient/nurse contacts in the ward. Patients not infrequently open up more to a nurse than to anyone, and this gives valuable data for the doctor's assessment.

But the nurse's role is more than the obtaining of information. By her attitude she can direct a patient's attention to his special obligations. Not infrequently patients are vague in their appreciation of social values – they have no idea why they are fighting, or the national issues or group issues. Their concern is too frequently for themselves, or their own interest, or that of the family and these concerns they conceal from themselves by a curtain of symptoms. The nurse, guided by the doctor, can force the issue and make the man understand the simple psychological mechanisms which foster a disability not founded on physical disease.

Apart from observation and simple treatment, nurses are trained in special investigations and therapy. They carry out many of the routine psychometric tests, help as technicians in the ward laboratories, and are instructors in occupational therapy. Furthermore, they are carefully trained in the physical methods of psychiatric treatment and the care of patients undergoing continuous narcosis or electric shock therapy.

The document then turns to an account of group therapy. The interest of the document as a whole lies in the acknowledgement of the value of the nurse's observations and patient assessment. The pattern of writing nurses' notes on such matters and sharing them with the doctors was to become a standard feature of Maudsley procedure, and served not only as communication but also as a training function. Also of interest is the development of interaction strategies, the awareness of group dynamics, the concern of a nurse for particular patients and the use of specialised skills. Slightly alarming is the assumption that the ward staff will combine to make the patient face up to his social obligations, in this case to return to the War, to fight and possibly to die for his country, and not to indulge in selfish concerns for his family.

After World War II, there were still Charge Nurses at Bethlem who worked in a custodial way as caretakers, feeling that when they had seen that the ward morning routines had been carried, they could retreat to their offices and take their ease. Some of these were men with army service who were used to serving in hierarchical situations but took a pride in doing their part of the work well. Yet beside them, and not apparently in conflict, there came into being in the 1950s a new kind of nurse, who was questioning and looking for new roles that were centred on active participation in psychiatric treatment. The Mill Hill nurses had returned to the Maudsley Hospital, where they initially resumed old-fashioned routines, yet a new spirit was abroad, and that was to be fostered by developments in nurse education.

There was initially a dearth of female staff, and more especially there was no Sister Tutor in post. Fortunately, a nurse returned to the hospital with a Sister Tutor's Diploma, and recruitment of student nurses with pay above the usual Rushcliffe scale commenced.

A healthy feature of that period was an openness to the wider world, with students coming from Denmark and other European countries, and also from what were then the British colonies. There were visitors, too, from the Royal College of Nursing, the Mental Hospital Matrons Association and the International Congress of Nurses.

Nurses finding a new role – the post World War II years

The union of the two prestigious hospitals (in 1948), like many arranged marriages, was expected to be to the advantage of both parties. Bethlem was cast as the comely bride bringing her dowry, while Maudsley was the intelligent, eligible groom. The first House Governor of the Joint Hospitals, K.J. Johnson (1953), wrote, 'Into the marriage of the two hospitals Bethlem has brought the fine buildings at Monks Orchard [Beckenham] and the accumulated wealth of centuries, and Maudsley the revivifying influence of a virile teaching hospital of international reputation. The planners have done their work well. They have given us the freedom of a teaching hospital and the money to make the most of it.' In this case, somewhat unusually, the bride proposed the match. Bethlem was a worthy hospital at this period, offering care of a high standard in a spacious country estate, but the intellectual ferment was at the Maudsley, which, in just over twenty years, had established itself on the international scene and under the guidance of Dr Edward Mapother, attracted some of the brightest medical minds.

In spite of the long World War II dispersal of the hospital and the death of Dr Mapother, the Maudsley teams reassembled after the war, led by Professor Aubrey Lewis. The money that Bethlem would bring to the partnership was expected to further the development of research into new treatments and so assist the advance of psychiatry. The danger for Bethlem was that it would lose something of its distinctive identity and traditions, becoming a country appendage to the Maudsley. To some extent, this became true, because of the continuing renown of the Maudsley. This also received impetus from the decision in the early 1990s to let the two hospitals and the Institute of Psychiatry be known collectively as 'The Maudsley'. However, the organisation became officially known in 1994 as The Bethlem and Maudsley NHS Trust. Whatever else happened, the marriage of the two hospitals facilitated the development of a unique range of specialist psychiatric units such as neither hospital was likely to have been able to produce on its own.

The amalgamation was planned by a Joint Transitional Committee, which concerned itself with matters of structure. There was no nurse on this planning team. The Committee decided to have one Matron or Lady Superintendent of Nursing for the whole establishment, and the post was to be filled by someone who would take a leading part in the world of mental nursing.

The new age was inaugurated on July 5, 1948. The two Nurse Training Schools united in the course of the first year, and the Matron of Bethlem was appointed overall Superintendent of Nursing.

During the next decade, nursing developments appear to have centred around the ideas and person of Miss Annie Altschul, later to be Professor of Nursing Studies at Edinburgh University. She is remembered as a some-what small Viennese lady, prone to wearing flowered dresses instead of official uniform, who had penetrating eyes and a questioning manner of speaking that commanded attention. Although only qualifying as a mental nurse in 1946, she speedily made her mark in nurse education, becoming a tutor in 1948, graduating in psychology and progressing to Senior Tutor and Principal Tutor at the Maudsley and Bethlem School of Nursing.

Researchers look at the function of nurses

Curiosity about what nurses did and what motivated them led to two research studies at the Maudsley in the early 1950s. This was a new development, using scientific enquiry for anything centred on nursing. The smaller study into nurses' attitudes and motivation was carried out by Dr Erwin Stengel (1955), later Professor at Sheffield University. He interviewed 67 Maudsley nurses with the aim of finding out why nurses took up mental nursing and remained in it, given its apparent unpopularity compared with general nursing. Nurses said they preferred mental nursing because it was more patient centred, gave more latitude in arranging one's work and had better teamwork than did general nursing. Set against that were the crowding of patients, the custodial functions, aggressive patients, periods of inactivity and mental strain. Dr Stengel, in his conclusions, presciently drew attention to the fact that the nurse–patient relationship, together with the doctor–patient relationship, would come to take its place among curative factors. More significantly still, he thrust aside the traditional view that what was most important about a nurse was his or her personal qualities and virtues. 'Even today the mental nurse, to make a contribution, has to have knowledge and skill. Humanity and devotion are not enough.'

The other study by a psychologist, Oppenheim, was carried out in 1952, although not published until later (Oppenheim and Eeman 1955). It was one of the very first job analyses carried out on nursing in this country, using work-study techniques. Oppenheim divided nurses work into five functions that provided the spectrum of nursing activities, which can be summarized as follows:

1. *Care of patients.* Talking to patients, helping patients, working with a special patient, restraining patients, working in the clinic preparing trays and trollies, administering medicines and injections, taking temperature, pulse and blood pressure, keeping charts and rosters, preparing and helping with ECT and insulin treatment.
2. *Supervision of patients.* Bathing patients, assembling patients and being with patients at occupational therapy, physical training, dances and entertainments; watching patients.
3. *Household duties.* Scrubbing, cleaning, polishing, dusting, tidying, attending to flowers, making beds, preparing meals, setting tables, serving meals, clearing tables, washing up and drying cutlery and crockery, counting cutlery, cleaning wastebins, caring for everything connected with linen and laundry.
4. *Duty Room.* Writing notes and reports.
5. *Reception and management.* Receiving doctors, matron, psychologist, other staff and visitors, receiving new admissions, checking and marking their clothes, running errands off the ward, answering the telephone, organising the work of other nurses, talking with Sister and others.

Oppenheim found that the prime determinant of a nurse's duties was her rank; the Sisters spent up to 34% of their time on office work and had low contact with patients, while the student nurse might spend up to 45% of time on domestic duties not directly with patients. Perhaps most significant were Oppenheim's comments on nurses' attitudes:

> *a similar substantial increase of 40% in Care of Patients could be accomplished on numerous occasions in all wards if nurses realised that talking to patients maybe part of treatment. The evidence indicates that a considerable increase in nurse–patient contacts could be accomplished by a change of attitude, without any extra staff.*

Oppenheim was convinced of the need for better contact between nurses and patients, and that nurses must overcome their fears that talking to patients might be problematic or a waste of time. Apart from an unelaborated reference to psychotherapy, he did not make it clear what he thought the rationale and framework for these discussions with patients might be. Oppenheim acknowledged that the value of nurses' contacts with patients had not been assessed.

Having collected considerable data on the duties of nurses, Oppenheim came back to his basic problem – namely, what the role and function of a mental nurse should be. He cautioned that without defining the function of the mental nurse, reforms would lack purpose and direction.

Around this time, there were other studies by the Manchester Hospital Board (1956) and the Liverpool Regional Hospital Board (1954), which also found mental nursing difficult to define and questioned the relationship to patient care of some of the tasks being carried out (Nolan 1993).

Developments from 1957 in training and acquiring psychosocial skills

A step forward in 1957 was the introduction of a new General Nursing Council syllabus for mental nurse training. Key aspects were, firstly, the concept of the mental hospital as a therapeutic community, with the nurse responsible for total nursing care having a place in the psychiatric team and, secondly, that learning needed to be directly related to the practical situation that the nurse was experiencing. The content of the syllabus had been enriched by sections on sociological aspects of behaviour, social structures and much more on the principles and practice of psychiatric nursing, as seen in relation to psychiatric treatment.

In the same year, Annie Altschul published a book entitled *Psychiatric Nursing*, in which she gave her description of what the nursing care of the mental patient should be. This was a brave statement of position, in an age when there was so little consensus of opinion as to what mental nurses should do, and few nurses who were prepared to define their proper function. There was evidently some medical apprehension about nurses defining or perhaps extending their role. In the foreword to Annie Altschul's book, there was a warning from a Maudsley psychiatrist about nurses falling into error. Dr D.L. Davies' view was that:

> *The relationship between doctor and patient is still, despite the success of certain physical methods of treatment, the true basis of therapy in psychiatry. Accepting this, nurses may well be tempted, in their endeavours to help the patient, either to usurp the role of doctor, or to become mere attendants.*

The psychiatrist admitted that, if nurses understood clearly what mental nursing consisted of, they would be less likely to fall into error. Annie Altschul made two useful points in her preface to the book, which were designed to assist a nurse to think more clearly about his or her own role within the psychiatric team. Firstly, although each hospital, each doctor and each group of patients make different demands on the nurse, what is expected of the nurse is determined by her own interpretation of her function; this puts the responsibility firmly with the nurse herself. Secondly, although a nurse's greatest asset is knowing people and knowing about people, knowledge should be increased by reading widely, avidly and critically to foster a broader and deeper understanding of human nature. Today, this might appear too obvious to say, but, at that time, there had been little emphasis on the nurse as a reader, so all-consuming were the practical aspects of her function. It was significant progress from the time 150 years before when the carers could not even sign their own names.

Annie Altschul travelled the world, going to America, Canada, Australia, Austria and Holland, picking up insights to enliven the debates about psychiatric nursing at the Maudsley and elsewhere. Some of the themes of the late 1950s sound very similar to those of today. In America, she found that nurses spent very little time looking after the mentally ill. What 'nursing therapy' was carried out there was confined to a few hours a week of 'one-to-one relationships'. People other than nurses were trained to look after patients. In Holland, she found that there were problems of roles within the psychiatric teams. Because more treatment was taking place in the community, mental nurses had moved out of hospital, taking over parts of social work roles and perhaps abdicating their original roles. There was confusion, too, about professional responsibility – how far could nurses be held responsible for what eventually became of the patient, and how far should they act independently of doctors. There were misgivings about the World Health Organization (WHO) strategy for nurse education – perhaps psychiatric nursing was, after all, fundamentally different from general nursing and required a prolonged but separate training.

*Miss Annie Altschul, Head of the School of Nursing,
photo from the 1950s*

One of the most memorable innovations in training made by Annie Altschul, helped by others, was the introduction of 'working in groups'. Some ward sisters, such as M. Charles and D. Coutts, had already in 1955 adopted the practice of daily nurses' group discussions, at which criticism of each other's work and ventilation of feelings were encouraged (Ackner 1955). By 1959, student nurses were already having some teaching sessions, sitting in a circle and discussing a topic, as a replacement for some of the traditional didactic teaching where the teacher stood at the front of the class and gave out information, although that sort of teaching also took place. This new method was adopted at least in part to satisfy the suggestions of the WHO Committee on Psychiatric Nurse Training that there should be more concentration on nurses acquiring psychosocial skills. Annie Altschul, with Dr Brian Ackner, engineered the setting up of a group of ward sisters to discuss psychosocial aspects of nursing, although not without resistance from some of the older nurses, who saw this as seditious. Nevertheless, the use of group methods of learning, especially of social psychology through experience, became the distinctive approach of the Maudsley School of Nursing, as pioneered by Annie Altschul (1964) and her successor, Reg Everest.

Publications continued to stream from Annie Altschul, an example being *Aids to Psychology for Nurses* (1962), a book that covered not only developmental psychology, but also psychological problems related to illness and the social psychology of a hospital ward. Another unusual paper was 'Trends in psychiatric nursing', her chapter in Freeman and Farndale's *Trends in Mental Health Services* (1963), which compared nursing on both sides of the Atlantic. While the USA was making every effort to have better all-round nurses, the UK had developed successful specialisation, which would, in turn, allow for specialisation within psychiatric nursing itself. Annie Altschul also commented, against the background of a general trend to community care, on the potential of mental nurses for work in the fields of preventive medicine and health education.

On leaving the Maudsley in 1964, she tried to sum up her thoughts on nursing by outlining the main principles of care:

> *1. Nurses provide the patient, admitted to hospital, with a feeling of safety and security.*
> *2. No one is sick in every aspect of living. Nurses help the patient to retain every bit of health he still has – not only his physical health, but any ability he still has to keep or make friends, to work, to retain responsibility and self respect.*
> *3. Most patients who are mentally ill suffer to some extent in the ability to live with others. Ward life must afford the opportunity to practise living with other people.*
> *4. Many patients need specific nursing care, either specific to the illness, or specific to the patient's age and personality. Some of the specific nursing care is physical, but much of it is specific in the relationship the nurse forms with the patient.*

She went on to say that, in training, the nurse must learn to provide a therapeutic atmosphere, to give the patient the opportunity to retain a maximal degree of self-determination and responsibility, to give the patient a say in planning his own day, and to maintain a focus on specific nursing care, especially nurse–patient relationships and interactions. There was more on these lines, including the need for clinical supervision of students and the development of leadership skills – all of which, with a little rephrasing into current terminology, sound like much that is still of concern to the modern nurse today.

Nurses find a voice through the Trade Unions

At the same time as the above educational activities were taking place, nurses were slowly learning to become articulate in other spheres. It had become established that talking with the patient was a central part of the nurse's role, but what about talking to doctors and managers? Whatever dialogue nurses achieved with doctors, there is little evidence that nurses gained much power to influence events, even in matters that directly concerned them. Doctors, controlling the voting in the Nursing Committee, still made major nursing policy decisions right up to the early 1970s. There is also scant evidence of negotiation with administrators over conditions of employment. Nurses eventually began to feel the need to speak out about their situation and influence policy making in their particular workplace and beyond. This the ward nurses did at first through the trade unions.

Trade union activity was not much in evidence in the first half of the twentieth century in either hospital, not even at the time of asylum strikes and disputes from 1918 to 1922. Reasons for this remain obscure but could be related to the dominance of the medical establishment over a group of low-status, inarticulate nurses. In the early years of the Maudsley, the National Asylum-Workers Union had written protesting about the levels of pay, but there had been virtually no organised union activity within the hospitals. In the immediate post-World War II period, Bethlem nurses, mainly the men, felt strong enough to form a trade union branch, in this case a branch of the Confederation of Health Service Employees (COHSE). Perhaps it was an increased awareness of the world outside Bethlem, or a premonition of major changes to come, that made nurses band together.

The first serious battle with management was to come in 1948 over arrangements for the amalgamation of the two hospitals. The male Charge Nurses felt that their chances of promotion, and therefore improved pay, were being threatened by the new arrangements. They wrote to the Board of Governors:

> *Dear Madam [Chairman]*   *28.10.1948*
>
> *We accept the ruling of the Board, that in future promotion will be by merit giving opportunity to singly and doubly qualified members of staff. There is however, still great dissatisfaction amongst the male nursing staff of this hospital. This is due to the continuous rumours circulating at the hospital regarding the prospects for promotion and the position of the Male Nursing staff, after the reorganisation of the hospital is carried out. The rumours to which we refer are:*
>
> *a) that in future, Nursing Sisters may be in charge of Male Wards.*
> *b) the possibility of the Female Staff taking over all the Male Wards except 2 wards.*
>
> *If either of these rumours are true, then the prospects of promotion for Male Staff is very remote ... In view of these facts, if the rumours are true, and we cannot gain promotion, we shall have to ask the Confederation of Health Service*

Employees, and the London Trades Union Congress to lay our case before the Minister of Health. If he cannot do anything in this matter, we shall ask him to provide facilities at other hospitals for staff who cannot gain promotion here . . .

Yours sincerely

signed by 18 Charge Nurses

This letter was a notable development for Bethlem nurses, in that it was the first time that they had dared to challenge management, especially as it included a threat to broaden the dispute and ultimately take their labour elsewhere. The male nurses were not successful in their challenge, being talked out of their determination by officers of the Board and suffering from their lack of will to take the matter further. In due course, female staff started to be placed in charge of male wards when they had earned it on the basis of merit. This trade union action, however, marked some progress, in that a group of nurses spoke collectively with a common view about their terms of employment.

The development of political activism

Pay remained the most significant topic to provoke staff unrest, although nurses were often confused about what could be done at local level and what could only be changed by national pay bargaining. This was evident in the troubles of the early 1970s. It was a time when a Labour government was in power and the trade unions in England were powerful. The seeds of discontent were sown at the time of the Royal College of Nursing's 'Raise the Roof' campaign to improve nurses' salaries. COHSE was the militant health service trade union at Bethlem with most nurse members, among whom junior staff were very prominent in planning what they would say to management and the wider community. Marches were the preferred form of action. There was much demonstrating but no actual strike, so pay was not withheld. Feelings ran very high on one occasion, and Maudsley nurses marched off with banners to the headquarters of the Department of Health in south London, but many came back disappointed, feeling that little had been achieved. Management tended to see this new behaviour – marching the streets shouting slogans – as 'unprofessional', but later on management attitudes changed and became more accepting. There was, nevertheless, the expectation of an honourable relationship between management and unions, which included the concept of 'fairness' in negotiation and an acknowledgement that the patients' interest was paramount. This agitation about pay was eventually settled by the Halsbury report of 1974.

The trade union agitation of the 1980s came at the time of Thatcherite ideas in British politics, which were driven by consideration for the individual as opposed to the needs of society. The action at the Bethlem and Maudsley was organised by a group of nurses who were radical, left-wing activists and opposed government thinking. This time because the nurses had the open backing of some junior doctors, they were empowered to become more vocal and politically active. This was a break from the consultant-dominated behaviour of the past. In May 1982, the NHS entered a period of industrial dispute, which lasted for the rest of that year. It was again, on the surface, a dispute about pay. Royal College of Nursing members refused to take an active part in the withdrawal of labour, but that still left nurses in COHSE and other unions, such as NUPE, who were willing to take strike action. There were planned periods of withdrawal of labour, sometimes for two hours and sometimes for twenty-four hours, but there were always sufficient staff left on the wards to ensure basic cover. There were also some limitations on the normal admissions policies of the hospitals. Non-urgent cases were deferred, and transfers from other institutions were not regarded as urgent. This was significant in that it provoked a wider debate about responsibilities for admissions. Although the decision to admit patients rested legally with the doctor, other members of the multidisciplinary team wanted to have a say in who came in to the wards. Nurses felt an urgent desire to have their views taken into consideration. When only the more disturbed and difficult patients were admitted, it was chiefly the nurses who had to face threats and violence on a daily basis. Had they not some right to say how many highly dependent patients could be managed at any particular time?

This national pay dispute gave rise to an internal dialogue in which nurses had an unprecedented say. The next large dispute of 1986 was set in an even broader political context in which issues such as the funding and management of the NHS mingled with local concerns. In view of a 1% revenue cutback, Eric Byers, the General Manager, announced in March 1986 the need to save £800 000 over two years, and an across-the-board selection of ward closures and restrictions of service was proposed. Some downgrading of charge nurses was also mooted. A Bethlem and Maudsley Action Committee was speedily formed, largely comprising nurses and junior doctors fighting, not only for their jobs, but also for the preservation of patient services and the maintenance of standards of care. This was a time when nurses became more vocal in their role as, what would later be called, 'patient's advocate'. Such was the strength of feeling that the debate polarised between managers, who said the hospital was overspent, which was felt to imply waste and bad management by the clinical teams, and the Action Committee, who said

Staff demonstrating outside Maudsley Hospital, 1986.
Photo: A Baxter

that the hospital was underfunded. By comparison with international standards, health services in the UK were underfunded. In 1982, the USA was spending 10.6% of the gross domestic product on health, and the UK only 5.9% (Teeling Smith 1986).

The dispute was also about the introduction of general management principles, by which it was feared that clinical considerations would be set aside in favour of methods that were cost effective, i.e. quick and cheap. National television news and radio became interested in the Maudsley dispute, and letters appeared in the daily press. The media had been deliberately drawn into the dispute by the junior medical staff.

On the one hand, the dispute was bitter and personal, with defamatory notices about individuals being placed around the hospital, and, on the other hand, it caused some useful questioning of traditional roles. For nurses, there were conflicts of loyalty, between what were their obligations – to patients, to their peer group, to the profession, to the unions, to employers, to the NHS and political affiliation. It is difficult to resist the conclusion that nurses suffered some erosion of belief in the NHS as a sustainable ideal. The Action Committee succeeded in diverting the major cuts away from the psychiatric services that it held most valuable. This was at the cost of a campaign that was thought to have damaged relationships of trust and opened up divergences of priorities between managers and clinical staff.

Most noteworthy for nurses was that they grew into an awareness of wider political issues and the possibilities and limitations of action. In the meantime nurses had also been developing their confidence, knowledge and skills in clinical areas. This will be discussed in Chapter 13.

References and further reading

Ackner B (1955) Training the psychiatric nurse on the ward. *Lancet*: **CCLXIX** (6890) 606–608.

Altschul A (1957) *Psychiatric Nursing*. London: Baillière, Tindall and Cassell.

Altschul A (1962) *Aids to Psychology for Nurses*. London: Baillière, Tindall and Cassell.

Altschul A (1963) Trends in psychiatric nursing. In H Freeman and J Farndale (eds) *Trends in Mental Health Services*. Oxford: Pergamon Press.

Altschul A (1964) Group dynamics and nursing care. *International Journal of Nursing Studies*, **1**: 151–158.

Altschul A (1964) Reflections on Nursing. *Bethlem and Maudsley Hospital Gazette*, September: 85–90.

Hayward V (1980) Nursing in the 20s. *Inter Nos* January: 3–5.

Nolan P (1993) *A History of Mental Health Nursing*. London: Chapman & Hall.

Oppenheim AN and Eeman B (1955) *The Function and Training of Mental Nurses.* London: Chapman & Hall.

Stengel E (1955) Psychiatry from the nursing point of view. *Nursing Mirror* **100** (2595–6): 1097–8, and **100** (2596): 1169.

Teeling Smith G (1986) *Health the Politician's Dilemma.* London: Office of Health Economics.

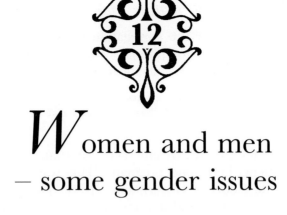

Women and men
– some gender issues

Consideration will be given here to a wide sweep of gender issues as they arose at the Bethlem and Maudsley hospitals, in the light of a felt need for reappraisal in the latter part of the twentieth century. There can scarcely be another area where so many unquestioning assumptions have been made as about the way women and men should be treated. This was highly apparent in the oral history interviews covering the 1930s to 70s. Whenever the interviewer asked questions related to a person's treatment as a woman, or a man, the answer was almost always an assertion that that was the way things were and that the interviewee never thought about it. Questions of gender-related cultural issues, for many people not easily separated from sexual and biological issues, seem to have been subject to taboos to which the usual reaction was silence. At the Bethlem and Maudsley, there is little evidence of open discussion of gender-related subjects among the carers until the late 1970s, coming in the wake of the women's liberation movement.

Topics touched on in this chapter range from the beginnings of planned segregation of women and men, through to the rising awareness, in the late twentieth century, of women's needs. On the way, we note the balance of the sexes among inpatients and their accommodation, sexual harassment, parity and disparity of male and female staff, differences in male and female patients' pastimes and occupations, and the integration on the wards of patients and staff of both sexes. These matters have been hardly considered at all by previous Bethlem historians, and can only be sketched in outline in this chapter. Further research could be worthwhile.

Segregation of female and male patients

The first hint of a need for the segregation of the sexes is read in the Court of Governors minutes for June 12, 1657. On Sundays and public holidays, the Governors would henceforth allow:

> no man to walk about, and the men and women to be kept asunder, and the Governors to consider how best the men and women may be lodged and kept asunder.

A possible reason for this which emerged years later was the desire to avoid female patients becoming pregnant. This was highlighted in the deliberations of the Court of Governors of 1681. The minute of March 30 showed the exasperation and disapproval of the Court at the laxity of the staff:

> At this Court came Joseph Matthewes the Porter of the hospitall of Bethlem and was told that this Court is very sensible of the great miscarriages lately committed in the hospitall of Bethlem by one of the beadles or basketmen in the said hospitall . . . And that his wife [the Matron] was much to blame for suffering the beadles to goe among the Lunatike women when shee was not present herselfe with them. And that shee did not make a sooner discovery of one of the said Lunatike women that is with child and is within three monthes of her tyme.

The next month, the Court considered ways and means to prevent any further similar occurrences, decreeing that two locks should be put on the doors of the cells where the women were lodged:

> And that shee [the Matron] cause all the said Cells to be locked up every night and every Sunday. And that shee do not suffer any of the said Cells to be opened any morning till such tyme that shee or some of the maidservants are there present. And that none of the manservants be permitted to have a key to any of the Cells wherein any of the Lunatike women who by reason of their great distraction lie naked. And that none except the matron or maidservant shall have recourse to them.

The Governors' concerns were plainly justified for in August of the same year, two brothers of a patient, Mary Loveland, petitioned for maintenance of a newly born child. The Governors felt obliged to pay for the wet nursing and clothing of the child.

Five years later, the hospital moved to Moorfields, where the patients were clearly segregated, and we read no more of menservants impregnating patients. The male and female patients evidently still wished to mingle, for the Governors in 1751 found it necessary to appoint a person to 'attend at the Iron-gates of the Womens Ward to prevent the Women from coming out and the Men from going into that Ward'. The basketmen continued to attend to the needs of patients on the Women's Side. For instance, as laid down in 1765, after lighting the fires in the morning, the basketmen carried the female patients to the Stove Room, turning out the 'low spirited and such as are mopish' (depressed), removing the old straw bedding, providing fresh straw, removing patients that were dirty from one cell to another and washing their dirty cells.

There was no legal requirement to separate insane men from insane women, and, even when an Act of 1784 required the separation of male and female prisoners in English gaols, no legal provision was made for the insane in this matter. The possibility of sexual misbehaviour by male staff has remained a potential danger in the management of mental patients, and there were attempts to avoid this problem in the nineteenth century by dividing the Bethlem staff, so that only female staff cared for female patients.

These management strategies became codified in the Lunacy Acts Amendment Act 1889 and the Lunacy Act 1890. The 1890 Act stated that:

> *53. It shall not be lawful to employ any male person in any institution for lunatics in the personal custody or restraint of any female patient, and any person employing a male person contrary to this section shall be liable to a penalty not exceeding twenty pounds.*

This item went on to make an exception for occasions of urgency. Another item covered 'abuse of the female lunatic':

> *324. If ... any person having the care or charge of any single patient, or any attendant of any single patient, carnally knows or attempts to have carnal knowledge of any female under care or treatment as a lunatic in the institution, or workhouse, or as a single patient, he shall be guilty of a misdemeanour.*

The item goes on to state that a conviction for such an offence can lead to imprisonment of up to two years, with or without hard labour.

The Bethlem and Maudsley records are largely silent on staff misdemeanours with patients in the twentieth century, although a very few individual examples are remembered by experienced managers, mostly concerning male staff who became involved with female patients and did not remain for long in the service of the hospital. The legal requirements were taken with due seriousness. The Mental Health Act of 1959 maintained the stance of the previous legislation, defining various offences and related punishments. Any man employed in a hospital or mental nursing home who had unlawful sexual intercourse with a woman who was receiving treatment for a mental disorder in that hospital or home was liable on conviction to imprisonment for a term not exceeding two years (see Section 128).

British law continues to protect the mentally disordered from the staff of hospitals or mental nursing homes. The ill-treatment or wilful neglect

183

of patients was the subject of Section 127 of the Mental Health Act 1983, which made this a prosecutable offence, carrying a penalty, on indictment, of up to two years imprisonment, or a fine, or both.

The balance of the sexes among in-patients

The earliest record of patients, at the beginning of the fifteenth century, stated that on a sample day – March 6 1402 – six out of the nine patients were men. The other three were merely recorded as 'sick', and their gender is not mentioned. There was a mention of a female patient at Bethlem some short time earlier. Figures are sparse for the mediaeval period. A sample count in 1598 included nine women and eleven men. About thirty years, later the balance was not dissimilar, at thirteen women and eighteen men. There is no information available from the documentation of Bethlem's early history on any policy for the balance of gender in patients admitted.

The balance of male and female patients remained roughly equal for much of the eighteenth century, but, from the early nineteenth century, there started to be a swing towards a marked preponderance of women as shown in Table 12.1.

The last of these years shows an excess of women over men by almost 50%, which leads one to ask whether there were any indicators, for example in the recorded diagnoses, to explain this state of affairs. The Bethlem apparent and assigned causes of disease, in curable patients admitted in 1845, were divided into moral and physical causes. The most common 'moral' cause of disease for women was 'death of relatives or friends' (18 out of 93), a cause that hardly appeared in the list for men at all (only 1 out of 62). Where the single word 'love' is listed as a cause, women also score more highly – twelve women as opposed to three men.

Perhaps more significant in the physical causes list were those that were sexuality or gender related for women and were not paralleled by corresponding causes in the men's list, for example uterine derangement, puerperal cause, change of life, prolonged lactation, weaning, and milk fever – 35 out of 56 in all. In the men's list out of 29 admissions, the main cause was intemperance (16 patients), and the only ones related to sexuality or gender were syphilitic infection (1 patient), and sexual excess (1 patient).

Charles Dickens (1852) commented that insanity was proving more prevalent among women than among men, illustrating this figure from St Luke's Hospital, London, where, over a century, 59.5% of the admissions had been women. He added that it was well-known that female servants

Table 12.1 Numbers of Male and Female Patients: 1780–1845

Inpatient figures at Moorfields

	Curable men	Curable women	Incurable men	Incurable women	Total
April 1 1780	70	75	49	49	243
December 27 1788	68	79	60	50	257

Annual admission figures for the following years at Southwark

	Males	Females	Total
1820	56	68	124
1830	83	118	201
1840	127	181	308
1845	110	205	315

were more frequently afflicted than were any other class of person, although he does not tell us anything about the causes or diagnoses. The rise in the admission of women has been commented on in detail by Showalter (1985), but it has not yet been possible to uncover the particular reasons for this phenomenon at Bethlem. It is tempting to hypothesise on the existence of a covert sexual agenda. In mid-Victorian times, the male, middle-class doctors could have encouraged the admission of young partially educated, somewhat refined females, whom they could dominate. One recalls the impressive numbers of governesses referred to in Chapter 4. Although these young women were not the social equals of the doctors, they were persons with whom the medical staff might have felt comfortable. They were more desirable as patients than were the males of the criminal classes, some of which Bethlem had been able to dispose of to Broadmoor Hospital. An analysis of case notes could reveal more about doctors' attitudes to these admissions.

By 1900, when the Commissioners visited on July 12, they found 90 male patients and 130 females, a 1:1.4 ratio, and something similar to this was maintained in the fourth Bethlem at Beckenham. The new hospital there in 1930 opened with places for 103 men and 147 women, and by November 1932, when the hospital had filled up, there were 92 men and 119 women, a 1:1.3 ratio. The preponderance of women continued, reaching about double the numbers of men in 1947 (51 men and 103 women). The picture fluctuated with the amalgamation of the hospitals, although the figures for 1967–9 show some levelling out in the new inpatient ratio of males to females, being 1:1.1. Women dominated the number of patients readmitted, at 1:1.4. This was shortly prior to 1972 when the national figures showed that two-thirds of admissions in England to psychiatric hospitals were women.

Patient accommodation

The earliest description of accommodation at Bishopsgate is in the muniment book of 1632 (quoted in Report of the Commissioners for Inquiring concerning Charities 1837) which lists:

> *Item, the old house, containing below stairs a parlour, a kitchen, two larders, a long entry throughout the house, and 21 rooms wherein the poor distracted people lie, and above the stairs eight rooms more for the servants and poor to lie in, and a long waste room now being contrived and in work, to make eight rooms more for poor people to lodge where there lacked room before.*

To this, ten years later, the Governors planned:

> *To erect a new building thereon for the enlargement of the said hospital, and would allow of 12 rooms being made on the ground, and eight over them for lunatics, and garrets for servants, and another yard for lunatics.*

John Stow (see Strype 1734) thought that the house could not accommodate more than fifty or sixty patients. There is no indication of the division of patients being made by gender, but, bearing in mind the known numbers of patients and available rooms, it seems likely that many patients were accommodated in single cells.

Constraints on the admission of either men or women might have arisen from the nature of the accommodation or the needs of observation and management, but alas we know nothing about this. When the hospital moved to the second site at Moorfields in 1676, the patients were accommodated in 120 small, single cells along the sides of the galleries, which were clearly separated by an iron grille into equal male and female sides.

The tradition of single rooms was carried on at Southwark in the third building to house Bethlem (Anonymous, 'A Constant Observer' 1823), and it was not until the fourth hospital building at Beckenham that dormitories for women only, or men only, were introduced. These dormitories did not usually hold more than about six beds.

The Maudsley started with only a few single rooms, the sleeping accommodation being planned more like the open wards of general hospitals, with beds against the walls. On the verandahs at the Maudsley, eight or more beds were sometimes accommodated. With the rebuilding of the

Maudsley in the late twentieth century, the trend to dormitories was reversed, with a return to the individual sleeping spaces favoured at Bethlem in earlier times.

Sexual harassment

Quite apart from the harassment of female patients by male staff recounted above, one must note the harassment of female staff by male staff, and female patients by male patients. Bethlem history does not often record the sufferings of female staff at the hands of their colleagues, but there was one scandalous case in 1818 when a Mr Capper was the Inspector of Criminal Lunatics allocated to Bethlem. He was noted to be making frequent visits to Matron's quarters. This was Mrs Forbes, whom the patients privately called 'Beauty'. Mr Capper frequently stayed late at night and was seen leaving by the Porter. On one occasion he was alleged to have been seen leaving Mrs Forbes bedroom at 9 in the morning. This got her into serious trouble with the management, and other skeletons began to fall out of the cupboard. It was told against her that she had been improperly intimate with another man on a previous occasion. There was also the question of the identity of the child that Matron's maid was looking after in their quarters. There were also the mysterious payments that Mrs Forbes was making to various members of staff. History, alas, does not declare whether Mrs Forbes was a victim of the harassment of her senior officer, or if she welcomed his attentions.

Regarding sexual relations between patients, the Bethlem and Maudsley hospitals have a long tradition of discouragement, ostensibly to help protect patients from sexually transmitted diseases and unwanted pregnancies. This negative approach is not surprising if one follows Foucault's analysis, which postulated that where sex and pleasure were concerned, power could 'do' nothing but say no (1976). Until recently, the hospital policy stated baldly that sexual intercourse between patients was not allowed. Patients caught 'in flagrante' were firmly told by the nurses to stop at once. Because so many of the hospital patients were acutely disturbed, it was thought more proper to protect them by enforced abstinence, than to allow any possiblity of choice or exploration of sexual relationships. This was not just for the sake of the patient, but also for the relatives, who were sometimes afraid that harassment might occur. In the 1970s, one man, whose wife was intimate with another patient, went to the news-papers to say that Bethlem was running a brothel. Later Stephen Firn (1992) reported the experience of a number of female patients with manic illness who felt that men took advantage of their disinhibited behaviour to have unprotected sex. There was also the possibility of harassment and abuse between people of the same sex, but there do not appear to be any historical records of this at Bethlem, which is not to say that it did not occur.

The psychiatric nurse has to face in her work especial problems with expressions of sexuality. Sampson (1992), a ward manager at Bethlem, wrote:

> *The institutional denial of patient sexuality has been slowly eroded by external influence, social change and a desire to be seen to support practice on the rational conclusions of research. Gone are the days when the ward sister was viewed as the arbiter of sexual morality and a well run ward would include tucking the patients in at night with their hands outside the blankets! No other professional discipline struggles with the conflicts involved more than psychiatric nurses – who are caught between the need for social control, policy implementation and society's double values.*

There is more recognition today of the need for sexual expression and the development of fulfilling sexual relationships, and this is finding expression in more enlightened hospital policies, empowering staff and patients to challenge the processes that perpetuate the difficulties. Maudsley guidelines on sexual activities involving adult patients affirm the principle that patients' rights to make their own decisions are respected, although this is hedged around with necessary provisos.

The parity or disparity of male and female staff

Our understanding of the hierarchies of caring staff over the last two or more centuries is mainly shaped by the records of salaries paid (see Chapter 3). From 1777, the Matron was paid the most, then the basketmen and then the maids. Thus the grading remained for almost one hundred and fifty years with the male attendants getting around twice as much as the Sisters.

The only major change had been the addition of a Head Attendant below the Matron in the hierarchy. Although a Mr James Simmonds was named as Head Keeper in the 1816 Inquiry Report, his position seems to have been that of the most senior of a group of keepers, as he was named first in the list of keepers in the Salary Book, but received the same remuneration as other male keepers. It was not until the mid-nineteenth century that there was the development of the post of Head Attendant, appointed to lead the staff on the male side, with a higher salary than the other keepers, although nothing like the salary of the

Matron. The first occupant of this post was Charles Neville in 1853. The post, later entitled Head Male Nurse, continued until amalgamation with the Maudsley. The men who held this post took over parts of the role previously belonging to the Apothecary, who had supervised the male staff in earlier times. The Head Attendants never achieved parity with the Matrons, being paid only about half as much as them, in spite of the similarity of duties. The role of Matron had been a long time developing, growing from an unpaid job for the Porter's wife to an occupation for a forceful woman able to make her mark with the male establishment. Men, in the shape of Masters, Governors, Stewards, Apothecaries, Physicians and Medical Superintendents, had for ever ruled Bethlem, so it was something of a surprise when a woman became discontented with a subservient role; the domination was challenged in 1847 by Mrs Hunter, the Matron (see Chapter 5). Dr John Conolly of Hanwell remarked in the same year that Matrons often tried to usurp authority from the medical Superintendent.

The higher profile of the Matron was not reflected in the status of her junior staff. Here the male attendants, successors to the keepers, were rewarded with larger salaries, more beer and a better diet than were their female counterparts. This superiority of status continued for most of the nineteenth century but was gradually eroded by the change of female staff from female attendants to nurses. This was finalised in 1901 with the adoption of the titles used by general hospitals, namely Sister and Staff Nurse. The men remained as attendants, being first mentioned as male nurses in 1923.

The principle of equality of opportunity came only in 1948 with the amalgamation of the hospitals. Before that, in the early years of the Maudsley, there was no question of equality, or even competition, as the nurses were almost exclusively women, apart from a mere handful of male nurses. There were precedents for this dominance of women, for example at Fife and Kinross, Scotland, in 1896 (Santos and Stainbrook 1949). Dr Mapother at Maudsley clearly preferred it that way: witness his evidence to the Royal Commission on Lunacy, 1925, on the beneficial presence of female nurses on male wards. Perhaps Mapother inherited this idea from Dr Henry Maudsley himself, who in 1868 pointed out that a hostile and deluded patient would yield more readily to a woman's persuasion. Nevertheless men were gradually taken on as nurses at Maudsley, ironically to control the more disturbed patients.

The possibility of parity of esteem with other senior staff for women with a nursing background only became a reality in the 1980s, with the appointment as Chief Nurse of Julia Brooking, who had a doctorate but, in the absence of a suitable professorship, left for a Chair elsewhere.

Female and male pastimes and occupations

Before the nineteenth century, there were no detailed reports on patients' amusements, although we know from passing references that they sometimes read and wrote. In *Sketches in Bedlam* (Anon. 1823) there were references to pastimes such as keeping pets (small animals or birds), chewing tobacco, taking snuff and trading in small artefacts in order to supplement the hospital diet with tea, sugar and fruit-cakes.

Judging from the Annual Reports from 1845, the pastimes and work of male and female patients were divided largely according to stereotyped role models. Male patients amused themselves with billiards, bagatelle, chess, draughts, dominoes and card games; females with every kind of sewing, feeding the birds and reading. Elaine Showalter (1985) perceptively comments on these passive activities, remarking that:

> *these artifacts of the feminine role were less for the patients' pleasure than for their training in the discipline of femininity.*

This pattern was continued in the daytime occupations, which for the women were laundry, needlework and cleaning, and for the men gardening, carpentry, metalwork, plumbing and stone masonry.

There were not really any mixed activities at Bethlem except dancing. The dances were an exercise in producing acceptable behaviour in gender stereotypes, rather like the tea parties instituted by George Jepson, Superintendent and Apothecary, with Katherine Allen, the Matron, Chief Nurse and Housekeeper, at The Retreat in York. The ballroom in Bethlem was built in 1838, and, at the monthly balls held there, the patients of both sexes mingled. These events were tightly controlled, only the well-behaved patients being allowed to attend, and medical officers in attendance. A reporter from the *Illustrated Times* attended a Christmas Ball in 1859 and wrote:

> *The ballroom at Bethlem Hospital is a spacious apartment in the wing corresponding to that in which the billiard room is situated, and is lighted by large louvre windows. On the festal occasions it is very prettily decorated, and might vie with many a more pretentious and high-sounding area for the display of the Terpsichorean art. During the Autumn and Winter months balls are constantly given for the inmates, who seem thoroughly to enjoy the innocent and cheerful amusement provided for them.*

The reporter did not comment on the social interactions between the patients but reflected with bemused humour on the odd nature of the Ball. While many young, comely, peaceful and well-behaved people were making merry, others took no part in the dance but sat on the benches indifferent or insensible to what was happening around them:

190

A Christmas Ball in 1859 at Bethlem, Southwark

You feel in the midst of the merriment that there is something wanting, that the wine is corked, that the cake has a leaven of madness in it, that there is only elevenpence-halfpenny out of the shilling in the pockets of the dancers, that there is a tile loose off the roof of the ballroom.

As late as the 1930s, this pattern was still continuing, when the dances were held in the Outpatients Department. These, and the outings by coach for picnics and to the cinema, were the only mixed-sex activities. Eventually, the dancing tradition lost its impetus and withered in the post-war years to an Annual Dance for patients and staff.

The separation of the sexes was maintained in other areas. At church services in the 1920s, male and female patients sat on opposite sides of the chapel, with nurses flanking the appropriate wall. This was paralleled in the hospital grounds, where male and female staff walked on opposite sides of the roadway.

Integration of patients and staff of both sexes

First steps to mixing male and female patients were made in 1930 at Bethlem when the new convalescent unit, Witley House, opened for

191

'associated patients'. In this two-storey building there were places for twenty-five men and thirty-five women, and it was designated to be 'one building for both sexes'. While the sleeping accommodation was in separate wings, there was a communal dining room and lounge where patients mingled. This was confirmed by retired staff through the oral history project. In the programme for the opening of the new hospital, it said that 'the unit was designed as far as possible to eliminate any obvious suggestion of a mental hospital'. This is an early expression of the aim that underlay later thinking, that in integrating wards one would move nearer to normal social conditions.

At the Maudsley, increased proximity of the sexes started more from reasons of staff convenience when nursing disturbed patients. It was thought desirable to group together in a detached building a relatively small number of patients who were causing a state of unrest in other wards. With the opening of this Villa ward in the garden in 1932, there was accommodation for eighteen patients, usually seven men and eleven women, although this could be varied by shifting two moveable wooden partitions in either direction on the long verandah, so changing the balance of single rooms. As Dr Mapother said, the patients were 'only separated by a partition round which they could run at any moment'.

The male and female staff on the wards at Bethlem were largely kept apart up to 1948 when Bethlem merged with the Maudsley, although regrets were occasionally voiced, as in the Annual Report for 1928, where we read 'no woman nurse is employed on the male side which is a pity'.

In the early days of amalgamation of the two hospitals, there were specialised wards that included both male and female patients, where duplicating facilities might have looked wasteful. Examples of this were Tyson West Two Ward at Bethlem, treating patients with insulin coma, and Ward Two at Maudsley. The latter ward was where the consultant Denis Hill pioneered the study of epilepsy and ran a 'family ward' containing a wide age group of women and men down to late childhood. The argument for mixing patients on specialised wards was not based on what might be most desirable for patients but on the suitability for staff, from the point of view of keeping down the number of placements that doctors in training had to complete. Arrangements for nursing both sexes on the same ward were questioned in 1953 when there had been a complaint involving nursing staff discipline. The upshot was that the Medical Committee made two nursing policies:

> 1) *That male nurses should not, at any time, be placed in charge of a ward containing female patients.*
> 2) *That male nurses should not be concerned in the restraint or physical nursing of female patients.*

Gradually the number of 'bisexual' wards, as they were ineptly called, was increased. In 1958, this was thought desirable to ensure that the optimum number of beds was in use. One consultant went ahead on his own and mixed his psychogeriatric wards without consultation, even appointing a male nurse to be in charge. This arrangement was still the subject of discussion in 1963 when the danger of 'physical sexual relationships, actual or imagined' was aired in Committee. The existing rules were thought to have been designed:

a) to protect patients from improper and harmful sexual advances by male nurses, and b) to avoid the danger of scandal or legal action due to unjust accusations by female patients against nursing staff, with the resulting damage to career of the nurses and to the good name of the hospital.

The Superintendent of Nursing argued strongly for a balanced staff of men and women, while ensuring that there was always adequate female coverage. It was then accepted that male nurses could take charge of mixed wards, so opening up many more chances of promotion for men. By 1963, there were three wards at Maudsley and five at Bethlem that had some integration. This meant, in practice, that the sexes slept on separate sides of the ward in single rooms or dormitories with their own washing and toilet facilities, while in the middle of the ward were the day rooms, offices and dining room.

The widespread integration of male and female wards did not occur in both hospitals until the late 1960s. This was in accord with a movement across the UK in other psychiatric hospitals following the same policy. It caused alarm to some nurses, particularly at the COHSE Conference in 1965, when the debates centred on the difficulties of adequate chaperonage and the possibilities of patients making allegations against nurses that would be difficult to disprove. The Bethlem and Maudsley Medical Committee was already planning in 1964 to build ward units to accommodate patients of both sexes, although no rationale was given in the minutes for this decision.

The impetus that came in 1966 to mix more wards centred on the allocation of beds in view of consultant vacancies, the need to reduce the number of consultants on each ward and the need to reduce unnecessary changes of placement for trainee doctors.

In June 1967, the *Kentish Times* reported that Eileen Skellern, the Superintendent of Nursing, was pleased with the success of an experiment whereby nursing staff were looking after mixed wards of men and women patients. This reduced the numbers of consultants and registrars required for each ward. One of the ward sisters reported that working with fewer medical staff gave a greater facility for communication and forced people to recognise individual requirements within their professional roles.

193

The final seal of approval for the mixing of selected male and female patients on the same ward, and the mixing of male and female staff on all wards, came in the Ministry of Health Report *Psychiatric Nursing: Today and Tomorrow* (1968). The remaining single-sex wards eventually came to seem anachronistic. The Junior Common Room doctors in 1973 commented in the Gazette that:

> *the need for single sex wards (Wards 5 and 6) should be rethought and we suggest that these restricted uses should cease, since we do not think that these limitations are necessary. Indeed they may well be harmful.*

Ultimately, towards the end of the 1970s these wards were integrated, and so it remained, with mixed-sex wards holding sway even when new buildings were erected in the 1980s and 90s. More recently, with the increased consciousness of the rights and needs of women, this policy has been questioned. It may be seen as desirable that there can be a flexible use of beds, as single specialty wards can then more easily be viable. The danger is that insufficient possiblity of choice will be available to users, unless at least a few single-sex wards are maintained.

Raising consciousness of women's issues

A women's group at the Maudsley, organised as a collective, started to bring forward issues in 1981 about why women become mentally ill and possible actions arising from that. They identified anxiety and depression as being the two largest components in the distress leading to women being classified as having psychiatric disorders. They also emphasised the social construction of women's distress as opposed to the medical model of illness. Instead of treating symptoms, the group said that it would be more useful to assist women to identify areas of situational stress. Such stress was found where tensions appeared between human needs and demands, and those of social institutions, such as work and family.

In 1987, a 'Women in Psychiatry' group was formed to discuss such issues as role stereotyping, traditions in the medical hierarchy, balancing professional and family considerations, the effects of pregnancy and the lack of child-care facilities. Means of dealing with some of these latter problems were suggested, including job sharing, part-time employment and better cover arrangements for night duty. There was a staff nursery at the Maudsley, but demand, especially for baby places, often outstripped supply. The concern of this women's group was paralleled by the work of managers who were trying to improve practices for employees across the board, for instance offering facilities for job sharing and more flexible working.

Not only were personnel employment policies improved, but also, in the wake of the government's 'Opportunity 2000' initiative (1991), in order to meet the Department of Health goals for health-care providers, a Maudsley group mounted a programme to help women focus on themselves, their careers and how they would like to develop in the future. In spite of this, Staples (1993), for the 'Women in Psychiatry' group, could write that there was still blatant sexual harassment, sexism and problems with maternity rights and child-care provision. At the Maudsley, women occupied only 13.5% of consultant posts, as opposed to 23% nationally. Less tangible, but still worrying, was the pervasive feeling women had that they were taken less seriously by consultants than were men. It would seem that watchdog and support groups run for and by women will be needed for some time.

References and further reading

Anon. ('A Constant Observer') (1823) *Sketches in Bedlam*. London: Sherwood Jones and Co.

Conolly J (1847, reprinted 1968) *The Construction and Government of Lunatic Asylums and Hospitals for the Insane*. London: Dawsons.

Connolly J, Ellis L, Lemburger C, Mahoney P and Peto H (1981) Why women become mentally ill. *Bethlem and Maudsley Hospital Gazette*, **29**(3): 27–28.

Dickens C (1852) A curious dance round a curious tree. *Household Words*, **IV**(95): 385–389.

Firn S (1992) No sex, please . . . *Nursing Times*, **90**(14): 57.

Foucault M (1976) (translated by R Hurley 1979). *The History of Sexuality*, vol.1, *An introduction*. London: Allen Lane.

Ministry of Health (1968) *Psychiatric Nursing: Today and Tomorrow*. London: H.M.S.O.

Pilowski L and Gerada C (1987) A Woman's Place. *Bethlem and Maudsley Hospital Gazette*, **34**(3): 8–9.

Sampson K (1992) Sex and the psychiatric nurse. *Bethlem and Maudsley Hospital Gazette*, **39**(1): 15–17.

Santos E and Stainbrook E (1949) A history of psychiatric nursing in the Nineteenth Century. *Journal of the History of Medicine and Allied Sciences*, **IV** 48–73.

Showalter E (1985) *The Female Malady*. New York: Pantheon.

Staples E (1993) Women in Psychiatry. *Bethlem and Maudsley Hospital Gazette*, **40**(1): 10–11.

Strype J (1734) *A Survey of the Cities of London and Westminster . . . Written at First in the Year MDXCIII*, by John Stow. London: A. Churchill.

A search for excellence – the last three decades

*T*he Maudsley and Bethlem hospitals have often been conscious that, just as their origins were different from the majority of mental hospitals in England, so their function and role would be different and distinctive. Bethlem, with its endowments and centuries of experience, and Maudsley, with its background of selective admission of voluntary patients, had united into a privileged teaching and research institution from which much was expected. All disciplines have willingly accepted an obligation to provide services that were among the best of their type currently available and might offer a pattern for services developing elsewhere. In the decades since World War II, the institution has been seeking to offer high-quality clinical care for patients, developing treatments to relieve suffering, and has often been recognised as a centre of excellence in research, teaching and services.

This chapter recounts some Maudsley achievements in caring and treatment, in the hospital and community, and also in nurse education. It touches on the problem of violence and concludes with thoughts on future directions in caring.

The accent on psychosocial nursing that Annie Altschul had introduced was broadened by Eileen Skellern, formerly of the Cassel Hospital, who became Superintendent of Nursing shortly before Annie Altschul left for Edinburgh University. Eileen Skellern was well known for her work at the Social Rehabilitation Unit, Belmont Hospital, Surrey. She had written a series of articles for the *Nursing Times* (1955) describing the therapeutic community there, where people learnt to modify their antisocial behaviour by passing through an intensive socialising experience. In a lecture on the change from custodial to therapeutic care (1957), she had set out her views on how the necessary change in the social organisation of the ward involved a fundamental change in nurse–patient relationships, whereby

196

the nurse and patient got to know each other as individuals and developed into a state where the nurse was working *with* the patient rather than for him. From her long experience, she advocated the use of regular ward meetings of doctors, nurses and patients, where there could be free discussion, helping to resolve the problems of both treatment and administration. Skellern also saw the necessity for regular meetings of all staff. These developments during her time at the Maudsley became widespread across the hospital. In 1964, she wrote that the patient's rehabilitation would involve new adjustments within the controlled social environment of the hospital. The nurse, while developing relationships with individual patients based on trust, would relate to the patients as a group through the medium of shared activities. Increasing socialisation was expected of the patients. In the 1960s, nurses would insist that meals must be taken in the hospital canteen and the occupational therapy department was attended regularly, and, when patients were well enough, full attendance was, if at all possible, also required at hospital socials and dances.

Nurse therapists

A major move forward in 1972 was the experimental scheme set up between the hospital and the Department of Health and Social Security to assess the feasibility of training psychiatric nurses to act as therapists under psychiatric and psychological supervision, and to see whether their performance would match that of psychiatrists and psychologists. This move to use nurses for treating outpatients, as an alternative to using doctors, was paralleled in Colombia and the USA (Helzer and Holmes 1979, cited in Marks 1985).

The techniques used have been collectively called 'behavioural psychotherapy'. The programme, known as the Nurse Therapist Scheme and described by Lindley (1972), was in two phases, the first of which included theoretical instruction and a practical experience of treatment under supervision. Each nurse therapist worked with a small case load of in- and outpatients, designing a treatment programme with a supervisor, administering treatment and carrying out follow up procedures. A psychiatrist, often Dr Isaac Marks, later Professor of Experimental Psychopathology, made the initial examination of patients and offered guidelines for treatment. This was accompanied by twice weekly seminars and patient conferences, allowing for detailed discussion of treatment techniques and problems. The second phase of the programme was less formal, allowing the students to extend their practical experience and allowing researchers to evaluate and make treatment benefit and cost-effectiveness calculations.

Problems treated ranged from specific phobias (e.g. of birds, of spiders) to complex phobic states (social phobias or agoraphobia), obsessive–compulsive disorders, personality problems and sexual problems (impotence and frigidity). Treatment techniques involved 'in vivo' flooding, imaginal desensitisation, implosion, thought-stopping, assertiveness training, role rehearsal, aversion and operant techniques of shaping, fading and token economies.

The Maudsley Nurse Therapist Scheme became established by 1975 as an ongoing Joint Board of Clinical Nursing Studies course, with a nationally agreed syllabus. The course was also soon mounted at Graylingwell Hospital, Chichester. At the time, this seemed an unsettling development, as nurses started to launch out as therapists into uncharted waters, albeit under careful medical supervision. There were possible problems of new independence, responsibility and changed relationships with patients, colleagues and other groups. The nature of some of the problems treated, particularly the sexual ones, might expose nurses to ethical dilemmas if the nurses were to become overinvolved with their patients. In practice, the problems were fewer than anticipated and capable of resolution.

The nurses recruited for this work adopted a more scientific and research-orientated approach to their work than had previously been common. This development was of key significance for the Maudsley, as it demonstrated by research that nurses could be taught and successfully practise the use of specialist therapeutic techniques to the benefit of the patient. Nurses achieved results that compared very favourably with those obtained by other professionals and were obtained potentially more cheaply. It was a clear example of an advanced clinical role in both the hospital setting and primary health care, and a gradual move towards nurse therapists becoming autonomous case managers or nurse practitioners. A characteristic of this development has been the rigorous research that has accompanied it (Marks et al 1977, Marks 1985).

At the same time, some individual nurses were following up interests in psychodynamic methods of treatment, by having either group or individual training psychoanalyses, with a view to becoming lay psychotherapists or teaching group psychotherapeutic methods to others. Also in the 1970s, various postregistration courses in special fields, for example the child and adolescent psychiatric nursing course and the behaviour therapy course in mental handicap nursing, were started to prepare nurses for more advanced roles. Some nurses in the late 1980s trained as cognitive therapists.

Community psychiatry

It is not really possible to say when Bethlem started in the field of community psychiatry. It seems that patients in former times were allowed outside the hospital walls and that this was given positive encouragement from the late nineteenth century onwards by persons such as Dr George Savage, the Medical Superintendent (1884), who believed in giving as much liberty to patients as he could, although there was some risk to be run: 'During the past year hundreds of patients have been on short or long leave and a fair number have been allowed to go out alone on parole, one only broke his word and instead of returning enlisted'.

Again in the next year he advocated this 'social treatment' as a reward for self-restraint. Yet this did not lead to treatments based outside the hospital, and it was not until 1919 that a Bethlem outpatient department was established. At about the same time as the first psychiatric outpatient nurses were beginning to emerge at Warlingham Park Hospital, Croydon, the Maudsley set up its first Day Hospital in 1953. This was modelled on a pioneer unit in Montreal. Dr A. Harris, who set up this service, was partly motivated by reasons of economy, but the Day Hospital was expected to make for improved contact between families and hospital staff, avoid the break with home and so reduce problems of rehabilitation. The nursing staff had a role in offering care and support with supervised activities, along with the administration of ECT. It was initially a small endeavour; as Sister Eileen Waller (1982) said, 'we were given a few rooms and a pack of cards'. There was, in addition, an occupational therapist who came with cane and embroidery for the ladies. At Bethlem, the Day Hospital opened in 1956, following a similar pattern to that at Maudsley, with treatments and occupational therapy in the mornings, and social and group activities in the afternoons (Farndale 1961).

All this changed in the 1960s with the arrival of Dr Douglas Bennett and a new stress on rehabilitation through industrial and clerical work, to add realism to the treatment. A Maudsley industrial workshop was opened in 1967. In the same year, a research nurse was appointed to investigate the role to be played by psychiatric nurses working in the community, and, although the topic was explored, there were no major developments in this direction at that time. It is necessary to reflect at this stage on the Maudsley's special situation regarding the community. It was, and is, placed in an inner city area with a high incidence of psychiatric morbidity. The Maudsley worked then almost exclusively with acutely ill patients, and there was as much work as could be coped with flowing into the hospital without going out into the district to look for it. In 1967, the first joint appointments were made to a community psychiatric service for Camberwell and East Lambeth, for which the Maudsley, with King's

College Hospital, was to take responsibility. Although there were some qualms about restricting the Maudsley's previous freedom in selecting patients, the district service was to offer new opportunities for research, development and teaching. This fresh commitment in the field of social psychiatry was to weld together the work of community agencies and hospital inpatient work. Help would be received from the Medical Research Council Social Psychiatry Unit, via the Camberwell Register, which provided epidemiological information. In the local London Borough, there were some day centres, no hostels or community psychiatric nurses, but a large active team of social workers belonging to the Borough's mental health department.

So it was that the first community psychiatric nurse employed from Bethlem in the 1970s was a specialist nurse, attached to the psychogeriatric team, monitoring discharged patients and supporting them in their home environment. Gradually, other units started to employ community psychiatric nurses. This process was almost certainly encouraged by the decline in specialist psychiatric social workers following the change to generic social work training after the Social Services Act of 1970.

The Maudsley could not be described as having been in the forefront of the development of community psychiatric nursing in the UK. This was partly caused by having a tiny catchment area of only a few miles around the hospital, from which patients could come in fairly easily. There were, from the early 1970s, nurses from speciality areas, such as old-age psychiatry and learning disabilities, working outside the hospital in patients' homes. The long-stay patients of the district were in a country mental hospital many miles away. For them, David Russell from the Maudsley developed dependency rating scales, which he used in a survey to plan the provision of services for the return of the patients to the community.

The orientation of new nurses towards the community was assisted by the inclusion of a community module in their training, whereby students took up a wide variety of placements in Social Services and the voluntary sector. Day and weekend care was increasing, alongside the provision of sheltered accommodation and a sheltered factory in the community, but the services remained largely hospital based. Yet even this was preferable to the admission of patients to a distant mental hospital in the countryside. The Day Hospital pressed on further into family work, using group therapy techniques throughout the 1970s, until this service was replaced in 1981 by a new concept in community services.

The District Services Centre was built to be the hub of a wheel of services offered to the long-term mentally ill of Camberwell. A particular aim was to achieve continuity of care, so that whether the individual was a day patient, inpatient or outpatient, he would be treated by the same staff team. Nurses were not so confined to the Centre as they had been to the ward, and they were able to work with patients in their homes. Ward nurses made preadmission assessment visits and also postdischarge visits for patients in their homes, places of work or schools, as well as contributing to case conferences in the community. For example, in 1981, 873 patients received 1645 visits between them. During the next decade, the number of community psychiatric nurses greatly increased, and, apart from those with a particular specialist role, they became established in community teams with responsibilty for a defined locality, following the assumption of responsibility for the whole of the Camberwell mental health services in 1991. As types of intervention have diversified across differing settings, age groups, and subspecialties, nurses have been at the forefront of schemes which display innovative practice. Illustrations of this have been:

- the Daily Living Programme, an alternative to hospitalisation for serious mental illness;
- the Community Drug Team;
- the Mental Impairment Evaluation and Treatment Service;
- the Maudsley Outreach Support and Treatment project (MOST), designed for those difficult to engage in care from three local electoral wards;
- the Adolescent Outreach Service;
- the Psychiatric Acute Care and Emergency Team (PACE), a crisis prevention service for those in the early stages of their illness;
- the Psychiatric Assertive Outreach and Continuing Care Team (PACT), a twenty-four-hour service for patients with long-term mental illness;
- the Children's Learning Disabilities Outreach Team.

Thorn Nurses

Another development of benefit to the community has been the Thorn diploma course on 'Problem centred interventions for people with serious mental illness', which was set up to commence in 1993 at two training centres, the Maudsley and Manchester University. It fits in with the government policy in *Health of the Nation – A Strategy for England* (Department of Health 1992), the aim of which for the community is to 'improve the health, social functioning and quality of life of people who are seriously mentally ill'. The course facilitators encourage the use of psychosocial interventions and a psycho-educative model of family work, hoping to enhance skills in both case management and family therapy. The course members focus on mental state assessment, problem-solving, advocacy, assertive community care and psychological interventions, addressing the needs of individuals and their families. Intensive evaluation of the effect of the practice of skills learnt on the course is a feature of the overall programme. It is intended that the Thorn Nurses, trained through the generous funding of the Sir Jules Thorn Charitable Trust, will disseminate knowledge by becoming trainers themselves.

Primary nursing

At the same time as refining the implementation of the nursing process in the early 1980s, the Maudsley nurses were pressing forward with a movement away from task orientation and towards other systems of organisation, such as team nursing and primary nursing. As early as 1955, Ackner reported that each nurse admitted the particular patient who was allocated to her. The nurse would write detailed descriptions, on admission, of the patient's physical state, behaviour and mood, and would meet with the psychiatrist at least once a week to discuss the patient's progress notes that that nurse had written. The writings of Marie Manthey of Minnesota (1970, 1980) on primary nursing were in accord with the Maudsley trend to have one nurse who was identifiable as being the nurse for one particular patient. The adoption of the primary nursing system was an evolutionary process, often pioneered by innovators at clinical level who wanted to encourage more active involvement by the patient. Hardiman (1984) and his team planned the introduction of primary nursing for the new Secure Unit. The primary nurse would ensure that the patient could identify her or him as the nurse responsible for his care. Besides assessing and planning the nursing interventions and supervising associate nurses, the primary nurse would communicate with other team members about his or her patient and maintain records.

Ritter (1985), then a Senior Ward Sister, also described the implementation of primary nursing on a Maudsley ward, claiming that no other system had more to offer the mentally ill. Her paper pictured a grief-stricken woman of 55 years old being helped towards rehabilitation. The woman had already been a patient in the ward for some time when a Staff Nurse was allocated as her primary nurse, in association with a final year student nurse and a seconded nurse. The woman had expressed some distress over her husband's last illness and death, so the team decided to embark on abreactions and guided mourning. One nurse planned the care, supervised its implementation and recording, and evaluated it. The Staff Nurse maintained an exposure to cues or triggers for the patient's grief, in what was virtually a flooding programme. The patient went

202

through a suicidal stage, while improving in posture, sociability and concentration. The advantages of the primary nursing system were that the nurses were clear about their professional relationship with the patient, and that the written data were available, documented as a composite picture, not only from the nurses' viewpoint. Everyone knew who the primary nurse was, and the patient recognised her as central to the changes that took place. It established a base from which the patient could plan to leave hospital.

By the time of the national arrival of the government-endorsed concept of the named nurse (1991), the Maudsley was operating the primary nursing system in almost all clinical areas. This system has enabled nurses to focus their thoughts on which problems would be amenable to nursing interventions and what contributions the individual patient and the nurse would be expected to make. It was in harmony with the model recommended by the national Mental Health Nursing Review Team (Department of Health, *Working in Partnership*, 1994), which wished good practice to include 'a clearly informed assessment of client needs, which involves the clients and their carers'. However, mental health nurses need to beware of assessing and developing plans of care oblivious of what other professionals are doing (Gournay 1995). All relevant disciplines need to make an input to the process of care planning. Current thinking and practice in the context of the care programme approach will take account of key worker responsibilities, supervision registers and discharge planning.

A Nursing Development Unit

An area of clinical work of special interest is Bridging Therapy, as carried out in the Maudsley Nursing Development Unit. Bridging Therapy is a technique, pioneered in Cairo by Dr N.A. Mahgoub, that seemed to a ward team at the Maudsley to be apt for their purpose in reducing the 'revolving door syndrome', whereby patients go through a repeating cycle of discharge and readmission. The nursing team, with Mike Farrell, Senior Staff Nurse, enthusiastically constructed a package to implement their ideas. Eilis Rainsford, the Ward Manager, took the decision to press forward. From admission, the primary nurse plans the discharge with the client, who is subsequently followed up in the community. Thus the primary nurse achieves some continuity of care by bridging the gap between hospital and community. With the associate nurses, the primary nurse is involved in follow-up by means of negotiated ward appointments, a Bridging Therapy clinic, a discharge group with relatives and home visits. The nurses receive back-up from their multidisciplinary team and liaise with other follow-up agencies to maintain a constant level of support. The views of the client as a consumer of service are seen as important, and measures, such as a patients' satisfaction survey, are taken to maintain awareness.

In 1992, the unit was chosen by the King's Fund Centre to be designated as a national Nursing Development Unit. The King's Fund Centre wrote, 'The Nursing Development Unit aims to promote excellence in nursing by evaluating practice and encouraging innovation, thus acting as a power base for the development of clinical practice.' Evaluation is being carried out with the aid of a grant over three years.

Developments in nurse education and research

A combined degree course with Brunel University, Uxbridge, was set up in 1968. An educational emphasis of Annie Altschul was the strong stress laid on the sociological aspects of behaviour and psychiatric care, and this led to the link with Brunel University. Professor Elliot Jacques, in liaison with Eileen Skellern and Reg Everest, then Head of the School of Nursing, set up a sandwich course, which would lead over four years to a social science degree combined with a professional qualification, in this case the Certificate of Mental Nursing. The aim was to give a sound academic grounding, accompanied by a coherent professional training, rather than just experience with various social agencies. From the hospital's point of view, there was a need to develop graduate nurses who would not only enrich the clinical care given to patients, but also be equipped to contribute to nursing and research developments in a rapidly changing climate. One must remember that, in the UK at that time, there were hardly any strictly nursing degree courses, and that this combined degree/RMN course was the only degree-linked course approved for the training of psychiatric nurses. The course produced a small but significant stream of highly articulate nurses, quite a few of whom remained in clinical work, while others gravitated to university posts.

A side-effect of the course was the generation of small-scale research studies, which sometimes turned into thought-provoking papers. An example of this was 'Voices of concern' by Hilary Allen (1981). This was a study of professional talk about patients in a psychiatric day unit. Allen noticed that much more time was spent on talk than was technically necessary. This followed on from Oppenheim (1955), who had observed that nurses spent more time talking to each other and other health professionals than in direct contact with patients. She therefore constructed a typology of talk that covered presenting the case, ongoing observations, interpretation and reformulation, action decisions, instructions and policies, chinese whispers, speculation, love and hate talk, anecdotes, digressions and pleasantries. Given that staff had areas of stress connected with their work, irrational talk served to provide legitimate time off from contact with patients, emphasising the underlying inequality of staff–patient relationships, reinforcing professional structures and offering some intellectual stimulation. 'Talk' about patients may be fulfilling the social, personal and professional needs of staff, and this is an important part of work.

The work of the School of Nursing continued to expand from the 1960s under the strong leadership of Reg Everest, and, in addition to the new degree course, other courses were started, including a modular course leading to the qualification of Registered Mental Nurse. This course was introduced in 1971 to offer an eight-module training, in which a teaching module was followed by practical experience in the subject just studied, in an attempt to overcome the old problem of the gap between the theory that was taught and the realities of clinical practice.

The group methods of teaching started in the 1960s were developed, notably for the postregistration courses run by Gunna Dietrich. This was in combination with a range of educational methods also in regular use. These experiential teaching methods made use of current ward experience, by asking students to describe nursing practice, consider alternatives and evaluate them. The student group would use discussions based on written work and set topics, group dynamic discussions and projects, psychodrama exercises and supervision classes (Dietrich 1978). Role play and non-verbal exercises helped to increase perception of how others saw them. Touching exercises helped the students to gain practice in handling others, as they would later have to do in the course of restraining or moving patients. The use of the student's current clinical experiences ensured that in no way could the school work be thought to be irrelevant to ward work. It was as if the attention of the teachers and students had at last been focused on the client, rather like the French medical teachers in the eighteenth century who had put theory behind them and focused their gaze on the patient (Foucault 1963). The development of self-awareness skills and the use of experiential techniques were recognised nationally and adopted in the English and Welsh National Boards Syllabus of Training in 1982.

The numbers of graduate nurses joining the staff as students, tutors or ward staff rose sharply from the early 1970s. This was a considerable change from the early days of Annie Altschul, who was then one of the few members of nursing staff with a degree. From the end of the 1970s onwards, there were nurses with higher degrees working in clinical areas. This change towards a more academically able type of nurse, reflecting the increase in university education nationally, was appropriate for the

205

intellectually challenging atmosphere of the Maudsley. Such nurses wrote about their work in books, either as authors or contributors, for example, Skellern to the RMPA *Handbook for Psychiatric Nurses* (Ackner 1964), Dodd to Scott and Dodd's *Neurological and Neurosurgical Nursing* (1966), Wilkinson's *Child and Adolescent Psychiatric Nursing* (1983), Ritter's *Manual of Clinical Psychiatric Nursing Principles and Procedures* (1989) and Brooking, Ritter and Thomas's *A Textbook of Psychiatric and Mental Health Nursing* (1992). Published papers increased from ten during the year 1982 to forty-six during 1992. This trend to nurses becoming involved in the writing of textbooks, descriptive papers of service developments and research reports looks set to continue, now that academic nursing is again expanding with a Masters degree in Clinical Mental Health Nursing and a PhD programme.

The effects of this increasing shift of focus towards academic activities, leading to a possible reduction of clinical contact time with patients, are yet to be assessed. Ward (1993) found that, in New York City, that nurses with a higher academic professional profile were concentrating on preparing others for carrying out therapeutic roles. This situation might become reflected in the UK.

Many research grants have been awarded to Maudsley nurses, and two projects that received support (Thorn Nurses and the Nursing Development Unit) have been outlined above. This is very much in line with the mission of the Maudsley, which gives research a high priority.

Together with the change to Project 2000 for preregistration courses, the postbasic nurse education courses have been established at diploma level. In the field of HIV/AIDS, the first course validated by the English National Board for Nursing, Midwifery and Health Visiting, focusing on the mental health care and management of people affected by HIV/AIDS, has trained social workers and nurses from all over the UK. Short courses have been held on topics such as:

- women, psychiatry and abuse;
- race, ethnicity and mental health;
- the assessment of depression, suicide risk and parasuicide.

For those without prior qualifications, there is the training programme for National Vocational Qualifications for Health Care Assistants.

The problem of violence

The recognition in the early 1970s that clinical staff needed a particular input of knowledge and skill in managing violence was an indicator of the disturbed times through which the hospital was intermittently passing. In the years following the arrival of the phenothiazine drugs in the 1950s, it was assumed that violence would gradually disappear as it was chemically managed more easily. Disillusionment set in when there was an upturn in violent incidents, perhaps related to the admission from 1970 onwards of patients subject to detention under the Mental Health Act. A small blue nursing procedure manual (1974) was written and a film produced to give detailed practical instructions on how to cope with personal attacks. It was thought that all nursing staff working as a team would manage violent incidents, and that one did not have to be a large heavy man to manage an attack satisfactorily. As there was a feeling that violence was increasing, a Violent Incidents Register (1976) was set up to monitor what was happening across the hospital. This showed an upward trend over the first few years of the Register up to 1984, followed by a slight decline (Noble and Rodger 1989). The violent patients were more likely to be schizophrenic and to have been repeatedly admitted. Among them was a high proportion of Afro-Caribbeans. The factors predisposing to the increase in violence were likely to include the need to deal with more seriously ill and chronic patients, the opening of new units, increasing violence in society and inner city area problems.

The practical management used in 1979 in an actual incident was described by Tibbles et al, who worked on the Villa ward for disturbed patients. The following extract came in the course of a longer paper that also covered prevention, teaching, attitudes, communications and follow-up. The approaches described were the best that could be envisaged at the time, but some different techniques have since been introduced. The 'specialling' referred to was when a nurse was assigned to make continuous observation of a patient, usually staying within arm's length of the patient all the time. This account involved a young patient who broke a curtain rod during an angry outburst and was threatening patients and staff. Extra resources were summoned:

> On the arrival of help, one of the helpers joined the nurse looking after the other patients. This is a very important factor that should never be overlooked. Two nurses were delegated to organise the medicines if necessary, one nurse collected a blanket. This is a safe recommended tool in managing violence. The Charge Nurse indicated this organisation and continued to retain contact with the patient. The communications with the patient were verbal and non-verbal and aimed at reducing the patient's fears in a hope of resolving the situation without violence. The Doctor joined the Charge Nurse in trying to persuade the patient, and both the Doctor and the Charge Nurse positioned themselves so that if the weapon was swung they would be clear. Although the area was sealed off to ensure that other patients could not enter this situation, the Doctor and the Charge Nurse could not turn away from the patient for fear of attack from behind.

> *The patient did not respond to verbal persuasion and his anger and fear and dangerousness were heightened. The decision to immobilise was indicated and all nurses prepared to help. The two nurses delegated to organise medicines were ready. The Manager continued to talk to the patient, distract him and closed in quickly, preventing the weapon being swung. All other staff then followed the immobilisation principles laid down in the Hospital Guidelines for the management of violence. Medicines were given and the patient taken to his bed where 'specialling' continued with two nurses at all times.*

Staff afterwards discussed critically how the incident was handled, and patients verbalised their feelings in the ward meeting.

Some of the clinical teams in the 1970s were preoccupied with the 'management' of violence, often through restraint, medication and seclusion, but this gradually gave way to a stronger emphasis on prevention. Topics that needed consideration were the way the nurse presented him or herself to the patient, how the nurse responded to the patient and offered information, how restraint could be used therapeutically, how to give time and space to converse and work with the patient, and how to plan for the needed resources (Rix 1985).

Continuing difficulties over violence, not only on the wards, but also in the Emergency Clinic, meant that nurses were drawn to considering prosecuting patients in the courts for their violent behaviour. An injured member of staff might claim for Criminal Injuries Compensation, but might also bring a personal prosecution against a patient for assault, and might even expect to gain some financial assistance under certain circumstances. Reports from doctors and nurses in 1986 confirmed that violence had become part of hospital culture and that nurses saw violence as part of their lot. The Emergency Clinic, the twenty-four-hour psychiatric casualty department, became a place where more serious incidents occurred, which the following flashpoint incident (Lloyd 1987) illustrated:

> *On the evening of 29th July [1987] a man arrived in the clinic announcing his intention to perform impromptu brain surgery with the knife he was wielding. Nursing staff barricaded themselves in the office and called for help. Within minutes the duty doctor and other staff arrived, summoned by phone and ignorant of what awaited them. They were powerless as the man smashed up furniture and fittings. Order was only restored when two van loads of police arrived and the officers overpowered and led away the attacker.*

This led to a short-lived experiment in the employment of external security men, who turned out to be only familiar with night-club bouncing and whose deportment was considered unsuitable.

Attempts to understand and grapple with the problems led to further research studies and surveys, for example, Roscoe (see Fisher 1988), Owen (1988–9) and Whittington and Wykes (1991–2). The first of these came up with the sobering fact that, while the average person in England can expect to be assaulted once every hundred years, if that person was to work at the Bethlem and Maudsley, he or she would be assaulted once every nine months. The survey also contained an assault 'league table', showing the leaders to be Clinical Nurse Managers, receiving 5.2 assaults per year, with Charge Nurses receiving 3.8 assaults and nursing assistants 3.

These people were especially vulnerable because of their specific roles, but this needed to be set against a broader picture in which preventive measures were inhibited through lack of resources or staffing problems. Owen, noting that stress management within the nursing profession had usually concentrated on individual coping mechanisms, looked at organisational coping strategies and found that the staff did not think the existing strategies were useful, except for the weekly staff support groups and those groups following violent incidents. Whittington and Wykes looked at strain and social support following assault by a patient and found that most of the social support provided for victims was on an informal basis and that there was no agreed formal system. They also noted that support for subjects in the study was concentrated in the time immediately after the incident, in spite of the fact that symptoms persisted in some staff for at least two and a half weeks. Staff needed to be educated on how they could expect to feel should they become involved in a violent incident. Moreover, general principles, procedures and guidelines were published for Maudsley staff and others on preventing and managing violence by Ritter (1989), and by Hardiman (1994) who drew on the guidelines on physical restraint from the Department of Health and the Welsh Office (1990). Clinical practice must be informed by further research, increased self-awareness, knowledge and skills, and monitoring of the clinical situation. This will go hand-in-hand with whatever treatment strategies are available for managing aggression.

The above 1994 hospital policy makes reference to facilities to seclude patients as being a treatment option in some areas. Carroll et al, in the same year, showed that in the course of a year sixty-four individuals had been secluded in two hundred and seventy-two seclusion episodes, which is another illustration of the persistence of the use of this technique which the Royal College of Nursing has deemed antitherapeutic (1994), but which clinical staff still appear to find a useful and acceptable procedure.

Caring for individuals with mental health problems – where next?

The positive developments outlined above have been achieved against a background of long standing uncertainties about the nature of care and the environment in which it is delivered. There are innate stresses in daily contact with the mentally disturbed and coping with fears of unpredictable violence (Skellern 1974). Nurses in the past thirty years have often perceived the Maudsley and Bethlem hospitals as being stressful places to work, which has been reflected in a high turnover of staff (Bamber 1988). The comparatively rapid changes in management structures, from Salmon to Griffiths, and the market economy have been a troubled backcloth to preoccupations that mental health nurses have had about their role.

The Ministry of Health report *Psychiatric Nursing: Today and Tomorrow* (1968) foresaw the participation of the nurse in community mental health services but could not perceive a general pattern. The report expected nurses to play a more active advanced therapeutic role in some form of psychotherapy, such as had already been developed in the USA. Yet it remained unclear whether or not a formal psychotherapeutic role was necessarily of more value than the general caring supportive psycho-therapeutic role that nurses commonly adopted (Cormack 1976).

The absence of a clear theoretical basis for patient–nurse relationships (Altschul 1972) allowed confusion to proliferate among nurses and their colleagues in the multidisciplinary team. The branching off into specialisms, such as behaviour therapy, has not necessarily helped those working in a more conventional setting dominated by the medical model. Nurses tend randomly to pick up attitudes and practices from the clinical environment in which they work. Wondrak (1982), then a tutor at the Maudsley, wrote, 'It appears that the nurse's role is determined not by its own standards, but by the prevailing psychological ideology of the particular institution.' This accords with the research findings of David Towell (1975), who found that psychiatric nursing encompassed a cluster of different roles varying quite radically with the setting in which these were performed. It reminds one of Celia Davies' (1981) view of nursing as a 'conglomerate of divergent occupations'.

The confusing variety of practice at clinical level was compounded by the longstanding dichotomy between what was required to be taught in the School of Nursing to pass examinations, and what were the realities of what happened on the wards. Although the tutors had attempted to use accounts of students' interactions with patients as a basis for teaching nursing for much of the post-War period, there was still much course work that students did not find of obvious relevance. As Brooking (1989) remarked, 'we don't really know what sort of educational input is required to produce good psychiatric nurses'. It almost seems as if something of the archetypal chaos of legendary Bedlam was lingering on.

Yet for all this diversity and lack of illumination, there remained a widespread conviction that good practice in nursing would include the therapeutic use of relationships, within which the nurse would keep the patient safe, act in good faith with reasonable care, maintain confidentiality and avoid untruthfulness. The nurse–patient relationship is based on trust as an overriding first principle (Altschul 1984). Empathy is also a useful concept when considering the development of nursing theory (Thomas in Brooking et al. 1992). The relationships are expected to be psychotherapeutic in nature in the broad sense, and sometimes in a more specific sense if nurses have acquired skills through training.

One is left with a realisation of the complexity of the nurse–patient relationship, which defies simple analysis and could inhibit theory development but offers plenty of room for research, in addition to the existing body of North American literature. Mental health nurses need to be able to identify what they are able to offer in situations where the boundaries between the professions are more fluid, when blurring of roles and multiskilling are thought desirable. If the existing mental hospitals open in 1985 (including, by definition, the Maudsley and Bethlem), are all closed by the year 2002 as the Chief Nurses of the Department of Health have predicted (1994), many of the traditional frameworks for nursing interventions will be lost and the core culture carriers will have become community psychiatric nurses (CPNs). This is not an encouraging prospect, bearing in mind the recent doubts about CPNs' effectiveness, their orientation away from people with severe mental illness, and suggestions that the balance of the skill mix in community nursing staff should shift to a larger proportion of unqualified personnel (Audit Commission 1994).

The Department of Health review *Working in Partnership* (1994) considered the anxieties and uncertainty surrounding the future role of mental health nursing, but thought it should play a central role in high quality care. The Mental Health Nursing Review Team, led by Tony Butterworth, Professor of Community Nursing at Manchester University, emphasised a collaborative approach, agreeing that mental health teams have skills in common, such as counselling, but stressing that nurses also have caring, rehabilitation and medication supervision skills. Nurses found it difficult to lay exclusive claim to many of their skills, but it was said that with the values and practice common to the nursing profession as a whole, mental health nurses provided a unique expertise. Some of the skills listed include establishing a therapeutic relationship, constructing a care programme, providing assessments, monitoring medication, collaborating with other members of the multidisciplinary team and managing the therapeutic environment.

It is perhaps significant that monitoring medication is often commented on in reports on nursing in both community and inpatient facilities. It could be a reflection of what Peplau (1994) calls the 'biomedicalisation' of psychiatry. The increasing nurse's role in giving medication, recording it and observing for compliance and complications seemed to her to be turning the nurse into the eyes and ears of physicians. Maudsley nurses are involved in these procedures, although this is not new in a research-based establishment. The nursing involvement in drug treatment regimes might be a growing cause for concern, bearing in mind the dangers of high doses of neuroleptic drugs. Nurses could be instrumental in developing alternative strategies for the management of symptoms that are less dependent on medication.

The above medical based practices are the nature component of the age-old nature–nurture controversy which is once again being played out. To Peplau, nurses have their roots on the nurturing side of the divide, with their skills in counselling, psychotherapy, family therapy, crisis intervention and ward government being more in accord with nurturing than are emerging psychiatric theories. One would expect that nurses within the context of developed relationships should be able to offer a range of interventions and options for the patient.

A challenge for nurses remains the extent to which they are seen as giving value for money in a service that is part of a managed internal market. Maudsley nurses have developed as skilled practitioners in specialist units, producing work of the highest quality and standards. They have frequently given a lead in the field of care for mothers and babies, AIDS patients, the psychotic, children and adolescents, patients with eating disorders and those with learning disabilities. These nurses may still have to fear being too expensive, as much as others in less privileged areas do. White (1992), from his Delphi study on the future of psychiatric nursing, expected the increasing development of specialist practitioner roles in the community. White's respondents also predicted most therapeutic contact time for patients would be with junior psychiatric nursing staff and health care assistants. The latter group, with less training, may well be increasingly seen as able to provide the traditional caring therapeutic relationships and checks on safety, which remain a vital service component. Radical questions repeatedly need to be addressed – for example, what kind of person with what skills is appropriate for the present situation? Annie Altschul rightly centres her approach on the patient: 'I think we have got to start with the patient, and say "what kind of person does the patient need at different periods?" and then say "well, what sort of background?"' (personal communication 1994). In this and other ways, services become user-led. There will always be a group of people whose occupation is to deliver care. Those people may or may not be called nurses.

The scenes of Bedlam have shown patients suffering, protesting and sometimes being heard and helped. The aim of the carers at some earlier stages in its history seemed to be focused on control more than cure, as if the organisation existed for the welfare of the staff. The various needs of staff – for financial reward, job security, a safe regime, a place to work out their own problems, to write a research paper, acquire a qualification – have all been present to differing degrees. The relationships of caring staff and patients have varied from brutality to the essence of kindness and consideration; from denying individuality to empowering patients. Sometimes the carers were shackled by rules and routine; sometimes the situation was so open that a nurse was free to interpret her role as she wished. During the past hundred years, nurses have emerged from the servant role, acquiring knowledge and specialist skills that have improved their status. Advanced clinical roles were pioneered, which represented what was excellent of its kind for the period. Yet for all the 'improvements', many of the old problems were constantly being recycled – how to manage violence, expressions of sexuality, gender issues, struggles for power between staff and staff, and staff and patients, the use of medication, relationships between the institution and the community. There is still much to do for a practitioner who will centre on the needs of the patient, reflect on the past, use the research that charts experience to plan the future, and tirelessly search for excellence in clinical practice.

References and further reading

Ackner B (ed.) (1964) *Handbook for Psychiatric Nurses*, 9th edn. London: Baillière, Tindall and Cassell.

Allen H (1981) 'Voices of Concern' – a study of verbal communication about patients in a psychiatric day unit. *Journal of Advanced Nursing*, **6**: 355–362.

Altschul A (1972) *Patient–Nurse Interaction: A Study of Interactive Patterns in Acute Psychiatric Wards*. Edinburgh: Churchill Livingstone.

Altschul A (1978) A systems approach to the nursing process. *Journal of Advanced Nursing*, **4**: 333–340.

Altschul A (1984) Psychiatric nursing: Does good practice need good principles? *Nursing Times* July 11 and 18: 36–38, 49–51.

Audit Commission (1994) *Finding a Place: A Review of Mental Health Services for Adults*. London: HMSO.

Bamber M (1988) The great exodus. *Bethlem and Maudsley Hospital Gazette*, **35**(1): 11–12.

Bennett D (1991) The drive towards the community. In Berrios GE and Freeman H (eds) *150 Years of British Psychiatry 1841–1991*. London: Gaskell.

213

Brooking J, Ritter S and Thomas B (1992) *A Textbook of Psychiatric and Mental Health Nursing*. London: Churchill Livingstone.

Callaghan P (1989) Dr Julia Brooking. Interview Report. *Bethlem and Maudsley Hospital Gazette*, **36**(1): 33–35.

Carroll S, Thomas B, Hope S and Tunmore R (1994) The use of seclusion in a large psychiatric hospital. Unpublished paper.

Cormack C (1976) *Psychiatric Nursing Observed*. RCN Research Series. London: Royal College of Nursing.

Davies C (1981) *Rewriting Nursing History*. London: Croom Helm.

Department of Health and Welsh Office (1990) *Code of Practice: Mental Health Act 1983*. London: H.M.S.O.

Department of Health (1992) *Health of the Nation – A Strategy for England*. London: HMSO.

Department of Health (1994) *The Challenges for Nursing and Midwifery in the 21st Century*. London: HMSO.

Department of Health (1994) *Working in Partnership: A Collaborative Approach to Care*. London: HMSO.

Dietrich G (1978) Teaching psychiatric nursing in the classroom. *Journal of Advanced Nursing*, **1978**(3): 525–534.

Dunster C (1993) Nursing development. *Bethlem and Maudsley Hospital Gazette*, **40**(1): 16–17.

Farndale J (1961) *The Day Hospital Movement in Great Britain*. Oxford: Pergamon Press.

Fisher N (1988) The fear of assault. Report of a hospital survey of violence by J Roscoe. *Bethlem and Maudsley Hospital Gazette*, **35**(1): 39–40.

Gournay K (1995) Reviewing the review. *Nursing Times*, **91**(18): 55–57.

Hardiman F (1984) Primary nursing in a secure unit. Unpublished paper.

Hardiman F (1994) *Preventing and Managing Violence, Policy and Guidelines for Practice*. Bethlem and Maudsley NHS Trust.

Helzer JE and Holmes SJ (1979) *Evaluation of Psychiatric Nurse Practitioners*. American Psychiatric Association, Chicago.

Lindley P (1972) The Nurse Therapist Scheme. *Bethlem and Maudsley Hospital Gazette*, Autumn: 13–14.

Lloyd K (1987) Violent times. *Bethlem and Maudsley Hospital Gazette*, **34**(3): 11–12.

Manthey M, Ciske K, Robertson P and Harris I (1970) Primary Nursing. *Nursing Forum* **IX**(I): 65–83.

Manthey M (1980) *The Practice of Primary Nursing*. Boston, Oxford, London, Edinburgh and Melbourne: Blackwell Scientific Publications.

Marks IM (1985) *Psychiatric Nurse Therapists in Primary Care*. RCN Research Series. London: Royal College of Nursing.

Marks IM, Hallam RS, Connolly J and Philpott R (1977) *Nursing in Behavioural Psychotherapy – An Advanced Clinical Role for Nurses*. RCN Research Series. London: Royal College of Nursing.

Ministry of Health (1968) *Psychiatric Nursing: Today and Tomorrow*. London: HMSO.

Noble P and Rodger S (1989) Violence by psychiatric in-patients. *British Journal of Psychiatry*, **155**: 384–390.

214

Oppenheim AN and Eeman B (1955) *The Function and Training of Mental Nurses.* London: Chapman and Hall.

Owen S (1989) Under pressure. *Bethlem and Maudsley Hospital Gazette,* **35**(3 and 4): 8–9.

Peplau HE (1994) Psychiatric mental health nursing: challenge and change. *Journal of Psychiatric and Mental Health Nursing,* **1994**(1): 3–7.

Ritter S (1985) Primary nursing in mental illness. *Nursing Mirror,* **160**(17): 16–17.

Ritter S (1989) *Manual of Clinical Psychiatric Nursing Principles and Procedures.* London: Harper and Row.

Rix G (1985) Compassion is better than conflict. *Nursing Times,* **81**(38): 53–55.

Scott DF and Dodd B (1966) *Neurological and Neurosurgical Nursing – An Introduction.* Oxford: Pergamon Press.

Skellern E (1955) A therapeutic community. *Nursing Times,* **51**(16): 426–8, **51**(19): 533–5, **51**(21): 593–4, **51**(23): 642–3, **51**(25): 688–9.

Skellern E (1957) From custodial to therapeutic care. *Nursing Times* **53**(8): 209–211 and 220–221.

Skellern E (1964) The Role of the Psychiatric Nurse. In Ackner B (ed.) *Handbook for Psychiatric Nurses.* London: Baillière, Tindall and Cassell.

Skellern E (1974) *Stress and the Environment.* Unpublished lecture to the Association of Nurse Administrators, in the Bethlem Archives.

Stengel E (1955) Psychiatry from the nursing point of view. *Nursing Mirror,* **100**(2595): 1097–8, **100**(2596): 1169.

Tibbles P, Leiba T and Syson-Nibbs L (1979) The management of violence in a locked ward – the nursing approach. *Bethlem and Maudsley Hospital Gazette,* Winter: 7–11.

Towell D (1975) *Understanding Psychiatric Nursing.* London: Royal College of Nursing.

Ward M (1993) Culture shock. *Nursing Times,* **89**(21): 38–40.

White E (1992) *The Future of Psychiatric Nursing by the Year 2000: A Delphi Study.* Manchester: University of Manchester, Department of Nursing Studies.

Whittington R and Wykes T (1992) Staff strain and social support in a psychiatric hospital following assault by a patient. *Journal of Advanced Nursing,* **17**: 480–486.

Wilkinson T (1983) *Child and Adolescent Psychiatric Nursing.* Oxford: Blackwell Scientific Publications.

Wondrak R (1982) It's a mystery. *Nursing Mirror,* Jan 27: 18–19.

BIBLIOGRAPHY

*A*lthough many printed sources are listed at the end of each chapter, there is material that is either specific to the Bethlem and the Maudsley, or containing detailed reference to the hospitals, which is listed below.

Primary sources

Manuscripts in the Bethlem Royal Hospital archives

Bethlem Admissions Registers
Bethlem and Bridewell Court of Governors Minutes
Bethlem Salaries Books
Bethlem Stewards' Account Books
Bethlem Sub-Committee and Grand Committee Minutes

Bethlem and Maudsley Board of Governors Minutes
Bethlem and Maudsley Joint Transitional Committee Reports
Bethlem and Maudsley Nursing Committee Minutes
Maudsley Box 338 St.111
Mill Hill Emergency Hospital, Medical Superintendent's Reports.

Parliamentary and royal papers

Record of Visitation of the Commissioners of Henry IV (1403), Chancellor's court, Tower of London, Miscellaneous Roll no. 276. In Report of the Commissioners for Inquiring Concerning Charities (1837). See below.
Reports of the Select Committee on Madhouses in England (1815–16). London: House of Commons.
Report of the Commissioners for Inquiring Concerning Charities (1837). London: House of Commons.

Report as to the State of Management of Bethlem Hospital, and of All Correspondence Thereon (1852–53). House of Commons Sessional Papers 49.

Newspapers, magazines and periodicals:

Bethlem House Journals – *Under the Dome, Bethlem Star, Orchard Leaves*
Bethlem and Maudsley House Journal – *Inter Nos*
Bethlem and Maudsley Hospital Gazette
Illustrated Times
Illustrated London News
Kentish Times
Quarterly Review
Pearson's Weekly
The Times

Other printed primary sources:

Anon. ('A Constant Observer') (1823) *Sketches in Bedlam*. London: Sherwood Jones and Co.
Bethlem and Bridewell Annual Reports (1843–1947)
Bethlem and Maudsley Triennial Statistical Reports (1949–1975)
Bowen T (1783) *An Historical Account of the Origin, Progress and Present State of Bethlem Royal Hospital*. London (no publisher given).
Institute of Psychiatry and Bethlem and Maudsley Annual Reports (1983–93)
Maudsley Medical Superintendent's Reports to the London County Council (1923–35)

Secondary sources

Allderidge, P (1970) Richard Dadd (1817–86): painter and patient. *Medical History*, July: 308–313.
Allderidge, P (1971) Historical notes on the Bethlem Royal Hospital and the Maudsley Hospital. *Bulletin of the New York Academy of Medicine, New York*, **47**(12): 1537–1546.
Allderidge, P (1974) Criminal insanity: Bethlem to Broadmoor. *Proceedings of the Royal Society of Medicine*, **67**: 897–904.
Allderidge, P (1974) *The Late Richard Dadd*. London: The Tate Gallery.
Allderidge, P (1974) *Richard Dadd*. London: Academy Editions.
Allderidge, P (1976) *The Bethlem Historical Museum Catalogue*. London: Bethlem and Maudsley Hospitals.
Allderidge, P (1977) Cibber's figures from the Gates of Bedlam. *Victoria and Albert Museum Masterpieces Sheet 14*. London: Crown.
Allderidge, P (1979) Hospitals, madhouses and asylums: cycles in the care of the insane. *British Journal of Psychiatry*, **134**: 321–334.

Allderidge, P (1979) Management and mismanagement at Bedlam, 1547–1633. In Webster C (ed.) *Health, Medicine and Mortality in the sixteenth century.* Cambridge: Cambridge University Press.

Allderidge, P (1985) Bedlam: fact or fantasy? In Bynum WF, Porter P and Shepherd M (eds) *The Anatomy of Madness: Essays in the History of Psychiatry.* vol.2. London: Tavistock.

Allderidge, P (1991) The Foundation of the Maudsley Hospital. In Berrios GE and Freeman F (eds) *150 Years of British Psychiatry.* London: Gaskell.

Allderidge, P (1993) *Bedlam: the first four centuries.* Unpublished paper.

Allderidge, P (1993) Sketches in Bedlam. *Proceedings of the 1st European Congress on the History of Psychiatry and Mental Health Care, 1990*: 76–82. Rotterdam: Erasmus Publishing.

Andrews J (1991) *Bedlam Revisited: A History of Bethlem Hospital c1634-c1770.* Unpublished PhD thesis, University of London.

Cawley R (1975) History of the Joint Hospital. In the *Triennial Report 1970–75 of the Bethlem Royal and Maudsley Hospital, and the Institute of Psychiatry*, pp. 10–13.

Copeland AJ (1910) Short history of Bethlem Royal Hospital. *Under the Dome*, **19**(74) 47–68.

Johnson KJ (1953) Short history of the Bethlem Royal Hospital and the Maudsley Hospital. *Bethlem and Maudsley Gazette*, May: 2–5 and 14–15.

Lewis A (1969) Edward Mapother and the making of the Maudsley Hospital. *British Journal of Psychiatry*, **115**(529): 1349–1366.

Masters A (1977) *Bedlam.* London: Michael Joseph.

O'Donoghue EG (1914) *The Story of Bethlehem Hospital from its Foundation in 1247.* London: T. Fisher Unwin.

Porter Phillips JG (1943) Bethlem Royal Hospital. *The Medical Press and Circular*, (210): 5449 and 5450.

Sargant W (1967) The Maudsley Hospital. Chapter 4 in *The Unquiet Mind.* London: Heinemann.

Talbot C (c1969) Unpublished untitled paper in Bethlem Archives.

Tuke DH (1876) The history of Bethlem Hospital. *Proceedings of the Medico-Psychological Association at Bethlem Royal Hospital.* May 10: 201–221.

Tuke DH (1882) *Chapters in the History of the Insane in the British Isles.* London: Kegan Paul, Trench and Co.

White JG (1899) *A Short History of the Royal Hospitals of Bridewell and Bethlem.* London (printed privately).

Whittacker D (1947) The 700th anniversary of Bethlem Hospital. *Journal of Mental Science*, **93**: 740–47.

*I*ndex

accommodation 186–7
  see also basement wards; single-room
      system
Ackner, Dr Brian 173, 202
Action Committee 177, 179
admissions policy 55, 57, 58–60,
      153–4
admissions procedure 165
Allderidge, Patricia [Hospital Archivist]
      4
  quotations of work 4, 5, 36, 63
Allen, Hilary, talk study 204
Allen, Katherine [Matron/Chief
      Nurse/Housekeeper – The
      Retreat, York] 190
Altschul, Annie 169, 171–4, 196
  on Eileen Skellern 82
  on patient–carer relationships 174,
      210, 212
  publications 171, 174
amalgamation/merger of Bethlem Royal
      and Maudsley Hospitals 13, 16,
      168–9
Andrews, Jonathan, research work
      4, 41, 43, 49, 55, 63, 73, 127
animals, mad people treated as 5
antimony [drug] 66, 125
antiphlogistic measures 63–4, 125
Apothecary 37, 63
  see also Haslam; Jepson; Wood
artists 37, 111–15
assaults on staff, frequency 209
assistant keepers 92
attendants 37–8

complaints against 21, 129
duties 93, 94, 95, 129
job-title change 39, 96, 189
rise in status 12, 39, 50
training 39, 162–4
uniforms 44–5
see also basketmen; gallery maids;
      keepers; nurses
autobiographical writings 28–33

ballroom 190
basement rooms/wards 124, 156
basketmen 35, 36
  duties 35, 88, 89, 90, 91, 182–3
  misconduct 127
  promotion 128
  uniforms worn 44
  wages 50
  see also attendants; keepers
bathing
  cold 64, 66
  showers 66, 121
Battie, Dr William [Governor] 124,
      125
beating 62, 118
Beckenham site [Kent] 13, 16
  accommodation described 186
  admissions procedure 165
  nurse:patient ratios 42, 43
  patients
    male:female ratio 185
    numbers 43, 185
Beckett, Samuel
      [novelist/playwright/poet] 142–5

Bedlam, origin of name 4
beer allowance [for staff] 51, 74
behaviour therapy 69, 210
   electric shocks used 125
   introduction 81
Bellers, John, quoted 119
Bennett, Dr Douglas 199
Benson, Matthew [Steward] 46
'Bess O'Bedlam' 137
Bethlehem
   Bishop 1, 4
   Priory of St Mary of 1, 4, 35
Bethlem and Maudsley NHS Trust 16,
      169
Bethlem Nurses Home 48
Bettinson, Gladys [Matron] 83
Beyond the Glass [novel by Antonia White]
      145–8
bibliography [for this book] 216–18
Bicêtre [Paris hospital] 5, 120
biomedicalization 212
Bishopsgate site [London] 8–9, 15
   accommodation described 186
   patients
      male:female ratio 184
      numbers 41
      occupations 53–4
   staff:patient ratios 41
'blanket patients' 20, 65
bleeding [as treatment] 63, 64, 125
blister treatment 64, 125
Bowen, Thomas [Chaplain & Governor]
      5, 64
Bradbury, Eliza [Matron] 83
Bridewell [House of Correction] 9, 13,
      15, 71, 127
Bridging Therapy 203–4
Broadmoor State Criminal Asylum 12,
      113, 155, 157
Brockden, Mrs B. [Matron] 83
Brooking, Julia [Chief Nursing Adviser]
      83, 189
   on educational input required 210–11
Brothers and Sisters 35
Brunel University [Uxbridge], degree
      course 79, 204
Butterworth, Professor Tony 211
Byers, Eric [General Manager] 177

Camberwell District Services Centre
      200–1

Camberwell site [Maudsley] 14
Cantle, Kenneth [Chief Male Nurse] 47
care, principles of 174
carers 35–51
   nurse or care assistant? 212
   relationship with patients 82, 196–7,
      210, 211, 212, 213
   see also attendants; basketmen; gallery
      maids; keepers; nurses
caretakers, Charge Nurses behaving as
      168
Carkesse, James [patient] 27, 32, 63
chains and manacles 5, 119
The Changeling [play by Thomas
      Middleton] 138
Charge Nurses 40
   concerns about promotion 175–6
Charles I, King of England, Scotland &
      Ireland 100, 101, 102
chemical restraint 68, 69, 125–6, 156
chloral 66, 125, 156
chronology 15–16
   Beckenham site 13, 16, 43
   Bishopsgate site 8–9, 15
   Deed of Gift [of land/estate] 1, 15
   Moorfields site 9–11, 15
   Southwark site 11–12, 15, 42
Clare, John [poet & patient] 31
Clark, Ernest [Head Male Nurse] 51
Clark, J. [patient/poet] 22–3, 64
Clashby, Elizabeth [Nurse] 36
client-centred approach 18
clothing/dress policy 46
coercion 120
cold baths/showers 64, 66
community mental health services
      200–1, 210
community psychiatric nurses (CPNs)
      201, 211
   first appointed 80, 200
community psychiatry 199–201
complaint literature 24–7
Confederation of Health Service Em-
      ployees (COHSE) 175, 176, 177
confidentiality 99
congratulatory literature 22–4
conium [drug] 66, 125
Conolly, Dr John [Medical
      Superintendent – Hanwell
      Asylum] 42, 65, 120, 121, 154
   attitude to new-style matrons 78, 189

consultants, women 195
Coteneys, Agnes [patient] 20, 54
criminal injuries compensation 208
criminal patients 11, 12, 112, 185
    transfer to Broadmoor 12, 113, 155, 157
Crooke, Dr Helkiah [Keeper] 9, 15, 36, 46, 54, 127

Dadd, Richard [artist & patient] 37, 111–13
Davies, Dr D.L. [psychiatrist], quoted 172
Davies, Lady Eleanor [patient] 100–3
Day Hospital 199
Deakin, Harriet [Matron] 83
death rate 158
degree courses 79–80, 81, 204
Dekker, Thomas, plays by 134–6
dependency rating scales 200
Dickens, Charles, quoted 152, 184–5
Dietrich, Gunna 205
digitalis 66, 125
disciplinary procedures 129
drug-based treatments 66, 68, 69, 125
    monitoring of medication 212
dry-packing 121
The Duchess of Malfi [play by John Webster] 136–7
Dunn, Emma [Matron] 83

Eager, Sarah [Matron] 83
Edwardian period 16, 159–61
electroconvulsive therapy (ECT) 68–9, 125
Emergency Clinic 208
entertainment 6
equality of pay/opportunity 50, 188–9
Everest, Reg [Head of School of Nursing] 174, 205
exorcism, allegations 3

fear, use in management of patients 64, 124
Firmin, Fiona [Staff Nurse], reminiscence 67–8
Fitzgerald, Thomas [poet] 22
Fitz-Mary, Simon [founding benefactor] 1, 15
Fletcher, John, play by 137–8

flogging 124
    see also beating; whipping
food deprivation 119
Forbes, Elizabeth [Matron] 83
    changes made by 65, 120
    complaints against 26, 91, 187
    salary 49
forcible feeding 24, 158
foretelling/prophecies 100, 101
Foucault, Michel [French philosopher] 5, 118, 124, 187
Foye, George [Steward] 46
French practice, compared with English 5
funding of health care 179

gallery maids 36
    duties 88, 90
    wages 50
    see also attendants; keepers
galvanism 66
Gay, John, quoted 10–11
gender-related issues 181–95
    see also men–women segregation
General Nursing Council
    mental nurse training syllabus 171
    requirements 40, 164
George III, King of Great Britain and Ireland 105, 107, 108
Glass, Florence [Night Sister – Maudsley] 122
governesses, as patients 56, 57, 185
Governors
    interest in public image 151
    on Lady Davies/Douglas 101
    male nurses' concern voiced 175–6
    named 5, 7
    patient-care concerns 77, 121
    praised in poem 22, 23
    on recruitment of staff 162
    rules 85–97
    on segregation of sexes 182
    staff misconduct dealt with by 73, 77, 91, 126–9
    on staff uniforms 43
    view on wages 49
graduate nurses 169, 205
Green, John [basketman] 46
group learning methods 173–4, 205
group therapy
    first commenced 68
    patients' views 28–30

221

Hadfield, James [soldier & patient] 108–10
Halsbury Report [1974]   176
Hanwell Asylum
    attendants   42, 50
    Matrons   65
    physician   42, 120, 154
Harris, Dr A.   199
Haslam, John [Apothecary]   37, 64, 65, 78, 119
    daughter   74–8
    views
        on Keepers   37, 127, 128
        on restraint methods   119, 120, 124, 127–8
Hayward, Vicki, reminiscences   48, 97, 164–5
Head Attendant, duties   95, 188–9
Hearder, Sarah [Matron]   38, 83, 97
Henry VIII, King of England   9, 15
Hill, Denis [consultant]   192
historical writing, value   2
Hodges, Diana [Matron]   83, 88
Hogarth, William [painter]   6–7
holding technique   142
The Honest Whore [play by Thomas Dekker]   134–5
Hood, Dr Charles [Physician-Superintendent]   150–5
    admissions policy   153–4
    improvements made   12, 51, 152
    non-restraint policies   42, 123
    and Richard Dadd [artist & patient]   112, 113
Hopkins, John [Porter]   73
hunger, as method of restraint   119
Hunter, Henrietta [Matron]   74–8, 83, 92
Hunter, Richard, on chemical restraint   126
hydrotherapy   67

Illustrated London News, on Dr Hood   152, 153
Illustrated Times, on Christmas Ball   190–1
improvements listed   65, 74–5, 157–9
incurable patients
    accommodation for   11, 55
    percentage   157
industrial disputes   177–9

Inquiries   12, 19–22
    alterations as result   150, 151
insulin shock therapy   67–8, 125
integration of patients/staff of both sexes   191–4
International Psychiatric Nursing Congress   80
isolation   119–20, 123–4

Jacob, Hildebrand [poet]   22
Jacques, Professor Elliot   81, 204
Jepson, George [Apothecary – The Retreat, York]   65, 120, 190
job descriptions   87, 97
job titles   39, 40, 71, 83
Johnson, Jane [Matron]   83
Johnson, K.J. [House Governor], quoted   168
Johnson, Samuel [lexicographer]   6
Joint Transitional Committee   169
journalists' views [of Bethlem]   139–42

keepers   36–7
    complaints against   9, 15, 25, 27, 127
    duties   23, 27, 37, 91–2, 128, 142
    remuneration   48, 50
    see also attendants; basketmen; gallery maids
kindness, in treatment   65, 120
King, George [Charge Nurse], reminiscence   60
King's College Hospital [London]   14, 199–200
King's Fund Centre, on Nursing Development Unit   204
Kough, Alice [Matron]   83

lady probationers   38, 162
Langley, Richard [Steward]   72, 101
Lee, Nathaniel ('Nat') [dramatist & patient]   103–5
length of service   47, 127
leucotomy operations   68
locked doors   120
Loving Mad Tom [song]   32–3, 62, 119
Lunacy Acts   158, 163, 183
Lunacy Commissioners
    dissatisfaction   76, 151, 158
    Inquiries   12, 16, 21, 75–7, 150, 151
    on restraint methods   121–2, 123

McFarlane, [Baroness] Jean, on Eileen Skellern 82

The Madness of [King] George III [play by Alan Bennett] 105

Mahgoub, Dr N.A. 203

maidservants 36
  wages 50

Male, Mrs J. [Matron] 83

male/female parity/disparity of staff 175–6, 188–9

male/female ratios of patients 184–6

male/female segregation 11, 36, 182–4, 191

managers, nursing
  divergence with clinical staff 177, 179
  job titles 40, 71

Mapother, Dr Edward [Medical Superintendent – Maudsley Hospital] 13, 48, 51, 169, 189

Marks, Dr Isaac 81, 197

Martin, Jonathan [patient] 110

Mary, Queen 13, 48

Matron 36, 71–83
  alternative job titles 40, 71, 83
  complaints against 26, 46, 75–7
  duties 86, 87, 88–9, 91, 92–3, 95, 97, 182
  listed 83
  number of staff controlled 71
  recruitment 38
    requirements 91
  remuneration 50, 77
  status compared with Head Attendant/Male Nurse 50, 188–9

Matthews, Hannah [Matron] 83

Matthews, Joseph [Porter] 27, 46, 182

Matthews, Millicent [Matron] 46, 83

Maudsley Hospital 13–14
  accommodation described 186–7
  admissions policy 58–60, 61
  community service 199–201
  Day Hospital 199, 200
  merger with Bethlem 13, 16, 168–9
  mixing of male and female patients 192
  new-staff induction/orientation 166–7
  Nursing Development Unit 203–4
  restraint methods 122
  staff 40, 51
    numbers 43

pay 51
  qualifications requirement 166
  residence requirements 47–8
  treatments used 68–9

medical students 12, 150

medicine, use in treatment 62–4, 66, 68, 69, 125

Medico-Psychological Association (MPA) Certificate 39, 40, 163–4

Meikle, Edith [Matron] 83

men–women segregation 11, 36, 182–4, 191

Mental Health Acts [1959/1983] 183, 184, 207

mental hospitals, effect of closure 211

mental nursing
  beginnings 38–40
  formalization of training 39, 163–4, 171
  future developments 210–13

Metcalf, Urbane [patient] 25–6, 91

Middleton, Thomas, play by 138

'Midnight, Mary' [journalist], view of Bethlem 140–2

Mill Hill Emergency Hospital [north London] 166–8

mixed-sex wards 19, 191–4

monastic origins [of Bethlem] 1, 8

Monks Orchard estate [Kent] 13
  see also Beckenham site

Monro, Dr Edward Thomas 65, 74, 121

Monro, Dr John 65

Monro, Dr Thomas 64, 66, 106

Moorfields site [London] 9–11, 15
  accommodation described 186
  patients
    male:female ratio 185
    numbers 41, 185
    occupations 54–5
  staff:patient ratios 41

moral treatment 65–6, 120, 121, 150–1
  Foucault's objection 124

More, Sir Thomas, quoted 62, 118

Morison, Dr Alexander 65, 74, 121

Murphy [novel by Samuel Beckett] 143–5

name variants [for Bethlem] 4

named nurse approach 202, 203

National Asylum-Workers Union 51, 175

neurosurgery 68, 125
Neville, Charles [Head Attendant] 37, 44, 50, 112, 113, 189
Nicholson, Margaret ('Peg') [patient] 105–7
night staff 38–9
non-restraint policies
  effect on staff numbers 42, 121
  first introduced 65, 120–1
Norris, James [patient] 20–1, 44, 92, 119, 120, 152
Northward Ho [play by Dekker & Webster] 135–6
novelists 142–8
Nurse
  duties 87–8
  first appointed 36
  job combined with Matron 36
nurse therapists 80, 197–8, 210
nurse–patient relationship 82, 196–7, 210, 211
nurses
  duties 95–6, 143–4, 170
  male/female parity/disparity 188–9
  numbers 42, 43
  research into function 169–71, 204–5
  role 210
  salaries 51, 189
  trade union activity 175–9
  training 39, 79–80, 81, 96, 164–6, 173–4, 204–5
  uniforms 44–6
  see also Psychiatric Nurses Association; Royal College of Nursing
Nursing Committee, lack of nurse representation 81, 175

occupational therapy 13, 65–6, 190, 199
occupations of patients 53–61
  at Bishopsgate 53–4
  at Moorfields 54–5
  at Southwark 55–8
O'Donoghue, Revd E.G. 3, 7, 23, 73, 77, 159–61
Ogdon, John [pianist & patient] 29–30
Oppenheim, A.N. [psychologist], nurses' job analysis 170–1, 204–5

order-keeping
  of patients 118–26
  of staff 126–30
outpatient treatment 199

padded rooms 65, 121, 123, 156
paraldehyde 68, 125, 156
Parncutt, Florence Agnes [Sister Tutor] 164
patients
  class differences 57, 154
  keeping order among 118–26
  male:female ratio 184–6
  more notorious ones 99–115
  numbers 41, 42, 43, 53, 54, 185
  occupations 53–61
  opinions 18–34
  pastimes 190
  relationship with carers 82, 196–7, 210, 211, 212, 213
  taking law into own hands 123
  treatments 61–9, 123–6
patient's advocate, role of nurse 177
pay disputes 176, 177
Pearce, Arthur Legent [patient] 31–2
peer of realm, as patient 60
physiotherapy department 67
The Pilgrim [play by John Fletcher] 137–8
political activism 176–9
Pooler, Mrs H. [Matron] 83
Porter 35
  complaints against 20, 27, 46, 72–3, 126–7
  remuneration 50
Portrait of a Schizophrenic Nurse [book by Clare Marc Wallace] 30–1
postbasic nurse education course 206
postregistration nurse education course 205
primary nursing 202–3
private rooms 58
Privy Council 101, 106
protest literature 24–7
Psychiatric Nurses Association 80
Psychiatric Nursing: Today and Tomorrow [Ministry of Health report] 194, 210
psychosocial skills, acquiring 171, 173, 201

public perceptions   6–7, 132–48
publications, academic/textbook   81, 171, 174, 196, 206
punishment   64–5
purging [as treatment]   63, 64, 125

Rake's Progress [painting by William Hogarth]   6–7, 44
residence requirements   47–8, 91, 97
restraint methods   5, 62, 65, 117, 119–20, 121–2
   reduction in use   65, 120–1, 150
   reintroduction   158
[The]Retreat [York]   42, 65, 120, 124
Robinson, Margaret [Matron]   83
Rodbard/Rodbird, Thomas [Keeper]   25, 26, 49
Royal College of Nursing
   Fellowship   80
   on female staff   39
   pay campaign   176
   on seclusion as treatment option   209
   ward sister research   78
Rule Books   85, 86–97
   eighteenth century   87–91
   nineteenth century   91–5
   seventeenth century   86–7
   twentieth century   95–7
Rush, Benjamin, on use of fear/terror   64
Russell, David   200

St Luke's Hospital   49, 184
Sala, George, article about Dr Hood   152–3
salaries   48–51
Salmon [management] structure   40, 97
Salpêtrière [Paris hospital]   5, 120
Sampson, K. [ward manager], on sexuality   188
Savage, Dr George [Medical Superintendent]   158, 162, 199
School of Nursing   169, 174, 205
scope [of this book]   2–3
seclusion   123–4, 209
sedation   68, 125, 126
segregation of sexes   11, 36, 182–4, 191
Senior Male Nurse, duties   97

sex ratios of in-patients   184–6
sexual harassment   187–8
Shakespeare's portrayal of madness   6, 133–4
shower baths   66, 121
Simmonds, James [Head Keeper]   44, 188
single-room system   57, 112, 186
single-sex wards
   reason for maintaining   194
   see also mixed-sex wards
Skellern, Eileen [Superintendent of Nursing]   78–82, 83
   background   78, 196
   her relationships with medical staff   81
   on mixed-sex wards   193
   publications   81, 196
   on relationships in nursing   82, 196–7
   remembered as nurse manager   82
   on staffing levels and skills   42
Skene, M.I.H. [Matron]   83
Slack, Jane [Night Nurse]   39
Slater, Dr Eliot   68
Slattery, William [Head Attendant]   38, 163
Smart, Christopher [journalist]   142
   see also 'Midnight, Mary'
Smyth, James [Keeper]   5, 65, 92, 99, 110
social activities   74, 159, 190–1, 197
solitary confinement   119–20, 123–4
sources of information   3–4
Southwark site   11–12, 15, 42
   accommodation described   186
   nurse:patient ratios   42, 43
   patients
      male:female ratio   185
      numbers   43, 185
      occupations   55–8
Spencer, Mary [Matron & Nurse]   36, 83
staff   35–52
   job titles   39, 40
   keeping order among   126–30
   male/female parity/disparity   175–6, 188–9
   numbers   40–3, 71
   recruitment problems   39
   salaries/wages   48–51, 188–9
   uniform worn   27, 43–6

staff (*cont.*)
  see also attendants; basketmen; gallery maids; keepers; Matron; nurses; Porter; Steward
staffing ratios 41, 42, 43
Stein, Dr George, reminiscence 68–9
Stengel, Dr Erwin 170
Steward 36
  remuneration 50
strait-jackets 119
strait-waistcoats 119
stress management 209
Strype, John, quoted 63
suicidal patients 30, 94
  numbers 57, 156
  nurses' duties 95, 96, 144
suicide rate 156–7
Superintendent of Nursing 40, 71, 169
  holder(s) of post 78–82, 83
  uniform worn 45
surgical procedures 68, 125
Sutherland, Stuart [psychologist & patient] 28–9

Taverner, Peter [Porter] 20, 46, 127
terminology 4
theatrical images 6–7, 133–8
therapeutic community approach 171, 196
therapists, nurses as 80, 197–8, 210
Thomas, Ben [Chief Nurse Advisor], xi 83
Thorn Nurses 201–2
Tibbles, P. 207–8
'Tom O'Bedlam' 32–3, 133
Townsend, Joseph, quoted 119
trade union activity 174–9
training of staff 39, 79–80, 81, 96, 164–6, 173–4
tranquillizers 69, 125–6
treatments 61–9
  early methods 61–2
  medicines 62–5, 69, 125–6
  physical methods 61–2, 63–5, 66–7, 68, 123–5
  therapy 68, 198
Tryon, Thomas, on 17C practices 125
Tuke, William [The Retreat, York] 65, 120, 124
Tyson, Dr Edward [Physician] 54, 104

uniforms 27, 43–6
USA
  nurse training 174
  nurses as trainers 198, 206
  spending on health care 179
  time spent on nursing therapy 172

value for money 212
Victorian period 16, 150–9
Villa ward [Maudsley] 29, 192, 207
violence
  frequency of assaults on staff 209
  management of 206–9
visitors, fee-paying 5, 6, 7, 91
vomiting [as treatment] 63, 64, 125

Wain, Louis [artist & patient] 113–15
'Wallace, Clare Marc' [nurse & patient] 30–1, 145
Waller, Eileen [Sister], quoted 199
Ward, Ned [journalist], view of Bethlem 139–40
Webb, Elinor [patient] 21, 76
Webster, John, plays by 135–7
Weston, Thomas [Steward] 7
wet-packing 121
Whig interpretation of history 151
whipping 62, 118
White, Antonia [novelist & patient] 145–8
White, Mary [Matron & Nurse] 36, 83
Williams, Dr W. Rhys 66–7
Wiltshire, Juliette [Chief Nursing Officer] 83, 148
Withers, Elizabeth [Matron] 36, 72–4, 83
Withers, Humphrey [Porter] 72–3
Witley House [at Bethlem] 191–2
women's issues 194–5
Wood, Gartwright [Matron] 83
Wood, Mr [Apothecary] 75, 77
Wood, Rachel [Matron] 83
Working in Partnership [Department of Health review] 211
World Health Organization (WHO), nurse education strategy 172, 173
Wright, Elizabeth [Matron] 38, 83